CLINICS IN
LABORATORY
MEDICINE

Antimicrobial Resistance:
Challenges and Solutions

GUEST EDITOR
Michael R. Jacobs, MD, PhD

June 2004 • Volume 24 • Number 2

SAUNDERS

An Imprint of Elsevier, Inc.
PHILADELPHIA   LONDON   TORONTO   MONTREAL   SYDNEY   TOKYO

W.B. SAUNDERS COMPANY
A Division of Elsevier Inc.

The Curtis Center • Independence Square West • Philadelphia, Pennsylvania 19106-3399

http://www.TheClinics.com

CLINICS IN LABORATORY MEDICINE Volume 24, Number 2
JUNE 2004 ISSN 0272-2712
Editor: Kerry Holland

Clinics in Laboratory Medicine (ISSN 0272-2712) is published quarterly by W.B Saunders Company, a Division of Elsevier Science. Corporate and editorial offices: The Curtis Center, Independence Square West, Philadelphia, PA 19106-3399. Accounting and Circulation Offices: 6277 Sea Harbor Drive, Orlando, FL 32887-4800. Periodicals postage paid at Orlando, FL 32862, and additional mailing offices. Subscription prices are $153.00 per year (US individuals), $223.00 per year (US institutions), $77.00 (US students), $178.00 per year (Canadian individuals), $272.00 per year (foreign institutions), $104.00 (foreign students). Foreign air speed delivery is included in all *Clinics* subscription prices. All prices are subject to change without notice. POSTMASTER: Send address changes to *Clinics in Laboratory Medicine*, W.B. Saunders Company, Periodicals Fulfillment, Orlando, FL 32887-4800. **Customer Service: 1-800-654-2452 (US). From outside of the US, call 1-407-345-4000.** E-mail: hhspcs@harcout.com.

Clinics in Laboratory Medicine is covered in *EMBASE/Exerpta Medica, Index Medicus, Cinahl, Current Contents/ Clinical Medicine, BIOSIS* and *ISI/BIOMED.*

Printed in the United States of America.

GUEST EDITOR

MICHAEL R. JACOBS, MD, PhD, Professor of Pathology and Medicine, Case Western Reserve University; and Director, Clinical Microbiology, University Hospitals of Cleveland, Cleveland, Ohio

CONTRIBUTORS

DAVID ANDES, MD, Assistant Professor of Medicine, University of Wisconsin, Madison, Wisconsin

JACK ANON, MD, Associate Clinical Professor of Otolaryngology, University of Pittsburgh School of Medicine, Pittsburgh, Pennsylvania

PETER C. APPELBAUM, MD, PhD, Professor of Pathology, and Director, Clinical Microbiology, Hershey Medical Center, Hershey, Pennsylvania

SARALEE BAJAKSOUZIAN, MS, Senior Research Associate, Department of Pathology, Case Western Reserve University, Cleveland, Ohio

MICHAEL S. BENNINGER, MD, Chairman, Department of Otolaryngology-Head and Neck Surgery, Henry Ford Hospital, Detroit, Michigan

CHRISTOPHER R. BETHEL, MS, Research Service, Louis Stokes Cleveland Veterans Affairs Medical Center, Cleveland, Ohio

ROBERT A. BONOMO, MD, Research Service, Louis Stokes Cleveland Veterans Affairs Medical Center, Cleveland, Ohio

BÜLENT BOZDOGAN, MD, PhD, Department of Pathology, Hershey Medical Center, Pennsylvania State University, Hershey, Pennsylvania

WILLIAM A. CRAIG, MD, Professor of Medicine, University of Wisconsin, Madison, Wisconsin

THOMAS M. FILE, Jr, MD, MS, Professor of Internal Medicine, Northeastern Ohio Universities College of Medicine, Rootstown, Ohio; and Chief, Infectious Disease Service, Summa Health System, Akron, Ohio

SHIGEKI FUJITANI, MD, Critical Care Medicine Fellow, Department of Critical Care Medicine, University of Pittsburgh Medical Center, Pittsburgh, Pennsylvania

CARYN E. GOOD, MA, MPH, Research Analyst, Department of Pathology, Case Western Reserve University, Cleveland, Ohio

ANDREA M. HUJER, BS, Research Service, Louis Stokes Cleveland Veterans Affairs Medical Center, Cleveland, Ohio

KRISTINE M. HUJER, MS, Research Service, Louis Stokes Cleveland Veterans Affairs Medical Center, Cleveland, Ohio

MICHAEL R. JACOBS, MD, PhD, Professor of Pathology and Medicine, Case Western Reserve University; and Director, Clinical Microbiology, University Hospitals of Cleveland, Cleveland, Ohio

GENGRONG LIN, BS, Research Associate, Department of Pathology, Hershey Medical Center, Hershey, Pennsylvania

ELIZABETH PALAVECINO, MD, Assistant Professor of Pathology, and Director of Clinical Microbiology, Department of Pathology, Wake Forest University Health Sciences, Winston-Salem, North Carolina

GLENN A. PANKUCH, MS, Senior Research Associate, Department of Pathology, Hershey Medical Center, Hershey, Pennsylvania

DAVID L. PATERSON, MBBS, FRACP, Associate Professor of Medicine, Division of Infectious Diseases, University of Pittsburgh Medical Center, Pittsburgh, Pennsylvania

FERNANDA SILVEIRA, MD, Infectious Disease Fellow, Division of Infectious Diseases, University of Pittsburgh Medical Center, Pittsburgh, Pennsylvania

PHILIP TOLTZIS, MD, Associate Professor of Pediatrics, Divisions of Pharmacology and Critical Care and Infectious Diseases, Department of Pediatrics, Case Western Reserve University, and Rainbow Babies and Children's Hospital, Cleveland, Ohio

ANNE WINDAU, BS, Research Associate, Department of Pathology, Case Western Reserve University, Cleveland, Ohio

CONTENTS

Intensive care units (ICUs) frequently are the epicenter of nosocomial infections with antibiotic-resistant bacteria. Optimization of
antibiotic therapy for seriously ill patients with bacterial infections
appears to have a strong influence on outcome. Laboratories can
aid in provision of appropriate antibiotic therapy by providing
clinicians with "antibiograms" to aid empiric antibiotic choice and
by providing minimal inhibitory concentrations of key antibiotics
so that antibiotic dosing is optimized to key pharmacodynamic targets. Laboratories also play a crucial role in the prevention of antibiotic resistance in the ICU. Molecular epidemiologic evidence of
an oligoclonal outbreak of infections orients prevention measures
toward investigation of common environmental sources of infection and prevention of patient-to-patient transmission. In contrast,
evidence of polyclonality shifts prevention of antibiotic resistance
to antibiotic management strategies.

Geriatric patients frequently are cared for in long term care facilities (LTCFs), which are now a major component of our health care
delivery system. Nearly half of the 2.2 million people who turned
65 years old in 1990 will enter an LTCF at least once before they die.
Infections are one of the principal causes of morbidity and mortality in LTCFs. Because LTCFs are a less costly alternative to hospitalization, clinicians are treating many serious infections in the
nursing home. As a result of antibiotic use, LTCFs will increasingly
be recognized as sources of organisms resistant to multiple antibiotics. β-Lactams are a valuable class of potent antimicrobials with

broad-spectrum activity against Gram-negative and Gram-positive organisms. The safety and efficacy of this class of antibiotics make them easy choices for empiric treatment of infections in the elderly. Unfortunately, excessive use of these antibiotics has created serious threats to our therapeutic armamentarium: the emergence of methicillin-resistant *Staphylococcus aureus* and of Gram-negative pathogens resistant to third-generation cephalosporins such as cefotaxime, ceftazidime, and ceftriaxone. Of these third-generation cephalosporins, resistance to ceftazidime is most frequently recognized. The major mechanism responsible for ceftazidime resistance in Gram-negative bacteria is the production of β-lactamases. This article summarizes the diversity of β-lactamases, highlights the important enzymes that confer ceftazidime resistance in LTCFs, and details some methods used to identify and characterize these enzymes. A clear challenge is to apply these techniques to epidemiologic and molecular studies conducted in LTCFs.

Antibiotic-resistant Gram-negative bacilli are a prominent and growing problem among hospitalized children. Epidemics caused by these organisms have been implicated in many outbreaks in children's hospitals, primarily in neonatal intensive care units. These epidemics are characterized by efficient patient-to-patient transmission of the outbreak clone via the hands of caregivers and through exposure of contaminated inanimate sources. The epidemiology of these resistant organisms in pediatric hospitals during endemic periods is more complex. The isolates cultured from hospitalized individuals in the absence of an outbreak usually are unique to each individual and are derived from the patient's endogenous flora or other disparate sources. As in adults, chronic care facilities for children represent significant reservoirs of antibiotic-resistant bacilli that are circulated back into the acute care hospital environment when the child becomes ill.

Vancomycin resistance in enterococci, predominantly *Enterococcus faecium*, developed in the latter half of the 1980s, and the long anticipated development of vancomycin resistance in *Staphylococcus aureus* has now occurred. A number of vancomycin-intermediate strains have been described, and these strains have abnormal, thickened cell walls in the presence of vancomycin. Two mechanisms of resistance have been described in the strains: affinity trapping of vancomycin molecules by cell wall monomers and clogging of the outer layers of peptidoglycan by bound vancomycin molecules, and change in the structure or metabolism of teichoic acids. Of more serious concern has been the description in 2002 of two patients with vancomycin-resistant *S aureus* infections. In one instance, the patient had skin lesions coinfected with vancomycin-resistant, vanA genotype, *E faecalis*, and the vanA resistance genes could have been transferred to the *S aureus* strain. Expression of resistance was high in one *S aureus* strain and low in the other, making detection more challenging in the latter instance. These developments are of great concern, and every effort should be made to prevent further development and spread of vancomycin resistance in staphylococci.

Community-acquired Methicillin-resistant *Staphylococcus aureus* Infections

Elizabeth Palavecino

Staphylococcus aureus causes a variety of minor diseases but also is responsible for staphylococcal pneumonia and sepsis, both of which can be fatal. It is thought to be responsible for many of the pneumonia deaths associated with the influenza pandemics of the 20th century. The introduction of penicillin in the 1940s greatly improved the prognosis for patients with severe staphylococcal infections. However, after a few years of clinical use, most staphylococcal strains were able to hydrolyze penicillin by producing β-lactamases, making penicillin a useless antibiotic to treat staphylococcal infections caused by β-lactamase-producing *S aureus*. Methicillin, a semisynthetic penicillin introduced in 1959, was specifically designed to be resistant to β-lactamase degradation, but resistance developed soon after its introduction into clinical practice. Methicillin-resistant *S aureus* (MRSA) was first reported in the United Kingdom in 1961, followed by reports from other European countries, Japan, and Australia. The first reported case of MRSA in the United States was in 1968. Currently, MRSA is an important pathogen in nosocomial infections and is a problem in hospitals worldwide, and it is increasingly recovered from nursing home residents with established risk factors. More recently, community-acquired MRSA infections have been documented among healthy individuals with no recognizable risk factors, and it seems clear that community-acquired MRSA (CA-MRSA) strains are epidemiologically and clonally unrelated to hospital-acquired strains. This review focuses on the epidemiology, clinical significance, and virulence markers of CA-MRSA infections.

Mechanisms of Resistance Among Respiratory Tract Pathogens

Michael R. Jacobs, Jack Anon, and Peter C. Appelbaum

Antimicrobial resistance among respiratory tract pathogens represents a significant health care threat. Identifying the antimicrobial agents that remain effective in the presence of resistance, and knowing why, requires a thorough understanding of the mechanisms of action of the various agents as well as the mechanisms of resistance demonstrated among respiratory tract pathogens. The primary goal of antimicrobial therapy is to eradicate the pathogen, via killing or inhibiting bacteria, from the site of infection; the defenses of the body are required for killing any remaining bacteria. Targeting a cellular process or function specific to bacteria and not to the host limits the toxicity to patients. Currently, there are four general cellular targets to which antimicrobials are targeted: cell wall formation and maintenance, protein synthesis, DNA replication, and folic acid metabolism. Resistance mechanisms among respiratory tract pathogens have been demonstrated for all four targets. In general, the mechanisms of resistance used by these pathogens fall into one of three categories: enzymatic inactivation of the antimicrobial, prevention of intracellular accumulation, and modification of the target site to which agents bind to exert an antimicrobial effect. Resistance to some agents can be overcome by modifying the dosage regimens (eg, using high-dose therapy) or inhibiting the resistance mechanism (eg, β-lactamase inhibitors), whereas other mechanisms of resistance can only be overcome by using an agent from a different class. Understanding the mechanisms of action of the various agents and the mechanisms of resistance used by respiratory tract pathogens can help clinicians identify the agents that will increase the likelihood of achieving optimal outcomes.

Antimicrobial resistance is a growing problem among pathogens from respiratory tract infections. β-Lactam resistance rates are escalating among *Streptococcus pneumoniae* and *Haemophilus influenzae*. Macrolides are increasingly used for the treatment of respiratory tract infections, but their utility is compromised by intrinsic and acquired resistance. This article analyses macrolide-resistance mechanisms and their worldwide distributions in *S pneumoniae*, *S pyogenes*, and *H influenzae*.

The pharmacologic field that studies antimicrobial pharmacokinetics and pharmacodynamics (PK/PD) has had a major impact on the choice and dosing regimens used for many antibiotics especially those used in the treatment of respiratory tract infections. PK/PD parameters are particularly important in light of increasing antimicrobial resistance. Drug pharmacokinetic features, such as serum concentrations over time and area under the concentration-time curve, when integrated with minimum inhibitory concentration (MIC) values of antibiotics against pathogens, can predict the probability of bacterial eradication and clinical success. These pharmacokinetic and pharmacodynamic relationships also are important in preventing the selection and spread of resistant strains and have led to the description of the mutation prevention concentration, which is the lowest concentration of antimicrobial that prevents selection of resistant bacteria from high bacterial inocula. β-lactams are time-dependent agents without significant post-antibiotic effects, resulting in bacterial eradication when unbound serum concentrations exceed MICs of these agents against infecting pathogens for >40% to 50% of the dosing interval. Macrolides, azaolides, and lincosamides are time-dependent agents with prolonged post-antibiotic effects, and fluoroquinolones are concentration-dependent agents, resulting in both cases in bacterial eradication when unbound serum area-under-the-curve to MIC ratios exceed 25 to 30. These observations have led to changes in recommended antimicrobial dosing against respiratory pathogens and are used to assess the role of current agents, develop new formulations, and assess potency of new antimicrobials.

Michael R. Jacobs, Saralee Bajaksouzian, Anne Windau, Caryn E. Good, Gengrong Lin, Glenn A. Pankuch, and Peter C. Appelbaum

Pharmacokinetic/pharmacodynamic parameters were used to interpret susceptibility data for the oral agents tested in a clinically meaningful way. Among *S pneumoniae* isolates, >99% were susceptible to respiratory fluoroquinolones, 91.6% to amoxicillin, 92.1% to amoxicillin/clavulanic acid (95.2% at the extended-release formulation breakpoint), 90.6% to clindamycin, 80.4% to doxycycline, 71.0% to azithromycin, 72.3% to clarithromycin, 71.8% to cefprozil and cefdinir, 72.6% to cefuroxime axetil, 66.3% to cexime, 63.7% to trimethoprim/sulfamethoxazole, and 19.7% to cefaclor. Among *H influenzae* isolates, 28.6% were β-lactamase positive, but virtually all were susceptible to amoxicillin/clavulanic acid (98.3%, with 99.8% at the extended-release formulation breakpoint), cexime (100%), and uoroquinolones (99.8%), whereas 93.5% were susceptible to cefdinir, 82.8% to cefuroxime axetil, 78.1% to trimethoprim/sulfamethoxazole, 70.2% to amoxicillin, 25.1% to doxycycline, 23.2% to cefprozil, and 5% to cefaclor, azithromycin and clarithromycin. Most isolates of *M catarrhalis* were resistant to amoxicillin, cefaclor, cefprozil, and trimethoprim/sulfamethoxazole. Thus significant β-lactam and macrolide/azalide resistance in *Streptococcus pneumoniae* and β-lactamase production and trimethoprim/sulfamethoxazole resistance in untypeable *Haemophilus influenzae* are still present. The results of this study should therefore be applied to clinical practice based on the clinical presentation of the patient, the probability of the patient's having a bacterial rather than a viral infection, the natural history of the disease, the potential of pathogens to be susceptible to various oral antimicrobial agents, the potential for cross-resistance between agents with *S pneumoniae*, and the potential for pathogens to develop further resistance. Antibiotics should be used judiciously to maintain remaining activity and chosen carefully based on activity determined by pharmacokinetic/pharmacodynamic-based breakpoints to avoid these bacteria developing further resistance, particularly to fluoroquinolones.

FORTHCOMING ISSUES

RECENT ISSUES

THE CLINICS ARE NOW AVAILABLE ONLINE!

Access your subscription at:
http://www.TheClinics.com

ELSEVIER
SAUNDERS

CLINICS IN
LABORATORY
MEDICINE

Clin Lab Med 24 (2004) xiii–xiv

Preface

Antimicrobial Resistance: Challenges and Solutions

Michael R. Jacobs, MD, PhD
Guest Editor

Since the introduction of arsenical antimicrobial agents into our therapeutic armamentarium by Paul Ehrlich following his pioneering work on protozoal diseases and syphilis in the first decade of the twentieth century, use of these "magic bullets" has become universal in medical, veterinary, and agricultural practice in the first decade of the twenty-first century. This has led to major improvements in our ability to conquer many infectious diseases, but overuse and misuse of these powerful and valuable agents have led to the development of resistance in bacteria, fungi, protozoa, and viruses. This issue is dedicated to delineating the challenges posed by such development of resistance in bacteria, with emphasis on severe infections that are no longer responsive to currently available agents and on respiratory tract infections where the predominant bacterial pathogens have developed resistance to most of the available drug classes. Three articles in this issue address the challenges we face in severe infections in adults, the elderly, and in children. Two articles address key problems we are facing with *Staphylococcus aureus* infections—the development of vancomycin resistance and the problem of methicillin resistance in community-acquired infections.

The second half of this issue is devoted to the challenges posed by the development of resistance in bacterial respiratory tract infections and to solutions proposed for these problems. Two articles address the mechanisms of resistance that these versatile pathogens have developed, illustrating the futility of trying to produce the "ideal" agent without control of the overuse

0272-2712/04/$ - see front matter © 2004 Elsevier Inc. All rights reserved.
doi:10.1016/j.cll.2004.03.010

of these agents that will inevitably lead to resistance. The next article addresses the principles of pharmacokinetics and pharmacodynamics and the application of this knowledge to treating respiratory tract infections. This article is followed by those addressing the application of these pharmacokinetic and pharmacodynamic principles to recent surveillance isolates of the major bacterial respiratory tract pathogens and the development of new formulations of existing agents to address the development of β-lactam and macrolide resistance in *Streptococcus pneumoniae* and β-lactamase production in *Haemophilus influenzae*.

It is my hope that this issue of *Clinics in Laboratory Medicine* will illustrate the precarious state that has evolved from uncontrolled use of these valuable agents, with the hope that readers will be encouraged to advocate more responsible use of these resources in the future.

Michael R. Jacobs, MD, PhD
Case Western Reserve University School of Medicine
University Hospitals of Cleveland
11100 Euclid Avenue
Cleveland, OH 44106, USA

E-mail address: mrj6@cwru.edu

ELSEVIER
SAUNDERS

CLINICS IN
LABORATORY
MEDICINE

Clin Lab Med 24 (2004) 329–341

Antibiotic-resistant infections in the critically ill adult

Fernanda Silveira, MD[a], Shigeki Fujitani, MD[b],
David L. Paterson, MBBS, FRACP[a],*

[a]Division of Infectious Diseases, University of Pittsburgh Medical Center, Suite 3A,
Falk Medical Building, 3601 5th Avenue, Pittsburgh, PA 15213, USA
[b]Department of Critical Care Medicine, University of Pittsburgh Medical Center,
Pittsburgh, PA 15213, USA

Infections in critically ill patients exact a high price in morbidity and mortality. Because of significant underlying disease processes and deranged physiologic status, critically ill patients are more susceptible to infection and are also more likely to have an adverse outcome from infection. Critically ill patients have multiple breaches in host defense—central venous lines, endotracheal tubes, surgical wounds, nasogastric tubes, and indwelling urinary catheters may all breach mucocutaneous barriers. A significant proportion of critically ill patients also will be immunocompromised by neutropenia, iatrogenic immunosuppression for transplantation or auto-mimmune disease, or acquired immunodeficiency due to HIV infection.

Antibiotic-resistant bacteria thrive among populations of the critically ill. Given the high mortality caused by infections in critically ill patients, antibiotic use is frequently empirical and broad spectrum. This potentially allows for selection of multiply resistant bacteria. Critically ill patients are accommodated in intensive care units (ICUs) where patient-to-patient trans-mission of antibiotic-resistant organisms is common. Factors contributing to such horizontal transmission of bacteria include numerous occasions when critically ill patients are exposed to the hands of health care workers and their equipment (for example, stethoscopes), especially when health care workers have not cleaned their hands or equipment between patients. It is not surprising that in emergency situations hand hygiene is suboptimal.

ICUs are therefore usually the epicenter of antibiotic resistance within hospitals. Antibiotic resistance of both Gram-positive and Gram-negative

---

* Corresponding author.
E-mail address: patersond@msx.dept-med.pitt.edu (D.L. Paterson).

0272-2712/04/$ - see front matter © 2004 Elsevier Inc. All rights reserved.
doi:10.1016/j.cll.2004.03.002

bacteria is common. Commonly observed resistance profiles include methicillin-resistant *Staphylococcus aureus* (MRSA), vancomycin-resistant enterococci (VRE), and extended-spectrum β-lactamase (ESBL)–producing Gram-negative bacilli. This article delineates the epidemiology of antibiotic resistance in ICUs and describes potential means by which laboratories can contribute to the optimization of treatment of the individual patient and the control of such resistance.

Epidemiology of antibiotic resistance in critically ill patients

Data collected and reported by hospitals participating in the National Nosocomial Infections Surveillance (NNIS) System provide a useful starting point for examination of the epidemiology of antibiotic resistance in the ICU. The NNIS System was established in 1970. At that time selected hospitals within the United States began routinely reporting their nosocomial infection data for aggregation into a national database. More than 300 hospitals currently participate in the NNIS system. Infection control practitioners at these institutions collect data on nosocomial infection in ICUs by using standardized protocols. Rates of infection are calculated by using, as a denominator, variables such as the number of patient days within the ICU, the days of mechanical ventilation, the days of central venous cannulation, and the days of indwelling urinary catheterization [1]. Data are usually presented by specific ICU type (burn, coronary, cardiothoracic, medical, neurosurgical, surgical, trauma).

Data from the NNIS System from January 1998 to June 2002 show that of 18,397 *S aureus* isolates from 147 ICUs, 51.3% of isolates were MRSA [1]. Of 11,262 enterococcal isolates from these ICUs, 12.8% were VRE. In a quarter of the ICUs, at least 25% of enterococcal isolates were VRE. Additionally, 6.1% of *Klebsiella* isolates lacked susceptibility to third-generation cephalosporins, implying ESBL production. (Lack of susceptibility to third-generation cephalosporins by using conventional breakpoints is neither 100% specific nor sensitive for ESBL production.) In 10% of ICUs, more than 27% of *Klebsiella* isolates were probable ESBL producers. Finally, amongst *Pseudomonas aeruginosa* isolates, the pooled mean of ciprofloxacin resistance was 36.3%, imipenem resistance 19.6%, ceftazidime resistance 13.9%, and piperacillin resistance 17.5%. With all of these antibiotics, at least 10% of ICUs had substantially higher rates of resistance than the pooled mean [1]. *P aeruginosa* isolates are frequently multidrug resistant, such that resistance to ciprofloxacin, imipenem, ceftazidime, and piperacillin may occur simultaneously [2].

Optimizing antibiotic therapy against antibiotic-resistant bacteria: the role of the laboratory

Given the extent of antibiotic resistance in ICUs and the underlying severity of illness in patients in ICUs, it is clearly important that antibiotic therapy for serious infections be optimized. There are three important components to optimization of antibiotic therapy in the seriously ill patient: (1) empiric antibiotic choice, (2) optimizing dosing, (3) consideration of duration of therapy.

Optimizing empiric antibiotic choice: the role of the "antibiogram"

Although severity of underlying illness is undoubtedly a contributor to outcome from serious bacterial infection, adequacy of empiric antibiotic choice is also a determinant of outcome. Adequate therapy means using antibiotics to which the organism cultured from the patient is susceptible, as determined by in vitro tests. The importance of adequate empiric therapy has been well illustrated by a review of more than 600 patients with community-acquired or nosocomial infections in ICUs in the Barnes-Jewish Hospital, St. Louis [3]. The infection-related mortality rate of infected patients receiving inadequate empirical therapy (42.0%) was significantly greater than that of patients receiving adequate antibiotic therapy (17.7%). Using a logistic regression model, inadequate empirical therapy was found to be the most important independent determinant of mortality for the entire patient cohort hospitalized in ICU at the time of the study. These same investigators reported similar results with a subsequent study of inadequate therapy for bloodstream infections [4]. Several other groups have produced similar findings [5–7]. Although these studies are non-randomized and potentially suffer from a variety of confounding factors, it appears highly likely that appropriate empiric antibiotic therapy leads to improved outcome.

The choice of empiric antibiotic therapy should be dependent on the likely organisms at the site of infection and their likely antibiotic resistance profile. Although empiric antibiotic therapy should clearly be individualized (based on factors such as allergies and renal function), the laboratory can contribute significantly to empiric antibiotic choice by providing "antibiograms" (Box 1). An antibiogram is a cumulative antibiotic susceptibility profile for a health care facility for a certain period of time. The National Committee for Clinical Laboratory Standards (NCCLS) now provides guidance for creation of such antibiograms in its publication, "Analysis and presentation of cumulative antimicrobial susceptibility test data" [8]. This standard calls for elimination of duplicate isolates from such antibiograms by using only the first isolate per patient per reporting period.

Cumulative antibiotic susceptibility test data collated from an entire hospital may differ substantially from that collected in a single ICU [9]. This is particularly true if the hospital-wide antibiogram is collated from all specimens received by a hospital's clinical microbiology laboratory, whether they are from outpatient facilities, emergency departments, inpatient units, and ICUs. We recommend that ICU-specific antibiograms be created, in a timely fashion, for individual ICUs.

Box 1. The potential role of the microbiology laboratory in the critically ill patient with infection with antibiotic-resistant bacteria

Optimizing antibiotic therapy
- Provide ICU-specific antibiogram to increase chances of adequate empiric therapy
- Timely provision of Gram stain, identification, and susceptibility of bacteria
- Provide minimal inhibitory concentrations for key antibiotics to allow pharmacodynamic targets to be achieved

Prevention of infection
- Selective media to adequately assess for colonization with antibiotic-resistant organisms
- Molecular diagnostic tests for genes responsible for common resistance mechanisms
- Molecular epidemiologic tools (for example, pulsed field gel electrophoresis) to direct prevention strategies

---

Optimizing antibiotic dosing: the importance of the minimal inhibitory concentration

By the time that the identity and antibiotic susceptibility profile of a bacterium is known, it is usually assumed that the role of the clinical microbiology laboratory is over. However, the way in which antibiotic susceptibility testing is performed is an important consideration. It is our opinion that provision of the actual minimal inhibitory concentration (MIC) end-point of the antibiotic used in therapy, rather than just a categorical susceptibility result, is an important role of the laboratory in the management of infections in the seriously ill patient (see Box 1). Knowledge of the MIC can allow clinicians to optimize dosage of the antibiotic selected for therapy.

A number of pharmacodynamic "targets" are now acknowledged as critically important in the outcome of infection [10]. For concentration-dependent antibiotics, such as aminoglycosides, the peak concentration to MIC ratio correlates well to clinical outcome [11]. As aminoglycoside serum concentrations are so readily available, clinicians can ensure the peak concentration to MIC ratio is optimized, if the MIC of the antibiotic for the organism in question is known. For quinolones, the peak to MIC ratio and the 24-hour AUC (area under the concentration-time curve) to MIC ratio have correlated with outcome [12]. For time-dependent antibiotics, such as the β-lactams, the time the antibiotic concentration is above the MIC correlates best with efficacy. Use of a mathematical technique known as

Monte Carlo simulation has shown that some antibiotic susceptibility "breakpoints" for Gram-negative bacilli may be misleading even if the manufacturer's recommended doses of antibiotics are used [13]. This is particularly true for Gram-negative bacilli (such as *P aeruginosa*) with MICs of 8 µg/mL for certain β-lactam antibiotics [13]. Such MICs are within the "susceptible" range for antibiotics such as ceftazidime, cefepime or piperacillin/tazobactam, but conventional dosing may not allow a high probability of meeting certain pharmacodynamic targets correlated with good clinical outcome. For example, the probability of attainment of at least 50% "time above MIC" when cefepime is dosed at 1 g every 12 hours or piperacillin/tazobactam is dosed at 4.5 g every 8 hours is poor (< 80%) in patients with good renal function, when the MIC of the organism is 8 µg/mL.

A related area is the detection of specific resistance mechanisms by the clinical microbiology laboratory. The presence of ESBLs is not readily appreciated when conventional breakpoints are used. A significant proportion of ESBL-producing isolates will have MICs of third- and fourth-generation cephalosporins of 4 to 8 µg/mL and thus will be reported as susceptible to these antibiotics [14]. The NCCLS has promulgated guidelines for the screening and detection of ESBL producers [15]. Two screening methods can be used: the first uses conventional disk diffusion techniques and the second uses broth dilution. If organisms are "screen positive," they should undergo phenotypic confirmatory testing. The principle of phenotypic confirmatory testing is that zone diameters will increase (or MICs will decrease) when either ceftazidime or cefotaxime is combined with clavulanic acid. This is because ESBLs are inhibited by clavulanic acid, allowing enhanced activity of the cephalosporin.

Organisms that have positive phenotypic confirmatory tests for ESBL production should be reported resistant to cefpodoxime, ceftazidime, aztreonam, cefotaxime, ceftriaxone, and cefepime, regardless of the apparent "susceptibility" of the organism to these antibiotics. It is possible that the breakpoints themselves will be changed in years to come to reflect breakpoints that are consistent with pharmacodynamic studies. However, until such time as breakpoints are changed, it is recommended that the NCCLS screening and confirmatory testing for ESBLs be performed.

Duration of antibiotic therapy

There is renewed interest in consideration of optimal duration of antibiotic therapy for critically ill patients. Unnecessarily prolonged courses of therapy may add nothing to the outcome of the bacterial infection but may contribute to the selection pressure that leads to antibiotic resistance. Recent randomized trials have confirmed that, in patients with suspected or confirmed ventilator-associated pneumonia, prolonged courses of antibiotic therapy have a deleterious effect [16,17].

Prevention of antibiotic resistance in critically ill patients

The laboratory has a central role in the prevention of antibiotic resistance in ICUs. In particular, molecular epidemiologic investigations can direct the interventions necessary for the control of resistance. Apparent outbreaks of infections with a particular antibiotic-resistant organism are usually first recognized by observation of increased frequencies of isolation of the organism in clinical specimens. However, patients colonized with an antibiotic-resistant organism usually outnumber those with frank clinical infections due to the resistant organism in question and are a ready source of organisms to be passed from patient to patient [18,19]. This happens because patients with colonization of antibiotic-resistant organisms usually have skin colonization with the same organism. Transmission of antibiotic-resistant organisms from patient to patient is usually facilitated by health care worker contact with the skin of the patient.

The gastrointestinal tract is the most common site of colonization with VRE- and ESBL-producing organisms [18,19]. Although gastrointestinal tract colonization with MRSA has been observed [20], the nose is a more common site of colonization for this organism. Laboratories can contribute to delineation of the pool of colonized patients by use of selective media, particularly when gastrointestinal tract colonization is sought. Additionally, there is growing interest in use of molecular diagnostic methods for delineating carriage status of MRSA [21]. This may be particularly useful in terms of rapid cohorting of colonized and noncolonized patients.

Once patients who are colonized or infected with the antibiotic-resistant organism under question are identified, molecular epidemiologic techniques can be used to determine whether a common clone is responsible. Pulsed field gel electrophoresis (PFGE) is the molecular epidemiologic tool most frequently used, but polymerase chain reaction (PCR)-based methods are also available [22]. The prevention strategy for reduction in occurrence of antibiotic-resistant organisms will depend on the results of molecular epidemiologic investigations. If a common clone of antibiotic-resistant organisms is found, then action should be directed toward reduction in patient-to-patient transmission of the organism, or a common environmental source of infection should be identified. If the antibiotic-resistant isolates are not related, but have occurred at increased frequency compared with baseline, measures should be introduced to reduce selection pressure by antibiotics.

Control of antibiotic resistance in critically ill patients when a common clone of antibiotic-resistant organisms is identified

Classic infection control is used as the method for controlling spread of antibiotic resistance when a common clone of antibiotic-resistant organisms is identified. The first major question is whether a common environmental focus of infection is present or whether the antibiotic-resistant organism is predominantly being spread from patient to patient.

A common environmental source of resistant organisms needs to be considered, particularly when an apparent outbreak of infection with nonfermentative Gram-negative bacteria is detected. Bacteria such as *P aeruginosa* have been linked to water reservoirs in the hospital [23]. Examples of such sources include faucets and faucet aerators and immersion or whirlpool baths. Potable water itself may be a source, although *P aeruginosa* from potable water is rarely multidrug resistant unless faucets or faucet aerators are contaminated in a health care setting. As has been well documented in recent years, improperly cleaned bronchoscopes may be an important source of multidrug resistant *P aeruginosa* [24].

Bronchoscopes have also been implicated in an outbreak of ESBL-producing *Klebsiella* species [25], as has ultrasonography coupling gel [26], and glass thermometers (used in axillary measurement of temperature) [27]. Outbreaks of infection with *Enterobacter cloacae* and *Serratia marcescens* have been associated with unintentionally contaminated medications or human albumin solutions [28,29]. Health care workers wearing artificial nails have been linked to nosocomial outbreaks of infection due to *P aeruginosa* and *S marcescens* [30–32].

Discovery of a removable environmental focus that harbored genotypically related isolates to the outbreak strain should obviously lead to an investigation as to how that object became contaminated and removal of the focus from the ward involved. Three examples of such an intervention have been described in the context of controlling outbreaks of infection with ESBL-producing organisms. Gaillot and colleagues [26] found that gel used for ultrasonography was contaminated with ESBL-producing organisms. Replacement of this gel quickly curtailed the outbreak. Branger [25] found that a poorly maintained bronchoscope was colonized with ESBL-producing organisms and could be linked to respiratory tract infections with the same strain. Repair and proper maintenance of the bronchoscope stopped nosocomial transmission of the organism. Finally, Rogues and colleagues [27] found colonization of four of 12 glass mercury thermometers with ESBL-producing *K pneumoniae* and axillary colonization with the same strain in two patients. Disinfection of the thermometers curtailed the outbreak.

If a common environmental source of infection is not found, it is usually assumed that patient-to-patient transmission of infection has occurred by way of the hands of health care workers. Stringent contact isolation precautions are widely used as a means of preventing spread of MRSA or VRE [33]. However, there is also ample evidence of person-to-person transmission of ESBL-producing Gram-negative bacilli and carbapenemase-producing *P aeruginosa*. A review of more than 50 studies that used molecular epidemiologic techniques to analyze outbreaks of ESBL-producing organisms found that in all cases at least two patients in each hospital shared genotypically similar strains, implying person-to-person spread of the organism [34]. Environmental foci were discovered in fewer than 10% of these outbreaks. Several recent studies have demonstrated clonal spread of carbapenemase-producing *K pneumoniae* or *P aeruginosa* [35–37]. Multiply resistant Gram-negative bacilli should no longer be regarded as selected by antibiotic use to the exclusion of the possibility of person-to-person transmission by the hands of health care workers.

Hand carriage of resistant organisms by health care workers has been documented by most, but not all investigators, who have sought it [38,39]. In these instances, the hand isolates were genotypically identical to isolates which caused infection in patients. Hand carriage by health care workers is usually eliminated by hand hygiene with chlorhexidine or alcohol-based antiseptics [40]. Alcohol-based handrubs have higher acceptance by busy health care workers in ICUs and are rapidly becoming a new standard of care [40]. Gastrointestinal tract carriage of resistant organisms has been documented in health care workers, but is astonishingly rare and seldom prolonged, except with ESBL-producing *Salmonella* species [41].

In most instances, contact isolation is instituted when outbreaks of multiply resistant organisms are demonstrated. Contact isolation implies use of gloves and gowns when contacting the patient. Several studies have documented that this practice alone can lead to reduction in horizontal spread of resistant organisms [34]. However, compliance with these precautions needs to be high to maximize the effectiveness of these precautions [42]. Furthermore, we recommend that patients who have gastrointestinal tract colonization as well as those with frank infection should undergo contact isolation. Standard methods of hand hygiene, screening for colonization, and patient isolation may not always be effective in controlling outbreaks of resistant organisms. In some situations, temporary ward closure is necessary to adequately control an outbreak that had been unresponsive to conventional measures [43].

Control of antibiotic resistance in critically ill patients when isolates are of multiple different strain types

If molecular epidemiologic studies show that the antibiotic-resistant organisms in an ICU are of diverse strain types, it is unlikely that application of traditional infection control principles will be effective at reducing the rate of colonization or infection with the resistant organism. In this situation, attention to antibiotic-prescribing patterns is more likely to be successful. As noted earlier, reduction in duration of antibiotic courses in ICUs has been effective at reducing the occurrence of antibiotic-resistant organisms. However, other strategies used in the past include total avoidance of use of certain antibiotic classes and antibiotic cycling.

It is increasingly evident that third-generation cephalosporins may be linked to the emergence of many multidrug resistant organisms and therefore may be particularly useful as targets in an antibiotic-restriction campaign [44]. Heavy empiric use of third-generation cephalosporins has been linked to infections with MRSA, VRE, ESBL-producing organisms, and multidrug resistant *P aeruginosa* [45,46]. Reduction in use of extended-spectrum cephalosporins is the common theme underlying many successful interventions in outbreaks with VRE and ESBL producers [45,47–50]. However, drugs with anti-anaerobic activity, by interfering with gut flora [51], and fluoroquinolones, by upregulating efflux pumps [52,53], also may be potential culprits in selecting for multidrug resistance and therefore be targets for restriction as empiric therapy.

Antibiotic cycling, the scheduled rotation of antibiotics in a particular ICU, is another strategy used in the control of antibiotic-resistant organisms. It is theorized that withdrawal of an antibiotic from use for a defined period of time will limit antibiotic pressure as a stimulus for antibiotic resistance. Early experience with rotating amikacin and gentamicin use supported this concept [54]. However, examples also exist whereby resistance does not disappear in the absence of antibiotic use. For example, although streptomycin was virtually never used at a large teaching hospital, 20% of isolates of *Enterobacteriaceae* were resistant to this antibiotic [55]. Furthermore, mathematical models suggest that cycling is inferior even to a situation where just two antibiotics are used simultaneously in the same population [56].

Two studies have assessed the adequacy of antibiotic cycling as an approach to the prevention of antibiotic resistance in the ICU. A group of French investigators has assessed cycling in a comprehensive study of antibiotic resistance within their institution [57]. In the baseline period, ceftazidime plus ciprofloxacin was widely prescribed as empirical therapy for ventilator-associated pneumonia. No efforts were made to streamline this therapy on the basis of antibiotic susceptibilities. In the intervention period, ciprofloxacin and ceftazidime were rarely used. A rotating cycle of cefepime, piperacillin/tazobactam, imipenem, and ticarcillin/clavulanate was used, coupled with a rotating cycle of different aminoglycosides. Streamlining of therapy was performed if antibiotic susceptibilities allowed. The cycles were for approximately 1 month each. A significant decrease in the number of episodes of ventilator-associated pneumonia was observed in the intervention period. The susceptibility profile of *P aeruginosa* to multiple antibiotics improved from the baseline period to the intervention period. Ciprofloxacin use fell eight fold in the intervention period.

Secondly, a study in Virginia established a quarterly empirical antibiotic rotation schedule [58]. Different antibiotic cycles were used for empirical treatment of pneumonia and peritonitis/sepsis of unknown origin. Antibiotics used in the cycles included ciprofloxacin, piperacillin/tazobactam, imipenem/meropenem, and cefepime. Significant reductions in the incidence of antibiotic-resistant Gram-positive infections, antibiotic-resistant Gram-negative infections, and mortality associated with infection were observed in the rotation period compared with the preceding 1 year during which nonprotocol-driven empirical antibiotic use was performed. It should be noted that infection control practices changed during the course of the study. Alcohol hand-wash dispensers were distributed throughout the institution immediately before the transition from nonprotocol-driven empirical antibiotic use to antibiotic rotation. An antibiotic surveillance team, which assessed the necessity for antibiotic use, was in place for 4 months of the baseline period and for all 12 months of the antibiotic rotation period.

From a methodologic standpoint, the use of "historical controls" continues to raise questions as to whether antibiotic cycling is truly effective or whether other variables such as diminished use of ceftazidime or ciprofloxacin or introduction of infection control practices were the major influences on changed antibiotic-resistance profiles. A multicenter study sponsored by the Centers for Disease Control and Prevention assessing antibiotic cycling has been performed; results of this study will help determine whether antibiotic cycling is truly an effective strategy.

Summary

Antibiotic resistance in critically ill patients is a major concern. Such patients may have reduced physiologic reserve and hence suffer high morbidity and mortality from serious infections. Clinical microbiology laboratories have a substantial role in aiding clinicians in the treatment of individual patients and in the prevention of occurrence of antibiotic resistance (see Box 1). Trends in antibiotic resistance in ICUs worldwide are for resistance to become more widespread and antibiotic options to become more limited. Development of rapid molecular testing for presence of genes encoding antibiotic resistance may play an important future role in the prevention of antibiotic resistance in bacteria from patients in ICUs.

References

[1] NNIS. National Nosocomial Infections Surveillance (NNIS) System Report, data summary from January 1992 to June 2002, issued August 2002. Am J Infect Control 2002;30(8):458–75.

[2] Linden PK, Kusne S, Coley K, Fontes P, Kramer DJ, Paterson D. Use of parenteral colistin for the treatment of serious infection due to antimicrobial-resistant *Pseudomonas aeruginosa*. Clin Infect Dis 2003;37(11):e154–60.

[3] Kollef MH, Sherman G, Ward S, Fraser VJ. Inadequate antimicrobial treatment of infections: a risk factor for hospital mortality among critically ill patients. Chest 1999; 115(2):462–74.

[4] Ibrahim EH, Sherman G, Ward S, Fraser VJ, Kollef MH. The influence of inadequate antimicrobial treatment of bloodstream infections on patient outcomes in the ICU setting. Chest 2000;118(1):146–55.

[5] Alvarez-Lerma F. Modification of empiric antibiotic treatment in patients with pneumonia acquired in the intensive care unit. ICU-Acquired Pneumonia Study Group. Intensive Care Med 1996;22(5):387–94.

[6] Luna CM, Vujacich P, Niederman MS, et al. Impact of BAL data on the therapy and outcome of ventilator-associated pneumonia. Chest 1997;111(3):676–85.

[7] Rello J, Gallego M, Mariscal D, Sonora R, Valles J. The value of routine microbial investigation in ventilator-associated pneumonia. Am J Respir Crit Care Med 1997;156(1): 196–200.

[8] NCCLS. Analysis and presentation of cumulative antimicrobial susceptibility test data (M-39A). Wayne, PA: NCCLS; 2002.

[9] Namias N, Samiian L, Nino D, et al. Incidence and susceptibility of pathogenic bacteria vary between intensive care units within a single hospital: implications for empiric antibiotic strategies. J Trauma 2000;49(4):638–45.

[10] Goldberg J, Owens RC Jr. Optimizing antimicrobial dosing in the critically ill patient. Curr Opin Crit Care 2002;8(5):435–40.

[11] Moore RD, Lietman PS, Smith CR. Clinical response to aminoglycoside therapy: importance of the ratio of peak concentration to minimal inhibitory concentration. J Infect Dis 1987;155(1):93–9.

[12] Preston SL, Drusano GL, Berman AL, et al. Pharmacodynamics of levofloxacin: a new paradigm for early clinical trials. JAMA 1998;279(2):125–9.

[13] Tam VH, McKinnon PS, Akins RL, Drusano GL, Rybak MJ. Pharmacokinetics and pharmacodynamics of cefepime in patients with various degrees of renal function. Antimicrob Agents Chemother 2003;47(6):1853–61.

[14] Paterson DL, Ko WC, Von Gottberg A, et al. Outcome of cephalosporin treatment for serious infections due to apparently susceptible organisms producing extended-spectrum beta-lactamases: implications for the clinical microbiology laboratory. J Clin Microbiol 2001;39(6):2206–12.

[15] NCCLS. Performance standards for antimicrobial susceptibility testing. 14th informational supplement. Wayne, PA: National Committee for Clinical Laboratory Standards; 2004.

[16] Chastre J, Wolff M, Fagon JY, et al. Comparison of 8 vs 15 days of antibiotic therapy for ventilator-associated pneumonia in adults: a randomized trial. JAMA 2003;290(19): 2588–98.

[17] Singh N, Rogers P, Atwood CW, Wagener MM, Yu VL. Short-course empiric antibiotic therapy for patients with pulmonary infiltrates in the intensive care unit. A proposed solution for indiscriminate antibiotic prescription. Am J Respir Crit Care Med 2000;162(2 Pt 1):505–11.

[18] Paterson DL, Singh N, Rihs JD, Squier C, Rihs BL, Muder RR. Control of an outbreak of infection due to extended-spectrum beta-lactamase–producing *Escherichia coli* in a liver transplantation unit. Clin Infect Dis 2001;33(1):126–8.

[19] Murray BE. Vancomycin-resistant enterococcal infections. N Engl J Med 2000;342(10): 710–21.

[20] Squier C, Rihs JD, Risa KJ, et al. *Staphylococcus aureus* rectal carriage and its association with infections in patients in a surgical intensive care unit and a liver transplant unit. Infect Control Hosp Epidemiol 2002;23(9):495–501.

[21] Francois P, Pittet D, Bento M, et al. Rapid detection of methicillin-resistant *Staphylococcus aureus* directly from sterile or nonsterile clinical samples by a new molecular assay. J Clin Microbiol 2003;41(1):254–60.

[22] Arbeit RD. Laboratory procedures for the epidemiologic analysis of microorganisms. In: Murray PR, editor. Manual of clinical microbiology. 7th edition. Washington DC: ASM Press; 1999.

[23] Anaissie EJ, Penzak SR, Dignani MC. The hospital water supply as a source of nosocomial infections: a plea for action. Arch Intern Med 2002;162(13):1483–92.

[24] Srinivasan A, Wolfenden LL, Song X, et al. An outbreak of *Pseudomonas aeruginosa* infections associated with flexible bronchoscopes. N Engl J Med 2003;348(3):221–7.

[25] Branger C, Bruneau B, Lesimple AL, et al. Epidemiological typing of extended-spectrum beta-lactamase-producing *Klebsiella pneumoniae* isolates responsible for five outbreaks in a university hospital. J Hosp Infect 1997;36(1):23–36.

[26] Gaillot O, Maruejouls C, Abachin E, et al. Nosocomial outbreak of *Klebsiella pneumoniae* producing SHV-5 extended-spectrum beta-lactamase, originating from a contaminated ultrasonography coupling gel. J Clin Microbiol 1998;36(5):1357–60.

[27] Rogues AM, Boulard G, Allery A, et al. Thermometers as a vehicle for transmission of extended-spectrum-beta- lactamase producing *Klebisiella pneumoniae*. J Hosp Infect 2000;45(1):76–7.

[28] Wang SA, Tokars JI, Bianchine PJ, et al. *Enterobacter cloacae* bloodstream infections traced to contaminated human albumin. Clin Infect Dis 2000;30(1):35–40.

[29] Ostrowsky BE, Whitener C, Bredenberg HK, et al. *Serratia marcescens* bacteremia traced to an infused narcotic. N Engl J Med 2002;346(20):1529–37.

[30] Passaro DJ, Waring L, Armstrong R, et al. Postoperative *Serratia marcescens* wound infections traced to an out-of-hospital source. J Infect Dis 1997;175(4):992–5.

[31] Moolenaar RL, Crutcher JM, San Joaquin VH, et al. A prolonged outbreak of *Pseudomonas aeruginosa* in a neonatal intensive care unit: did staff fingernails play a role in disease transmission? Infect Control Hosp Epidemiol 2000;21(2):80–5.

[32] Foca M, Jakob K, Whittier S, et al. Endemic *Pseudomonas aeruginosa* infection in a neonatal intensive care unit. N Engl J Med 2000;343(10):695–700.

[33] Muto CA, Jernigan JA, Ostrowsky BE, et al. SHEA guideline for preventing nosocomial transmission of multidrug-resistant strains of *Staphylococcus aureus* and enterococcus. Infect Control Hosp Epidemiol 2003;24(5):362–86.

[34] Paterson DL, Yu VL. Extended-spectrum beta-lactamases: a call for improved detection and control. Clin Infect Dis 1999;29(6):1419–22.

[35] Cornaglia G, Mazzariol A, Lauretti L, Rossolini GM, Fontana R. Hospital outbreak of carbapenem-resistant *Pseudomonas aeruginosa* producing VIM-1, a novel transferable metallo-beta-lactamase. Clin Infect Dis 2000;31(5):1119–25.

[36] Yan JJ, Ko WC, Tsai SH, Wu HM, Wu JJ. Outbreak of infection with multidrug-resistant *Klebsiella pneumoniae* carrying bla(IMP-8) in a university medical center in Taiwan. J Clin Microbiol 2001;39(12):4433–9.

[37] Giakkoupi P, Xanthaki A, Kanelopoulou M, et al. VIM-1 Metallo-beta-lactamase-producing *Klebsiella pneumoniae* strains in Greek hospitals. J Clin Microbiol 2003;41(8):3893–6.

[38] Royle J, Halasz S, Eagles G, et al. Outbreak of extended spectrum beta lactamase producing *Klebsiella pneumoniae* in a neonatal unit. Arch Dis Child Fetal Neonatal Ed 1999;80(1):F64–8.

[39] Eisen D, Russell EG, Tymms M, Roper EJ, Grayson ML, Turnidge J. Random amplified polymorphic DNA and plasmid analyses used in investigation of an outbreak of multiresistant *Klebsiella pneumoniae*. J Clin Microbiol 1995;33(3):713–7.

[40] Hugonnet S, Perneger TV, Pittet D. Alcohol-based handrub improves compliance with hand hygiene in intensive care units. Arch Intern Med 2002;162(9):1037–43.

[41] Mhand RA, Brahimi N, Moustaoui N, et al. Characterization of extended-spectrum beta-lactamase-producing *Salmonella typhimurium* by phenotypic and genotypic typing methods. J Clin Microbiol 1999;37(11):3769–73.

[42] Lucet JC, Decre D, Fichelle A, et al. Control of a prolonged outbreak of extended-spectrum beta-lactamase-producing enterobacteriaceae in a university hospital. Clin Infect Dis 1999;29(6):1411–8.

[43] Macrae MB, Shannon KP, Rayner DM, Kaiser AM, Hoffman PN, French GL. A simultaneous outbreak on a neonatal unit of two strains of multiply antibiotic resistant *Klebsiella pneumoniae* controllable only by ward closure. J Hosp Infect 2001;49(3):183–92.

[44] Safdar N, Maki DG. The commonality of risk factors for nosocomial colonization and infection with antimicrobial-resistant *Staphylococcus aureus*, enterococcus, gram-negative bacilli, *Clostridium difficile*, and *Candida*. Ann Intern Med 2002;136(11):834–44.

[45] Quale J, Landman D, Saurina G, Atwood E, DiTore V, Patel K. Manipulation of a hospital antimicrobial formulary to control an outbreak of vancomycin-resistant enterococci. Clin Infect Dis 1996;23(5):1020–5.

[46] Landman D, Quale JM, Mayorga D, et al. Citywide clonal outbreak of multiresistant *Acinetobacter baumannii* and *Pseudomonas aeruginosa* in Brooklyn, NY: the preantibiotic era has returned. Arch Intern Med 2002;162(13):1515–20.

[47] Rahal JJ, Urban C, Horn D, et al. Class restriction of cephalosporin use to control total cephalosporin resistance in nosocomial *Klebsiella*. JAMA 1998;280(14):1233–7.

[48] May AK, Melton SM, McGwin G, Cross JM, Moser SA, Rue LW. Reduction of vancomycin-resistant enterococcal infections by limitation of broad-spectrum cephalosporin use in a trauma and burn intensive care unit. Shock 2000;14(3):259–64.

[49] Bradley SJ, Wilson AL, Allen MC, Sher HA, Goldstone AH, Scott GM. The control of hyperendemic glycopeptide-resistant *Enterococcus* spp. on a haematology unit by changing antibiotic usage. *J Antimicrob Chemother.* Feb 1999;43(2):261–6.

[50] Smith DW. Decreased antimicrobial resistance after changes in antibiotic use. *Pharmacotherapy.* Aug 1999;19(8 Pt 2):129S–32S.

[51] Donskey CJ, Chowdhry TK, Hecker MT, et al. Effect of antibiotic therapy on the density of vancomycin-resistant enterococci in the stool of colonized patients. N Engl J Med 2000; 343(26):1925–32.

[52] Livermore DM. Multiple mechanisms of antimicrobial resistance in *Pseudomonas aeruginosa*: our worst nightmare? Clin Infect Dis 2002;34(5):634–40.

[53] Villers D, Espaze E, Coste-Burel M, et al. Nosocomial *Acinetobacter baumannii* infections: microbiological and clinical epidemiology. Ann Intern Med 1998;129(3):182–9.

[54] Gerding DN, Larson TA. Aminoglycoside resistance in gram-negative bacilli during increased amikacin use. Comparison of experience in 14 United States hospitals with experience in the Minneapolis Veterans Administration Medical Center. Am J Med 1985;79(1A):1–7.

[55] Chiew YF, Yeo SF, Hall LM, Livermore DM. Can susceptibility to an antimicrobial be restored by halting its use? The case of streptomycin versus *Enterobacteriaceae*. J Antimicrob Chemother 1998;41(2):247–51.

[56] Bonhoeffer S, Lipsitch M, Levin BR. Evaluating treatment protocols to prevent antibiotic resistance. Proc Natl Acad Sci USA 1997;94(22):12106–11.

[57] Gruson D, Hilbert G, Vargas F, et al. Rotation and restricted use of antibiotics in a medical intensive care unit. Impact on the incidence of ventilator-associated pneumonia caused by antibiotic-resistant gram-negative bacteria. Am J Respir Crit Care Med 2000;162(3 Pt 1): 837–43.

[58] Raymond DP, Pelletier SJ, Crabtree TD, et al. Impact of a rotating empiric antibiotic schedule on infectious mortality in an intensive care unit. Crit Care Med 2001;29(6): 1101–8.

CLINICS IN
LABORATORY
MEDICINE

ELSEVIER
SAUNDERS

Clin Lab Med 24 (2004) 343–361

Antibiotic resistance in the institutionalized elderly

Andrea M. Hujer, BS, Christopher R. Bethel, MS,
Kristine M. Hujer, MS, Robert A. Bonomo, MD*

*Research Service, Louis Stokes Veterans Affairs Medical Center,
10701 East Boulevard, Cleveland, Ohio 44106, USA*

Geriatric patients frequently are cared for in long term care facilities (LTCFs) which are now a major component of our health care delivery system. These facilities provide a range of necessary services including rehabilitation, chronic care, adult daycare, assisted living, and skilled nursing. At present, approximately 2.5 million residents live in LTCFs. Nearly half of the 2.2 million people who turned 65 years old in 1990 will enter an LTCFs at least once before they die [1,2].

Infections are one of the principal causes of morbidity and mortality in LTCFs [3–5]. Prevalence of infections in the nursing home population ranges from 1.8 to 9.4 per 1000 resident-days depending on the patient populations studied and the detection methods used [6–10]. Because LTCFs are a less costly alternative to hospitalization, clinicians are treating many serious infections in the nursing home [11,12]. Consequently, LTCFs will increasingly be recognized as sources of endemic organisms resistant to multiple antibiotics [13–18].

β-Lactams are a valuable class of potent antimicrobials with broad-spectrum activity against Gram-negative and Gram-positive organisms. The safety and efficacy of this class of antibiotics make them easy choices for empiric treatment of infections in the elderly. Oral and parenteral β-lactams, particularly cephalosporins, are among the most frequently prescribed medications in LTCFs. Unfortunately, excessive use of these antibiotics has created serious threats to our therapeutic armamentarium: the emergence of methicillin-resistant *Staphylococcus aureus* and of Gram-negative

This work was supported by grants from the Veterans Affairs Medical Center Merit Review Program.

* Corresponding author.

E-mail address: robert.bonomo@med.va.gov (R.A. Bonomo).

pathogens resistant to third-generation cephalosporins such as cefotaxime, ceftazidime, and ceftriaxone [19]. Of these third-generation cephalosporins, resistance to ceftazidime is most frequently recognized.

The major mechanism responsible for ceftazidime resistance in Gram-negative bacteria is the production of β-lactamases. This article summarizes the diversity of β-lactamases, highlights the important enzymes that confer ceftazidime resistance in LTCFs, and details the methods used to identify and characterize these enzymes. A clear challenge is to apply these techniques to epidemiologic and molecular studies conducted in LTCFs.

β-Lactamases

β-Lactams are lethal for bacteria. By inhibiting bacterial cell wall–synthesizing enzymes (transpeptidases and carboxypeptidases), penicillins and cephalosporins rapidly kill bacteria. Because of their affinity for penicillin, the targets of penicillin are referred to as penicillin-binding proteins (PBPs). β-Lactams interfere with the synthesis of new peptidoglycan (N-acetyl glucosamine attached to N-acetyl muramic acid and short peptide chains that are cross-linked with a pentapeptide bridge) by acting as transition state analogs of penicillin. Unabated, bacterial autolytic enzymes then break down cell walls and permit the influx of water, resulting in cell lysis and death.

β-Lactamases are bacterial enzymes that protect bacteria from β-lactam compounds by hydrolyzing the lactam bond (C-N) of β-lactams in a two-step reaction. This results in the formation of an inactive product, referred to as a penicillinoate. β-lactamases are hydrolases and the presence of a strategically positioned water molecule in the active site is critical for efficient function.

As a rule, β-lactamases are located in the periplasmic space in Gram-negative bacteria or in the immediate external environment as in staphylococci. β-Lactamases are globular in shape and have two domains: α-helical and β-pleated sheets. Although the primary amino acid sequences of various β-lactamases may differ significantly among these enzymes, their overall shape and topology are similar (Fig. 1). Examination of the catalytic machinery of these proteins shows that there are four conserved motifs common to all β-lactamases and PBPs. Because of this structural and functional similarity, it is speculated that β-lactamases have arisen from PBPs [20,21].

β-Lactamase nomenclature

Is there is any logic to why β-lactamases are designated as they are, such as TEM-1, SHV-1, OXA-1, and PSE-1? In practice, β-lactamases have been named after the location they have been discovered (MIR-1 from Miriam Hospital in Rhode Island), a biochemical property (IRT-1, Inhibitor-

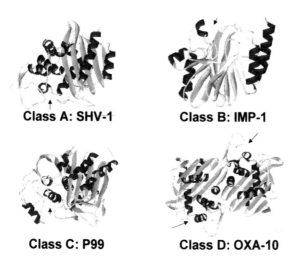

Class A: SHV-1   Class B: IMP-1

Class C: P99   Class D: OXA-10

Fig. 1. Ribbon diagrams of β-lactamases from Ambler Classes A to D drawn with the program WebLab ViewerLite 3.5. The coordinates were taken from the Protein Data Bank (www.rscb.org) for 1SHV, 2BLT, 1DDK, and 1FOF. Blue represents β-pleated sheets and red represents alpha helices. Arrows indicate the active site.

resistant TEM or CMT-1, complex mutant of TEM), the patient of origin (TEM-1 for Temionera), the bacterial species (PSE-1, *Pseudomonas aeruginosa*), or the country of origin (BSE-1, Brazil). A website is available that has enumerated the amino acid variants of TEM, SHV, OXA, CMY, IMP, CTX-M, and a variety of AmpC type β-lactamases (http://www.lahey.org/studies).

β-Lactamase classification

Two schemes are in use to classify β-lactamases: the Ambler classification method (four classes, A–D) and the Bush-Jacoby-Medeiros classification system (groups 1–4) [22,23]. These classification schemes assist in the understanding of the relationship of these enzymes to one another. The Ambler system classifies β-lactamases based on sequence homology, whereas the Bush-Jacoby-Medeiros system groups enzymes according to functional similarities. In the Ambler system, class A, C, and D β-lactamases are serine-based enzymes, whereas class B enzymes are metallo-β-lactamases. Metallo-β-lactamses use one or two zinc atoms in the active site to catalyze the hydrolysis of the β-lactam and are able to hydrolyze carbapenems [24].

Common β-lactamases found in enteric bacilli are either primarily penicillinases (benzylpenicillin is a favored substrate) or cephalosporinases (cephalothin as a substrate). For example, TEM-1, the class A enzyme that is found in *Escherichia coli*, demonstrates a turnover rate (k_{cat}) for penicillin that can reach 1000 to 2000 molecules/second. Despite class C β-lactamases having turnover rates that are not as fast as TEM-1, class C cephalosporinases are particularly well suited for the hydrolysis of ceftazidime, which has high affinity (K_m) for the active site of this enzyme [25]. Class D β-lactamases demonstrate a substrate specificity for oxacillin [26]. β-Lactamases that can confer resistance to third-generation cephalosporins such as ceftazidime are of three types:

1. Class A or group 2be. These are predominantly plasmid-encoded TEM-1 and SHV-1 derivatives that have "extended their substrate spectrum" and are commonly referred to as "extended spectrum β-lactamases demonstrate a substrate specificity for oxacilin [24]. β-lactamases" (ESBLs). There are numerous reports of novel non-TEM non-SHV β-lactamases that confer resistance to ceftazidime.
2. Class D or group 2f OXA β-lactamases.
3. Class C, or group 1 predominately chromosomally encoded β-lactamases (eg, AmpC).

Table 1 lists clinically important β-lactamases among the class A, C, and class D enzymes that confer resistance to ceftazidime. The reader is referred to references that summarize the numbering system used for class A β-lactamases and for the relationship between PBPs and β-lactamases [27,28]. An important question arises: what are the changes in these β-lactamases that confer new hydrolytic properties?

Extended spectrum β-lactamases

β-Lactamase–mediated resistance to ceftazidime is very worrisome when found in *Klebsiella pneumoniae* and *Escherichia coli*, the common enteric bacilli that colonize and infect elderly patients. Many *E coli* and virtually all *K pneumoniae* possess TEM-1 and SHV-1 β-lactamases, respectively. These class A enzymes confer resistance to the aminopenicillins (ampicillin, amoxicillin) and first-generation cephalosporins (eg, cefazolin), but not to third-generation cephalosporins (eg, ceftazidime) or to cephamycins (eg, cefoxitin). Specific nucleotide changes in the β-lactamase gene result in a TEM or SHV β-lactamase enzyme with altered amino acids and new hydrolytic capacities that can inactivate antibiotics like ceftazidime (Table 2) [29,30]. The structural explanation for this altered phenotype rests on

Table 1
Clinically important β-lactamases that confer ceftazidime resistance

| Class A | Class C | | Class D |
	Chromosomal	Plasmid	
TEM-10	P99	MIR-1	OXA-10
TEM-26	AmpC	CMY-2	OXA-17
CTX M-2		ACT-1	
PSE-2			

Table 2
Amino mutations responsible for extended spectrum profile in TEM and SHV β-lactamase

Wild type TEM or SHV	Extended spectrum β-lactamases
Glu104	Lys 104 (TEM-6)
Arg164	Ser164 (TEM-10, -12)
Asp179	Asn179 (SHV-8)
Glu238	Ser 238 (SHV-2, -5)
Glu240	Lys 240 (TEM-10, SHV-5)

Ambler numbering system used to show amino acid positions [27].

specific movement of the b3 β-pleated sheet of the enzyme with the formation of altered H bonds (see later discussion).

Frequently, the ESBLs present in *E coli* and *K pneumoniae* are on large plasmids that move from one genus or species to another. These plasmids also carry genes that confer resistance against other antibiotics such as amino-glycosides, trimethoprim, sulfamethoxazole, and so forth [31]. Resistance to β-lactam/β-lactamase inhibitor combinations (ampicillin/sulbactam, amoxicillin/clavulanate, ticarcillin/clavulanate or piperacillin/tazobactam) is usually not a characteristic demonstrated by ESBLs. In fact, TEM and SHV-type ESBLs are usually more susceptible to β-lactam/β-lactamase inhibitor combinations containing clavulanic acid or tazobactam [29,30].

Recent structural analyses explain why TEM and SHV β-lactamases develop these new hydrolytic properties [32]. In all of these proposals, key amino acid mutations result in structural modifications that influence the binding or turnover of third-generation cephalosporins. Movement of a critical part of the enzyme improves catalysis by permitting the large third-generation cephalosporin molecule to form favorable contacts in the active site. The crystal structure of the ESBLs, SHV-2 and TEM-52, reveal that there is a major movement of noncatalytic residue in the B3 β strand that expands the active site cavity to accommodate the large side chain of ceftazidime [32,33].

It is unknown why ESBLs arise predominantly in *K pneumoniae* [30]. TEM and SHV-type ESBLs are also being found in *Salmonella* spp, *Serratia* spp, *Morganella morganii*, *Proteus* spp, *Enterobacter* spp, and even *Pseudomonas aeruginosa* [30]. Gram-negative organisms commonly possess multiple β-lactamases [20]. This finding may not be entirely by chance or accident. One could envision a setting in which the presence of more than one β-lactamase confers an evolutionary advantage to the bacterium fighting to survive in "an ocean of β-lactam antibiotics."

Amp C β-lactamases

Amp C β-lactamases, also referred to as cephalosporinases, are commonly recognized in *Enterobacter aerogenes*, *Enterobacter cloacae*, *Citrobacter* spp.,

Morganella morganii, and *Pseudomonas* spp. [34]. As a rule, these β-lactamases are resistant to inhibition by β-lactam/β-lactamase inhibitor combinations, confer cefoxitin resistance, and are "inducible." These enzymes are "induced" by recycling of cell wall components (muropeptides), which triggers the synthesis of these broad-spectrum ceftazidime-hydrolyzing enzymes [35]. The regulatory process controlling their induction is now receiving a great deal of attention since the various steps in the process can be potential drug targets. The crystallographic structures of the AmpC β-lactamase of *E coli* and *Enterobacter cloacae* P99 is also known [36,37]. The active site is larger than that of wild-type class A enzymes, hence explaining their ability to hydrolyze third-generation cephalosporins.

Although typically found within the bacterial chromosome, growing numbers of AmpC β-lactamases are being found on plasmids [38–44]. Examples of these are CMY-2, ACT-1, ACC-1, LAT-1, and MIR-1β-lactamases. Based on their homology to AmpC β-lactamases, distinct groups exist. How frequently plasmid-mediated AmpC β-lactamases move from strain to strain is unknown. The presence of an AmpC β-lactamase in a bacterium missing an outer membrane protein, the channel that permits the entry of small molecules into the Gram-negative cell, can result in resistance to all β-lactams, including carbapenems [40–42]. The number of β-lactamases that can hydrolyze every β-lactam is limited to certain carbapenemases conferring resistance to imipenem, cephalosporins, and penicillins [28].

Non-TEM, non-SHV β-lactamases

In addition to TEM and SHV ESBLs and AmpC β-lactamases, other β-lactamases are being reported that confer third-generation cephalosporin resistance. Examples are PER-1 (from *Pseudomonas aeruginosa*), Toho-1, CTX-M-1, CTX-M-2, CTX-M-15, OXA-14, BES-1, VEB-1, GES-1, IBC-1, and IBC-2 β-lactamases [45–49]. Initially regarded as curiosities, these enzymes are now being discovered at an alarming rate and will assume greater importance in the next decade [47]. It must be kept in mind that unlike their wild-type TEM or SHV counterparts, these β-lactamases naturally possess the ability to hydrolyze third-generation cephalosporins and are usually not inactivated by currently available β-lactam/β-lactamase inhibitor combinations [46]. The threat here may be in the widespread dissemination of another line of β-lactamases conferring resistance to all β-lactams.

Scope of ceftazidime resistance

Since the discovery in 1983 of transferable resistance to third-generation cephalosporins in *K pneumoniae*, ESBL-mediated resistance to ceftazidime has been reported nationally [50,51]. The Centers for Disease Control

(CDC) and the National Nosocomial Infection Surveillance System (NNISS) reported that over the period 1987 to 1991, the percentage of *K pneumoniae* isolates that were resistant to ceftazidime increased from 1.5% to 3.6%. A more recent survey of 33,869 Gram-negative isolates from 400 intensive care units in the United States documented an even more impressive rise (14.4% among *Klebsiella* isolates) [52–54]. The prevalence of ceftazidime resistance among *Klebsiella* isolates now is close to 20% in some areas. Resistance to non-β-lactam antibiotics is also extremely common in these organisms; two thirds of ceftazidime-resistant *Klebsiella* strains were resistant to both gentamicin and tobramycin versus 3.6% among ceftazidime-susceptible strains, and nearly half were resistant to ciprofloxacin. Factors predictably associated with this increase are hospital length of stay and cephalosporin use [52].

Do ESBL-producing organisms also cause serious infections? In a survey by Sahm et al [54], ceftazidime resistance in *Klebsiella* isolates was more prevalent among isolates from blood (12.7%) than from urine (7.1%) or from respiratory sources (9.3%). In the most comprehensive analysis of ESBL-producing *K pneumoniae* to date, Paterson et al [55] have shown 43.5% of blood stream isolates of *K pneumoniae* from ICU patients produced ESBLs. Although not a significant risk factor for mortality in this study, close to 40% of the patients with *K pneumoniae* bacteremia were >65 years old.

Nearly 150 ESBLs of the TEM, OXA, and SHV varieties have been identified [56]. The TEM family of plasmid-mediated β-lactamases is the most prevalent. Usually, there is a dominant enzyme in a given city or institution [56]. These enzymes vary considerably in the level of resistance conferred to antibiotics such as cefotaxime and ceftazidime. Automated susceptibility systems, which are the most commonly used systems in microbiology laboratories nationally, occassionally miss this type of resistance due to the low inoculum used in testing isolates and the use of breakpoints that are too high [57–59]. Although these organisms are usually susceptible to β-lactam/β-lactamase inhibitor combinations, some ESBL-producing organisms will also display resistance to these combinations. When this occurs, a novel inhibitor-resistant TEM or SHV enzyme, overproduction of β-lactamase, or multiple β-lactamases (class C and class A) are suspected.

Establishment of ceftazidime resistance in skilled nursing facilities

Organisms resistant to third-generation cephalosporins can arise in LTCFs by one of two mechanisms. First, a patient that is colonized or infected with a third-generation cephalosporin-resistant enteric can be transferred from a hospital to an LTCFs. The ESBL-producing organism can be present as a colonizer of the perineum, the stool, or isolated from a urine sample of a patient with an indwelling bladder catheter. Second, excessive use of β-lactams eventually selects for mutations in the β-lactamase gene(s) that confers a selective advantage such as ceftazidime resistance. Surprisingly, clinicians do not appreciate how frequently spontaneous mutations in β-lactamase genes can occur. In the laboratory, resistance to ceftazidime (ESBL phenotype) in *E coli* possessing a plasmid-encoded SHV-type β-lactamase has been selected at a frequency of one ceftazidime-resistant organism per 100 million bacteria [60], which is approximately the number of organisms present in about 100 mL of infected urine. Hence, in the appropriate environment (chronic indwelling bladder catheter, multiple courses of antibiotics for catheter-associated bladder infections, infected pressure ulcers, or aspiration pneumonia), a resistant organism can have a selective advantage. Once established, the β-lactamase resistance genes can transfer on a plasmid from one species or genus to another [61–64]. Studies have also shown that novel ESBLs can remain endemic to an institution even when ceftazidime use is eliminated [64].

An emerging concern in the care of elderly patients in LTCFs is the development of complex infections with ceftazidime-resistant organisms. A number of very alarming reports have appeared in the past decade that detail this critical problem [64–67]. In each case, the link between ceftazidime resistance and antibiotic use is clear.

Rice et al [64] first described a novel ESBL (TEM-26) in an LTCFs in Massachusetts. Up to then, ESBLs were mostly found in Europe, were strictly nosocomial isolates, and had not been described in LTCGs in the United States. This report brought attention to the frightening possibility that excessive antibiotic use in LTCFs promotes the emergence and establishment of ESBLs. In 1995, Bradford et al [65] reported the discovery of SHV-7, a novel ceftazidime-resistant ESBL isolated from a patient living in a nursing home in New York. This ESBL, found in *E coli*, further highlighted the growing problem of ceftazidime resistance in LTCFs. To determine risk factors for the acquisition of resistant bacteria in LTCFs, Muder et al [66] performed a case control analysis examining the colonizing flora of nursing home residents. This group found 35 patients colonized with resistant enterobacteriacae; 55% of these were ceftazidime resistant. Here, the prior use of ampicillin was an important risk factor for colonization with a resistant pathogen. In a subsequent study by Schiappa et al [67], the debilitated elderly were the most common patient source of ceftazidime-resistant bloodstream isolates in patients admitted to the hospital. TEM-10 was the most frequent ESBL discovered in these isolates. A major outbreak of ESBL-producing pathogens has also occurred in the Cleveland Veterans Affairs Medical Center [68,69]. Here, the most frequent ceftazidime-resistant isolates were recovered from a geriatric chronic care ward. Again, this was associated with the use of third-generation cephalosporins.

A recently conducted epidemiologic survey in Chicago shows that LTCFs are important reservoirs for ceftazidime-resistant enteric bacilli [70]. In the cohort of 55 hospitalized patients infected or colonized with ceftazidim-resistant enterics, 35 came from LTCFs (60%). All these strains were also resistant to aminoglycosides, trimethoprim/sulfamethoxazole, and quinolones. Independent risk factors for colonization were the presence of multiple co-morbidities, the presence of a gastrostomy tube, pressure ulcers, and prior receipt of quinolones or trimethoprim/sulfamethoxazole. The plasmid-encoded TEM-10 β-lactamase was discovered in seven different strains of enteric bacilli in these patients, suggesting that poor infection control practices may have facilitated the spread of this highly mobile resistance determinant.

Subsequent studies at a single large LTCFs in Chicago documented extensive colonization with an ESBL-producing pathogen. Of the 163 patients, 67 (41%) had ceftazidime-resistant *K pneumoniae* or *E coli* isolated from rectal swabs. Although many different ESBLS were detected, most strains harbored TEM-10. Molecular typing studies documented that most *K pneumoniae* isolates were clonal, with two types accounting for 90% of strains, whereas no strain type predominated among the *E coli* isolates. Recent transfer to an acute care unit and antibiotic exposure were independent risk factors for acquisition of ESBL-producing strains in this setting [67].

As ceftazidime-resistant organisms in the institutionalized elderly become endemic, treatment options are rapidly becoming limited. Quinolones are highly effective, but resistance can emerge rapidly. In addition, geriatricians are often concerned with the potential neurotoxicity of carbapenems and quinolones. Carbapenems, available only in the parenteral form, are reserved as "last resort" β-lactams.

Despite our recognition of the seriousness of this problem, the molecular epidemiology of ceftazidime-resistant Gram-negative organisms possessing ESBLs or AmpC β-lactamases is unknown in the institutionalized, elderly population. If LTCFs are reservoirs for resistant pathogens, major challenges exist: how can we devise intervention strategies to halt the emergence of ceftazidime-resistant organisms in LTCFs? What are the factors that accelerate colonization by ceftazidime-resistant pathogens? Can we interrupt the transfer of ceftazidime-resistant pathogens from LTCFs to hospitals? To answer these important questions, one must begin by ascertaining the frequencies and types of ceftazidime-resistant organisms found in LTCFs, how often the institutionalized elderly colonized or infected with organisms harboring ceftazidime-resistant phenotypes are admitted from LTCFs to hospitals, and if there are any epidemiologic or clinical factors that can be modified to halt this progression.

Addressing antimicrobial resistance in the skilled nursing facility

The fecal flora represents a large potential reservoir for the evolution of antimicrobial-resistant organisms as well as a site where resistance genes transfer from commensal flora to virulent micro-organisms [71–75].

Antimicrobial agents and hospitalization have a major impact on the aerobic flora of the elderly. There are, however, few longitudinal prospective studies in the literature comparing the effects of these two factors on transfer of resistant organisms between LTCFs and hospitals. Given the prevalence of infections in the elderly and their increasing numbers, this is an alarming consideration.

The magnitude of risk for patients to be colonized with fecal aerobic Gram-negative bacilli resistant to β-lactams is related to length of stay and use of β-lactam therapy [71–75]. In this framework, we outline a paradigm to begin to assess this problem in LTCFs. This approach combines epidemiologic surveillance, use of molecular techniques, and the establishment of central laboratories. We have assessed the essential components of this paradigm in a descriptive study of elderly patients admitted to an inpatient ward [76].

Active surveillance

As a first measure, we propose the establishment of an active surveillance system. This approach samples, collects, and analyzes the enteric flora of debilitated or elderly patients who are at risk for colonization by resistant Gram-negative bacilli. This will permit clinicians to monitor the presence, characteristics, frequency, type, and dissemination of multi-resistant enteric pathogens. At present, the only indicators available for determining frequency of β-lactam-resistant pathogens are the clinical microbiology records at individual institutions. A network surveillance system for detecting the presence of colonizing organisms by obtaining rectal swabs or sampling fecal flora is the first step in the accurate detection of clinically significant nosocomial organisms possessing resistance determinants. After obtaining appropriate consent, a stool sample is obtained on admission to the LTCFs, sent to the laboratory, and plated on MacConkey agar containing a third-generation cephalosporin, such as ceftazidime (2 µg/mL). After 18 to 24 hours of incubation, any ceftazidime-resistant enteric isolates are identified.

Characterizing ceftazidime resistance

Ceftazidime-resistant organisms in fecal samples are characterized by using MIC interpretative categories established by the NCCLS [57]. However, the inocula recommended and the interpretative MIC break-points established often misclassify ESBL-producing isolates as being susceptible to ceftazidime and other third-generation cephalosporins. This is also the case with commercial systems in common use, such as MicroScan and Vitek systems [59]. To reliably detect ESBLs, it is necessary to test ceftazidime alone and ceftazidime/clavulanate in combination, either by disk diffusion or MIC determination. Both methods are available commercially in the form of disks or gradient-diffusion (E-test) strips [59]. ESBL-producing isolates demonstrate the pattern of being ceftazidime resistant and ceftazidime/clavulanate susceptible. Organisms resistant to ceftazidime and ceftazidime/clavulanate usually have AmpC type β-lactamases and are also resistant to cefoxitin. It is also possible to induce high-level ceftozidime resistance with cefoxitin [21].

After complete β-lactam susceptibility testing (ampicillin, ampicillin/sulbactam, amoxacillin/clavulanate, piperacillin, piperacillin/tazobactam, cephalothin, cefuroxime, cefoxitin, ceftazidime, cefotaxime, ceftriaxone, imipenem) has been performed, the next step is testing if the resistance to ceftazidime is transferable. Conjugation experiments can be designed using a recipient strain that is resistant to rifampin (example *E coli* J53-2) and selecting for ceftazidime and rifampin resistance. Once selected, the double disk diffusion test can again be repeated to verify that the ESBL was transferred to the transconjugant. It is common to find that the donor and transconjugant will demonstrate different levels of resistance against test β-lactams. This may be due to the permeability characteristics of the donor and transconjugant being different, the β-lactamase being expressed differently in one host versus the other, or the presence of more than one β-lactamase.

Molecular epidemiology

The principle techniques used in tracking and evaluating β-lactam-resistant organisms are analytical isoelectric focusing (aIEF), DNA finger-printing by pulsed-field gel electrophoresis (PFGE) of enzymatic DNA digests, and polymerase chain reaction (PCR) amplification of β-lactamase genes. A number of other methods can be used, such as Southern blotting and plasmid analysis, but their utility and specificity are not as great as with aIEF, PFGE, and PCR. Novel genetic methods are also being developed. These methods are described later.

Analytical isoelectric focusing

aIEF is a fast, efficient method of identifying β-lactamases based on protein charge [56,77,78]. aIEF has been used as a rapid screening tool for detecting β-lactamase enzymes in clinical isolates. A major limitation is that aIEF does not identify clonality, and it is not always diagnostic of new variants. We have developed a technique that can be performed after growing an overnight culture of bacteria [79]. Cell pellets are made, resuspended in buffer, and treated with lysozyme and EDTA to yield a crude extract. The proteins in this extract are electrophoresed on a gel with known standards. The β-lactamases are detected by overlaying the gel with filter paper containing nitrocefin, a chromogenic cephalosporin that turns from yellow to red when a β-lactamase enzyme hydrolyzes its β-lactam bond. Matching the red color bands produced by the hydrolysis of nitrocefin to standards gives the investigator a reasonable idea as to which

Table 3
Isoelectric points of select β-lactamases

TEM-1	5.4
TEM-10	5.6
TEM-12	5.25
TEM-26	5.6
SHV-1	7.6
SHV-2	7.6
SHV-5	8.2

β-lactamases are present (Table 3). This method also is a satisfactory way to demonstrate that a recipient strain possesses the same β-lactamase as the donor.

Polymerase chain reaction amplification of β-lactamase genes

Using primers specific to TEM and SHV β-lactamases, it is possible to amplify β-lactamase genes from individual clinical isolates. The sequence of the TEM and SHV primers needed to amplify these genes has been described and can be synthesized or obtained commercially, and PCR kits are readily available. To confirm that the primers amplified the β-lactamase genes, PCR products are electrophoresed on an agarose gel, and the presence of bands compared with those of known controls. One can also sequence the amplified DNA product directly or clone it into an appropriate vector and sequence the β-lactamase gene in the vector. This approach may be more difficult with other β-lactamases because sequence similarities are not as great as with TEM or SHV.

Pulsed-field gel electrophoresis of chromosomal DNA digests

PFGE of enzymatic digests of chromosomal DNA permits analysis of bacterial DNA fragments [80]. This technique is a variation of agarose gel electrophoresis in which the orientation of the electric field across the gel is changed periodically ("pulsed") rather than being kept constant as in conventional methods of using electrophoresis. This allows larger fragments of DNA to be effectively separated by size. Micro-organisms are embedded in agarose plugs or inserts, and the cell walls and cellular proteins are lysed and digested enzymatically. The isolated genomes are enzymatically digested with restriction endonucleases that have few recognition sites (eg, *Xba*I). The plugs are aligned on an agarose plate and placed in the electrophoresis chamber. Once electrophoresed and stained with ethidium bromide, the plate is then read and photographed. PFGE analysis is discriminatory and comparable or superior to other available techniques [81–88]. This technique has two notable limitations in that it is time consuming and requires specialized, relatively expensive equipment. Rapid methods of processing the bacterial plugs have made the process more efficient [87,88].

Other methods

Plasmid analysis, ribotyping, randomly amplified polymorphic DNA (RAPD), PCR based on repetitive chromosomal sequences (rep-PCR), restriction site insertion-PCR (RSI-PCR) are recently developed techniques to detect mutations of the β-lactamase genes to identify ESBLs. Chanawong et al [80] demonstrated that the combination of PCR-RFLP (restriction fragment length polymorphism) and RSI-PCR techniques can be readily applied to epidemiologic studies of the SHV β-lactamases. Another useful tool for the detection of certain variants is the combination PCR and single-strand conformational polymorphism (PCR-SSCP) and PCR-RLFP. Ligase chain reaction (LCR) is a recently developed technique also used to discriminate SHV variants. LCR uses a thermostable ligase and biotinylated LCR primers. It can detect single base pair changes [81].

A very promising method uses the sensitivity of PCR coupled with fluorescently labeled probes. Randeggar and Hachler [82] developed a technique using real-time PCR monitored with fluorescent-labeled hybridization probes followed by melting curve analysis. Their technique was able to detect SHV variants and discriminates between non-ESBLs and ESBLs. This method termed "the SHV melting curve mutation detection method" promises to save investigators hours of time. It remains to be established if this method can be applied to other ESBLs.

Enterobacterial repetitive intergenic consensus (ERIC)-based PCR has proven also to be an attractive method for epidemiologic investigations. Base on PCR amplification, this technique has been applied to investigations of clonality in *Salmonella* spp, *Mycobacterium tuberculosis, E coli, Brucella*, and *Lactobacillus.*

Our laboratory has recently developed immunologic methods to detect the presence of SHV and AmpC β-lactamases [84]. Using a highly sensitive and specific enzyme linked immunosorbent assay (ELISA) method, we have demonstrated > 95% sensitivity and specificity. Whether this can be readily applied to class D β-lactamases or class B metallo-enzymes remains to be established.

Clinical research centers

Because the techniques described previously are not readily available, we propose the establishment of central reference laboratories equipped to pursue these investigations. Instructions can be given to appropriately collect and handle samples and identify each type of resistant pathogen. Resistant organisms are sent to a central reference laboratory where the skills and techniques are in place to perform the appropriate analysis. Real-time data concerning resistance trends can be disseminated by the internet to all investigators. Treatment algorithms can be designed based on data collected institutionally or regionally [89].

Summary

Does finding Gram-negative organisms producing ESBLs and AmpC β-lactamases in LTCFs impact significantly patient morbidity and mortality? Studies have documented a significant mortality rate associated with ESBL-producing organisms. There is, however, a paucity of information on rates, risk factors, effects of colonization, and management of infections in LTCFs. The frequent transfer of chronically ill, elderly patients among institutions may accelerate the dissemination of ceftazidime-resistant Gram-negative enteric bacteria in LTCFs. Many of the chronically ill patients that reside in LTCFs are frequently admitted to acute care facilities, have chronic indwelling catheters, and have received multiple courses of antibiotic therapy. Once patients are colonized, it is unclear as to how long they remain colonized, or, more importantly, what role this new organism has in disease.

Identifying which organisms are involved and their relationship to clinically significant infections will permit us to introduce targeted, data-derived interventions that prevent and interrupt the nosocomial transmission of these organisms. This will enable us to understand the trends in molecular epidemiology of these emerging pathogens in the endemic setting. The results of such a study may also assist in the establishment of policies and infection control precautions necessary for admissions from, and discharges to, LTCFs. Now is the time to begin to address the impact and financial burdens of colonization and subsequent infection with multiresistant enterics that colonize patients from LTCFs. A systematic approach directed at understanding the results of antibiotic therapy is needed. Funding for these efforts should be a priority of agencies dedicated to quality care of the elderly.

References

[1] Yoshikawa TT, Norman DC. Infectious disease in the aging. Totowa, NJ: Humana Press; 2000.
[2] Kemper P, Murtaugh CM. Lifetime use of nursing home care. N Engl J Med 1991;324: 595–600.
[3] Irvine PW, Van Buren N, Crossley K. Causes for hospitalization of nursing home residents: the role of infection. J Am Geriatr Soc 1984;32:103–7.
[4] Rudman D, Mattson DE, Nagraj HS, Caindec N, Rudman IW, Jackson DL. Antecedents of death in the men of a Veterans Administration nursing home. J Am Geriatr Soc 1987;35: 496–502.
[5] Nicolle LE, Strausbaugh LJ, Garibaldi RA. Infections and antibiotic resistance in nursing homes. Clin Microbiol Rev 1996;9:1–17.
[6] Bradley SF. Infection and infection control in long term care settings. In: Yoshikawa TT, Norman DC, editors. Infectious disease in the aging. Totowa, NJ: Humana Press; 2000.
[7] Nicolle LE, Garibaldi RA. Infection control in long-term-care facilities. Infect Control Hosp Epidemiol 1995;16:348–53.

[8] Scheckler WE, Peterson PJ. Infections and infection control among residents of eight rural Wisconsin nursing homes. Arch Intern Med 1986;146:1981–4.

[9] Franson TR, Duthie EH Jr, Cooper JE, Van Oudenhoven G, Hoffmann RG. Prevalence survey of infections and their predisposing factors at a hospital-based nursing home care unit. J Am Geriatr Soc 1986;34:95–100.

[10] Darnowski SB, Gordon M, Simor AE. Two years of infection surveillance in a geriatric long-term care facility. Am J Infect Control 1991;19:185–90.

[11] Hing E. Effects of prospective payment system on nursing homes. Vital and Health Statistics, Series 13. Data from the National Health Survey. 1989;102:1–8613.

[12] Mylotte JM, Naughton B, Saludades C, Maszarovics Z. Validation and application of the pneumonia prognosis index to nursing home residents with pneumonia. J Am Geriatr Soc 1998;46:1538–44.

[13] John JF Jr, Ribner BS. Antibiotic resistance in long-term care facilities. Infect Control Hosp Epidemiol 1991;12:245–50.

[14] Weinstein RA. Resistant bacteria and infection control in the nursing home and hospital. Bull NY Acad Med 1987;63:337–44.

[15] Terpenning MS, Bradley SF, Wan JY, Chenoweth CE, Jorgensen KA, Kauffman CA. Colonization and infection with antibiotic-resistant bacteria in a long-term care facility. J Am Geriatr Soc 1994;42:1062–9.

[16] Yoshikawa TT. VRE, MRSA, PRP, and DRGNB in LTCF: lessons to be learned from this alphabet. J Am Geriatr Soc 1998;46:241–3.

[17] Bradley SF. Issues in the management of resistant bacteria in long-term-care facilities. Infect Control Hosp Epidemiol 1999;20:362–6.

[18] McCue JD. Antibiotic resistance: why is it increasing in nursing homes? Geriatrics 1997;52: 34–36, 39–43.

[19] Moellering RC Jr. Interaction between antimicrobial consumption and selection of resistant bacterial strains. Scand J Infect Dis Suppl 1990;70:18–24.

[20] Medeiros AA. Evolution and dissemination of beta-lactamases accelerated by generations of beta-lactam antibiotics. Clin Infect Dis 1997;24(Suppl 1):S19–45.

[21] Livermore DM. beta-Lactamases in laboratory and clinical resistance. Clin Microbiol Rev 1995;8:557–84.

[22] Ambler RP. The structure of beta-lactamases. Philos Trans R Soc Lond B Biol Sci 1980; 289:321–31.

[23] Bush K, Jacoby GA, Medeiros AA. A functional classification scheme for beta-lactamases and its correlation with molecular structure. Antimicrob Agents Chemother 1995;39: 1211–33.

[24] Rasmussen BA, Bush K. Carbapenem-hydrolyzing beta-lactamases. Antimicrob Agents Chemother 1997;41:223–32.

[25] Jaurin B, Grundstrom T. ampC cephalosporinase of Escherichia coli K-12 has a different evolutionary origin from that of beta-lactamases of the penicillinase type. Proc Natl Acad Sci USA 1981;78:4897–901.

[26] Ouellette M, Bissonnette L, Roy PH. Precise insertion of antibiotic resistance determinants into Tn21-like transposons: nucleotide sequence of the OXA-1 beta-lactamase gene. Proc Natl Acad Sci USA 1987;84:7378–82.

[27] Ambler RP, Coulson AF, Frere JM, et al. A standard numbering scheme for the class A beta-lactamases. Biochem J 1991;276(Pt 1):269–70.

[28] Massova I, Mobashery S. Kinship and diversification of bacterial penicillin-binding proteins and beta-lactamases. Antimicrob Agents Chemother 1998;42:1–17.

[29] Philippon A, Labia R, Jacoby G. Extended-spectrum beta-lactamases. Antimicrob Agents Chemother 1989;33:1131–6.

[30] Jacoby GA, Medeiros AA. More extended-spectrum beta-lactamases. Antimicrob Agents Chemother 1991;35:1697–704.

[31] Jacoby GA. Genetics of extended-spectrum beta-lactamases. Eur J Clin Microbiol Infect Dis 1994;13(Suppl 1):S2–11.

[32] Nakaga M, Mayama K, Hujer AM, Bonomo RA, Knox JR. Ultrahigh resolution structure of a class A beta-lactamase: on the mechanism and specificity of the extended-spectrum SHV-2 enzyme. J Mol Biol 2003;328(1):289–301.

[33] Orencia MC, Yoon JS, Ness JE, Stemmer WP, Stevens RC. Predicting the emergence of antibiotic resistance by directed evolution and structural analysis. Nat Struct Biol 2001;8: 238–42.

[34] Nordmann P. Trends in beta-lactam resistance among Enterobacteriaceae. Clin Infect Dis 1998;27(Suppl 1):S100–6.

[35] Jacobs C, Frere JM, Normark S. Cytosolic intermediates for cell wall biosynthesis and degradation control inducible beta-lactam resistance in gram-negative bacteria. Cell 1997; 88:823–32.

[36] Usher KC, Blaszczak LC, Weston GS, Shoichet BK, Remington SJ. Three-dimensional structure of AmpC beta-lactamase from Escherichia coli bound to a transition-state analogue: possible implications for the oxyanion hypothesis and for inhibitor design. Biochemistry 1998;37:16082–92.

[37] Lobkovsky E, Moews PC, Liu H, Zhao H, Frere JM, Knox JR. Evolution of an enzyme activity: crystallographic structure at 2-A resolution of cephalosporinase from the ampC gene of Enterobacter cloacae P99 and comparison with a class A penicillinase. Proc Natl Acad Sci USA 1993;90:11257–61.

[38] Bret L, Chanal-Claris C, Sirot D, Chaibi EB, Labia R, Sirot J. Chromosomally encoded ampC-type beta-lactamase in a clinical isolate of Proteus mirabilis. Antimicrob Agents Chemother 1998;42:1110–4.

[39] Bauernfeind A, Schneider I, Jungwirth R, Sahly H, Ullmann U. A novel type of AmpC beta-lactamase, ACC-1, produced by a Klebsiella pneumoniae strain causing nosocomial pneumonia. Antimicrob Agents Chemother 1999;43:1924–31.

[40] Stapleton PD, Shannon KP, French GL. Carbapenem resistance in Escherichia coli associated with plasmid-determined CMY-4 beta-lactamase production and loss of an outer membrane protein. Antimicrob Agents Chemother 1999;43:1206–10.

[41] Martinez-Martinez L, Pascual A, Hernandez-Alles S, et al. Roles of beta-lactamases and porins in activities of carbapenems and cephalosporins against Klebsiella pneumoniae. Antimicrob Agents Chemother 1999;43:1669–73.

[42] Bradford PA, Urban C, Mariano N, Projan SJ, Rahal JJ, Bush K. Imipenem resistance in Klebsiella pneumoniae is associated with the combination of ACT-1, a plasmid-mediated AmpC beta-lactamase, and the foss of an outer membrane protein. Antimicrob Agents Chemother 1997;41:563–9.

[43] Papanicolaou GA, Medeiros AA, Jacoby GA. Novel plasmid-mediated beta-lactamase (MIR-1) conferring resistance to oxyimino- and alpha-methoxy beta-lactams in clinical isolates of Klebsiella pneumoniae. Antimicrob Agents Chemother 1990;34:2200–9.

[44] Tzouvelekis LS, Tzelepi E, Mentis AF. Nucleotide sequence of a plasmid-mediated cephalosporinase gene (blaLAT-1) found in Klebsiella pneumoniae. Antimicrob Agents Chemother 1994;38:2207–9.

[45] Poirel L, Le Thomas I, Naas T, Karim A, Nordmann P. Biochemical sequence analyses of GES-1, a novel class A extended-spectrum beta-lactamase, and the class 1 integron In52 from Klebsiella pneumoniae. Antimicrob Agents Chemother 2000;44:622–32.

[46] Giakkoupi P, Tzouvelekis LS, Tsakris A, Loukova V, Sofianou D, Tzelepi E. IBC-1, a novel integron-associated class A beta-lactamase with extended-spectrum properties produced by an Enterobacter cloacae clinical strain. Antimicrob Agents Chemother 2000;44: 2247–53.

[47] Bush K. New beta-lactamases in gram-negative bacteria: diversity and impact on the selection of antimicrobial therapy. Clin Infect Dis 2001;32:1085–9.

[48] Ishii Y, Ohno A, Taguchi H, Imajo S, Ishiguro M, Matsuzawa H. Cloning and sequence of the gene encoding a cefotaxime-hydrolyzing class A beta-lactamase isolated from Escherichia coli. Antimicrob Agents Chemother 1995;39:2269–75.

[49] Danel F, Hall LM, Gur D, Akalin HE, Livermore DM. Transferable production of PER-1 beta-lactamase in Pseudomonas aeruginosa. J Antimicrob Chemother 1995;35: 281–94.

[50] Knothe H, Shah P, Krcmery V, Antal M, Mitsuhashi S. Transferable resistance to cefotaxime, cefoxitin, cefamandole and cefuroxime in clinical isolates of Klebsiella pneumoniae and Serratia marcescens. Infection 1983;11:315–7.

[51] Steward CD, Rasheed JK, Hubert SK, et al. Characterization of clinical isolates of Klebsiella pneumoniae from 19 laboratories using the National Committee for Clinical Laboratory Standards extended-spectrum beta-lactamase detection methods. J Clin Microbiol 2001;39:2864–72.

[52] Quinn JP. Clinical strategies for serious infection: a North American perspective. Diagn Microbiol Infect Dis 1998;31:389–95.

[53] Fridkin SK, Gaynes RP. Antimicrobial resistance in intensive care units. Clin Chest Med 1999;20:303–16[viii].

[54] Sahm DF, Marsilio MK, Piazza G. Antimicrobial resistance in key bloodstream bacterial isolates: electronic surveillance with the Surveillance Network Database–USA. Clin Infect Dis 1999;29:259–63.

[55] Paterson DL, Ko WC, Von Gottberg A, et al. International prospective study of Klebsiella pneumoniae bacteremia: implications of extended-spectrum beta-lactamase production in nosocomial Infections. Ann Intern Med 2004;140:26–32.

[56] Paterson DL, Hujer KM, Hujer AM, et al. Extended-spectrum beta-lactamases in Klebsiella pneumoniae bloodstream isolates from seven countries: dominance and widespread prevalence of SHV- and CTX-M-type beta-lactamases. Antimicrob Agents Chemother 2003;47:3554–60.

[57] NCCLS. Methods for dilution antimicrobial susceptibility tests for bacteria the grow aerobically: approved standards. 6th edition. M7–A6. Wayne (PA): National Committee for Clinical Laboratory Standards; 2003.

[58] Livermore DM, Chen HY. Quality of antimicrobial susceptibility testing in the UK: a Pseudomonas aeruginosa survey revisited. J Antimicrob Chemother 1999;43:517–22.

[59] Jacoby GA, Han P. Detection of extended-spectrum beta-lactamases in clinical isolates of Klebsiella pneumoniae and Escherichia coli. J Clin Microbiol 1996;34:908–11.

[60] Shlaes DM, Currie-McCumber C. Mutations altering substrate specificity in OHIO-1, and SHV-1 family beta-lactamase. Biochem J 1992;284(Pt 2):411–5.

[61] Bure A, Legrand P, Arlet G, Jarlier V, Paul G, Philippon A. Dissemination in five French hospitals of Klebsiella pneumoniae serotype K25 harbouring a new transferable enzymatic resistance to third generation cephalosporins and aztreonam. Eur J Clin Microbiol Infect Dis 1988;7:780–2.

[62] Chanal CM, Sirot DL, Labia R, et al. Comparative study of a novel plasmid-mediated beta-lactamase, CAZ-2, and the CTX-1 and CAZ-1 enzymes conferring resistance to broad-spectrum cephalosporins. Antimicrob Agents Chemother 1988;32:1660–5.

[63] Gutmann L, Ferre B, Goldstein FW, et al. SHV-5, a novel SHV-type beta-lactamase that hydrolyzes broad-spectrum cephalosporins and monobactams. Antimicrob Agents Chemother 1989;33:951–6.

[64] Rice LB, Willey SH, Papanicolaou GA, et al. Outbreak of ceftazidime resistance caused by extended-spectrum beta-lactamases at a Massachusetts chronic-care facility. Antimicrob Agents Chemother 1990;34:2193–9.

[65] Bradford PA, Urban C, Jaiswal A, et al. SHV-7, a novel cefotaxime-hydrolyzing beta-lactamase, identified in Escherichia coli isolates from hospitalized nursing home patients. Antimicrob Agents Chemother 1995;39:899–905.

[66] Muder RR, , Brennen C, Drenning SD, Stout JE, Wagener MM. Multiply antibiotic-resistant gram-negative bacilli in a long-term-care facility: a case-control study of patient risk factors and prior antibiotic use. Infect Control Hosp Epidemiol 1997;18: 809–13.

[67] Schiappa DA, Hayden MK, Matushek MG, et al. Ceftazidime-resistant Klebsiella pneumoniae and Escherichia coli bloodstream infection: a case-control and molecular epidemiologic investigation. J Infect Dis 1996;174:529–36.

[68] Rice LB, Carias LL, Bonomo RA, Shlaes DM. Molecular genetics of resistance to both ceftazidime and beta-lactam-beta-lactamase inhibitor combinations in Klebsiella pneumoniae and in vivo response to beta-lactam therapy. J Infect Dis 1996;173:151–8.

[69] Rice LB, Eckstein EC, DeVente J, Shlaes DM. Ceftazidime-resistant Klebsiella pneumoniae isolates recovered at the Cleveland Department of Veterans Affairs Medical Center. Clin Infect Dis 1996;23:118–24.

[70] Wiener J, Quinn JP, Bradford PA, et al. Multiple antibiotic-resistant Klebsiella and Escherichia coli in nursing homes. JAMA 1999;281:517–23.

[71] Shanahan PM, Thomson CJ, Amyes SG. Beta-lactam resistance in normal faecal flora from South Africa. Epidemiol Infect 1995;115:243–53.

[72] Weinstein RA. Epidemiology and control of nosocomial infections in adult intensive care units. Am J Med 1991;91:179S–84S.

[73] Levy SB, Marshall B, Schluederberg S, Rowse D, Davis J. High frequency of antimicrobial resistance in human fecal flora. Antimicrob Agents Chemother 1988;32:1801–6.

[74] Leistevuo T, Osterblad M, Toivonen P, Kahra A, Lehtonen A, Huovinen P. Colonization of resistant faecal aerobic gram-negative bacilli among geriatric patients in hospital and the community. J Antimicrob Chemother 1996;37:169–73.

[75] Leistevuo T, Toivonen P, Osterblad M, et al. Problem of antimicrobial resistance of fecal aerobic gram-negative bacilli in the elderly. Antimicrob Agents Chemother 1996;40: 2399–403.

[76] Bonomo RA, Donskey CJ, Blumer JL, et al. Cefotaxime-resistant bacteria colonizing older people admitted to an acute care hospital. J Am Geriatr Soc 2003;51:519–22.

[77] Mathew A, Harris AM, Marshall MJ, Ross GW. The use of analytical isoelectric focusing for detection and identification of beta-lactamases. J Gen Microbiol 1975;88: 169–78.

[78] Vecoli C, Prevost FE, Ververis JJ, Medeiros AA, O'Leary GP. Jr. Comparison of polyacrylamide and agarose gel thin-layer isoelectric focusing for the characterization of beta-lactamases. Antimicrob Agents Chemother 1983;24:186–9.

[79] Paterson DL, Rice LB, Bonomo RA. Rapid method of extraction and analysis of extended-spectrum beta-lactamases from clinical strains of Klebsiella pneumoniae. Clin Microbiol Infect 2001;7:709–11.

[80] Chanawong A, M'Zali FH, Heritage J, Lulitanond A, Hawkey PM. Discrimination of SHV beta-lactamase genes by restriction site insertion-PCR. Antimicrob Agents Chemother 2001;45:2110–4.

[81] Kim J, Lee HJ. Rapid discriminatory detection of genes coding for SHV beta-lactamases by ligase chain reaction. Antimicrob Agents Chemother 2000;44:1860–4.

[82] Randegger CC, Hachler H. Real-time PCR and melting curve analysis for reliable and rapid detection of SHV extended-spectrum beta-lactamases. Antimicrob Agents Chemother 2001;45:1730–6.

[83] Maslow JN, Slutsky AM, Arbeit RD. Application of pulsed field gel electrophoresis to molecular epidemiology. Diagnostic molecular epidemiology. Washington, DC: American Society for Microbiology; 1993. p. 563–72.

[84] Hujer AM, Page MG, Helfand MS, Yeiser B, Bonomo RA. Development of a sensitive and specific enzyme-linked immunosorbent assay for detecting and quantifying CMY-2 and SHV beta-lactamases. J Clin Microbiol 2002;40:1947–57.

[85] Arbeit RD, Arthur M, Dunn R, Kim C, Selander RK, Goldstein R. Resolution of recent evolutionary divergence among Escherichia coli from related lineages: the application of pulsed field electrophoresis to molecular epidemiology. J Infect Dis 1990;161:230–5.

[86] Murray BE, Singh KV, Heath JD, Sharma BR, Weinstock GM. Comparison of genomic DNAs of different enterococcal isolates using restriction endonucleases with infrequent recognition sites. J Clin Microbiol 1990;28:2059–63.

[87] Prevost G, Jaulhac B, Piemont Y. DNA fingerprinting by pulsed-field gel electrophoresis is more effective than ribotyping in distinguishing among methicillin-resistant Staphylococcus aureus isolates. J Clin Microbiol 1992;30:967–73.

[88] Matushek MG, Bonten MJ, Hayden MK. Rapid preparation of bacterial DNA for pulsed-field gel electrophoresis. J Clin Microbiol 1996;34:2598–600.

[89] Peri TM. Surveillance, reporting and the use of computers. In: Wenzel RD, editor. Prevention and control of nosocomial infections. Baltimore (MD): Williams and Wilkins; 1993.

ELSEVIER
SAUNDERS

CLINICS IN
LABORATORY
MEDICINE

Clin Lab Med 24 (2004) 363–380

Antibiotic-resistant gram-negative bacteria in hospitalized children

Philip Toltzis, MD

*Divisions of Pharmacology and Critical Care and Infectious Diseases,
Rainbow Babies and Children's Hospital, Department of Pediatrics, Case Western Reserve
University School of Medicine, 11100 Euclid Avenue, Cleveland, OH 44106, USA*

The past two decades have witnessed the emergence of a heterogeneous group of facultative, Gram-negative pathogens that are resistant to one or more classes of conventional parenteral antibiotics. Antibiotic-resistant Gram-negative bacteria primarily affect critically ill, hospitalized patients, particularly those in large tertiary care centers. The genera most frequently associated are those included in the family Enterobacteriaceae, most commonly *Enterobacter*, *Klebsiella*, *Citrobacter*, and *Serratia*, as well as nonenteric, nonfermenting bacteria such as *Pseudomonas* and *Acinetobacter*. The antibiotic susceptibility patterns of resistant bacilli have evolved over the years, reflecting the antimicrobial regimens in widest use at the time. Resistance was originally confined to kanamycin and gentamicin, then extended to all of the aminoglycosides, including amikacin, then to both the older and more recently developed extended spectrum β-lactam agents, including the advanced-generation cephalosporins and penicillins. Although most Gram-negative bacilli currently remain susceptible to the carbapenems and the fluoroquinolones, resistance to these agents has also been described.

Because antibiotic resistance among Gram-negative bacilli encompasses multiple resistance phenotypes, the mechanisms conferring resistance are multiple as well. The most prominent bacterial resistance mechanism among this group of organisms is enzymatic antibiotic inactivation. Among these reactions, hydrolysis of the antibiotic β-lactam bond by β-lactamase is the most common. A large array of β-lactamases has been identified in Gram-negative organisms, with additional enzymes reported almost monthly [1–7]. Most new enzyme variants represent single amino acid substitutions of previously characterized enzymes that have developed under antibiotic pressure [2,4,6]. Of particular note are the extended-spectrum β-lactamases

E-mail address: pxt2@cwru.edu

0272-2712/04/$ - see front matter © 2004 Elsevier Inc. All rights reserved.
doi:10.1016/j.cll.2004.03.001

(ESBLs); these primarily plasmid-borne enzymes have evolved to hydrolyze greater and greater numbers of advanced-generation β-lactam antibiotics. Many β-lactamase enzymes, particularly the chromosomal ampC β-lactamases, are substrate inducible, so that even organisms initially susceptible to a β-lactam antibiotic may become highly resistant during therapy. A second group of important inactivating enzymes elaborated by Gram-negative bacteria conjugates aminoglcosides through phosphorylation, adenylation, and acetylation [8]. All of the aminoglycosides in current use are susceptible to inactivation by one or more of these enzymes. β-lactamase–mediated resistance is often found in conjunction with other mechanisms of resistance; consequently, a single isolate may be resistant to multiple commonly used antibiotics [9,10].

In addition to the production of antibiotic inactivation enzymes, Gram-negative bacteria may express antibiotic resistance through two additional mechanisms. The first, prevention of antibiotic accumulation within the bacterial cell, may be partially the result of the hydrophobic outer membrane common to all Gram-negative organisms. Additionally, porins, aqueous diffusion channels on the surface of the bacteria, may be altered under selection pressure to become impermeable to some antibiotics. Sometimes these mechanisms work in concert with others; combinations of porin mutations and β-lactamase production has resulted in high-level resistance to virtually all the β-lactam antibiotics in selected isolates of *Pseudomonas* and *Klebsiella*, for example [11,12]. Additionally, some bacteria express efflux pumps to actively extrude the antibiotic from the intracellular space [13]. This mechanism is becoming particularly prominent in resistance to the fluoroquinolones. The other mechanism, biochemical alteration of the antibiotic's cellular target, results in the rapid development of resistance of Gram-negative bacteria to the fluoroquinolone antibiotics through single or cumulative amino acid substitutions on DNA gyrase or topoisomerase IV [14].

Prevalence and incidence of antibiotic-resistant Gram-negative bacilli

Initial reports of antibiotic-resistant bacilli emerged from Europe during the 1980s. A French survey published in 1992, for example, screened tens of thousands of isolates submitted from multiple hospitals and indicated that 28% of *Enterobacter*, 7% of *Klebsiella*, 19% of *Citrobacter*, and 38% of *Serratia* were resistant to cefotaxime and other β-lactam agents [15]. Subsequent reports documented that resistance among Gram-negative species to a wide variety of commonly used antibiotics continued to increase during the past decade. These studies were conducted primarily on isolates collected from adult intensive care unit (ICU) patients from widely distributed geographical regions [16–30]. Taken together, these reports indicated a growing incidence of infection by organisms resistant to the third-generation cephalosporins and the broad-spectrum penicillins (alone or in combination with a β-lactamase inhibitor), a more gradual increase in resistance to the aminoglycosides, and a relatively slow albeit inexorable emergence of resistance to the carbapenems and quinolones. At least in some regions the degree of resistance to parenteral antibiotics increased and the occurrence of co-resistance to multiple classes of agents became more common.

The specific incidence and prevalence of infections from Gram-negative bacteria in general, and antibiotic-resistant isolates in particular, in pediatric patients has been less well studied. In recent multi-hospital surveys, Gram-negative bacteria accounted for 15% to 40% of all pediatric nosocomial infections [31–35], but little data were presented regarding the proportion of isolates that were antibiotic resistant. A recent survey of nosocomial bloodstream infections in pediatric patients from 49 American hospitals conducted between 1995 and 2000 indicated that resistance to the late-generation penicillins, and, in the case of *Enterobacter*, to the third-generation cephalosporins was quite prominent. Yet most of the surveyed organisms remained susceptible to the aminoglycosides, the fluoroquinolones, and the carbapenems (Table 1) [35].

Pediatric nosocomial Gram-negative bacillary infections are reported most commonly in the neonatal intensive care unit (NICU), the pediatric intensive care unit (PICU), and on the oncology ward. In the NICU in particular, recent upward trends in Gram-negative infections may be at least partially a consequence of intrapartum antibiotic prophylaxis against early-onset Group B streptococcal (GBS) infections, a strategy widely applied since the mid-1990s [36]. Although maternal intrapartum ampicillin has been unequivocally successful in decreasing the incidence of early-onset streptococcal

Table 1
Rank order of nosocomial bloodstream pathogens in pediatric patients among 49 hospitals throughout the United States

Organisms	Total		
	No. of isolates	% of isolates	Crude mortality[a] (%)
Coagulase-negative staphylococci	1658	43.3	10.6
Enterococci	357	9.4	11.8
Candida spp.	355	9.3	19.6
Staphylococcus aureus	351	9.2	12.0
Klebsiella spp.	223	5.8	14.5
Escherichia coli	190	5.0	17.4
Enterobacter spp.	190	5.0	14.6
Pseudomonas aeruginosa	121	3.2	28.7
Streptococcus spp.	113	3.0	16.1

Adapted from Wisplinghoff H, Seifert H, Tallent SM, Bischoff T, Wenzel RP, Edmond MB, Nosocomial bloodstream infections in pediatric patients in United States hospitals: epidemiology, clinical features and susceptibilities. Pediatr Infect Dis J 2003;22(8)686–91.

Nosocomial bloodstream infections in pediatric patients in United States hospitals: epidemiology, Chemical features and susceptibilities.

[a] Crude mortality of patients with monomicrobial blood stream infection.

disease in the newborn, the effect of GBS prophylaxis on the incidence of Gram-negative bacillary infections has been a matter of ongoing concern. Most studies to date have suggested that the rate of non-GBS early-onset sepsis during the recent period of intrapartum antibiotic prophylaxis is stable or slightly decreasing [37,38]. Other investigators, however, have demonstrated that in selected NICU populations the incidence of early-onset Gram-negative bacterial infections increased toward the end of the last decade. Stoll et al [39], reporting data from the National Institutes of Health–sponsored Neonatal Research Network, examined the rates and causes of early-onset neonatal infection over two time periods among infants with birthweight <1500 g. Compared with the birth cohort born from 1991 to 1993 when GBS prophylaxis was not routine, infants delivered between 1998 and 2000 experienced a marked increase in sepsis due to *Escherichia coli* (from 3.2 to 6.8 per 1000 live births). Moreover, several reports suggest that early onset bacillary infections are becoming more resistant to commonly used parenteral antibiotics [38–40]. In the survey by Stoll and associates, [39] for example, most *E coli* isolates from infants with early-onset sepsis were resistant to ampicillin. This study and others [40,41] additionally documented that mothers of infants with ampicillin-resistant *E coli* infections were more likely to have received intrapartum antibiotics than mothers of infants infected with ampicillin-susceptible *E coli*. These findings suggest that maternal antibiotic exposure during labor, administered to prevent early-onset GBS infection in infants, may be shifting the susceptibility pattern of Gram-negative bacilli, particularly *E coli*, infecting the offspring.

Additionally, late-onset hospital-acquired NICU infections due to antibiotic-resistant Gram-negative pathogens also may be increasingly common. Nambiar and Singh [42] observed that Gram-negative bacteria were the predominate cause of late-onset infections at the Children's National Medical Center in Washington, DC during the period 1996 to 2001. Their retrospective study revealed that Gram-negative organisms represented 43% of pathogens causing nosocomial infections in the NICU during this period. Using weekly surveillance cultures, investigators from the same center determined that 17% of their NICU residents were colonized by antibiotic-resistant Enterobacteriaceae [43]. A survey completed in our NICU at Rainbow Babies and Children's Hospital in Cleveland similarly noted that 8.6% of all patients were colonized by at least one Gram-negative organism resistant to ceftazidime, piperacillin-tazobactam, or tobramycin at some time during their NICU stay [44]. In both the Washington and Cleveland units, antibiotic-resistant bacilli in the NICU tended to be isolated from the most premature and sickest patients. Risk factors for colonization or infection by resistant bacilli included low birth weight, prolonged stay, and antecedent exposure to antibiotics.

The incidence of antibiotic-resistant bacilli in PICU and pediatric oncology patients is less well studied. An estimation of the magnitude of antibiotic-resistant bacilli in PICU patients can be derived from surveys measuring colonization by resistant organisms. Patients studied in our PICU in Cleveland during the mid-1990s were assessed for colonization with Gram-negative bacilli resistant to either ceftazidime or tobramycin through daily rectal and nasopharyngeal swabs. Among those children admitted for >24 hours, 20.3% were colonized with at least one antibiotic-resistant strain before PICU discharge [45]. A wide variety of species was detected. Tobramycin resistance was expressed in 52.8% of the isolates, ceftazidime resistance in 35.6%, and both resistance phenotypes in 11.6%. Data regarding Gram-negative infections among pediatric oncology patients similarly are principally derived from the experiences of single centers [46–49]. Typical is a recent report from Turkey [46], which documented that about 35% of the infections among pediatric cancer patients were caused by Gram-negative bacilli, most frequently *Klebsiella*, *E coli*, *Enterobacter*, and *Pseudomonas*. Detailed data regarding antimicrobial resistance patterns among these organisms have not been presented, however.

Clinical consequences of nosocomial infections due to antibiotic-resistant Gram-negative bacilli

Nosocomial infection by Gram-negative bacilli increases hospital cost and length of stay. Although it makes medical sense that Gram-negative bacterial infections should increase mortality as well, studies examining this association, all conducted in adults, in fact have produced mixed results. Nosocomial infections occur mostly in very ill patients, and controlling for the many covariate factors that are associated with mortality in these subjects is a difficult task [50]. One recent single-center study found that microbiologically confirmed nosocomial infections from a variety of pathogens in adult ICU patients were strongly associated with an increased mortality (53.2% versus 37.2% among those not suffering from infection) even after controlling for confounding factors contributing to death [51]. Another single-center report, by contrast, found no such association [52]. Likewise, it is easy to imagine that infections due to antibiotic-resistant organisms are more likely to be initially treated with ineffectual antibiotics and therefore associated with a higher attributable mortality compared with infections caused by susceptible pathogens. Indeed, several recent studies have supported this contention [53–55]. Ibrahim and colleagues, for example, documented a mortality of 61.9% among 147 adult ICU patients with nosocomial bloodstream infections due to a variety of pathogens who were initially treated with inadequate antimicrobial agents [53]. This compared with a death rate of 28.4% among subjects who received adequate antibiotics from the onset. Other investigators have been unable to demonstrate that infection with an antibiotic-resistant bacillus is associated with an increased risk of mortality [56,57]. Indeed, in one study the survival curves for those infected by antibiotic-susceptible and antibiotic-resistant Gram-negative bacteria were essentially overlapping [57].

The consequences of nosocomial bacillary infection in children, particularly by those organisms expressing antibiotic resistance, have not been adequately examined. In general nosocomial infections produce the greatest adverse outcomes at the extremes of age, so it is likely that very premature infants fare worse than older children, even those with cancer or subjects admitted to a PICU. Crude mortality from Gram-negative bacteremia in all children is approximately 10% to 20% [35,58], lower than the statistics quoted for adults (15% to 40%) (see Table 1) [35,51,52,55,57]. In studies simultaneously surveying survival of Gram-negative bacillary bacteremia in children and adults, mortality has been lower in the pediatric age group [35,58].

Epidemiology of outbreaks of antibiotic-resistant Gram-negative bacilli

Epidemics of Gram-negative bacillary infections have been reported in critically ill children for decades, particularly in NICUs where outbreaks occur most frequently in the pediatric hospital. Accumulated experience indicates that NICU epidemics possess the following characteristics [1]. First, the outbreaks are caused by clonally related organisms of a single species. It is assumed that epidemic strains possess one or more characteristic that predisposes to their acquisition and spread compared with other bacilli, for example, resistance to commonly used antibiotics or disinfectants, enhanced adhesion to mucous membranes or inanimate surfaces, or prolonged survival [2]. Second, all acquisition after for the index case occurs through patient-to-patient transmission after hospital admission, primarily via the hands of caregivers [3]. Third, contamination of the inanimate environment frequently sustains the outbreak.

Recently reported NICU outbreaks have been caused primarily by *Enterobacter* [59–67], *Klebsiella* [68–74], and *Serratia* [75–80]. Typically the outbreak clone has been identified from numerous environmental sources, including rectal thermometers [60,62,73], incubator doors [75], pulse oximeter probes [73], re-used suction catheters and laryngoscope blades [76,81], and breast pumps [76]. *Serratia* in particular has been cultured from handwashing disinfectants [80]. Additionally, outbreak clones have been identified from nutritional sources, including parenteral nutrition solutions [63] and formula [61,78].

Given the primary role patient-to-patient transmission plays in ICU outbreaks of antibiotic-resistant Gram-negative bacilli, hand antisepsis is key to interrupting an epidemic and probably is critical in preventing an epidemic during nonoutbreak periods. Older studies indicated that hands of hospital caregivers frequently are positive for Gram-negative bacilli [82,83]. Hand cultures performed in NICU nurses in the early 1970s, for example, revealed bacillary contamination in more than 86% of samples [83]. Although simple soap and water are ineffective in ridding the hands of bacillary contamination when it becomes part of the permanent flora, antisepsis with chlorhexidine, povidone-iodine, or the more newly introduced alcohol-based hand gels are substantially more effective in reducing bacterial load [84–86]. The importance of frequent application of hand antisepsis in caring for critically ill children (and, of course, adults) before and after patient contact therefore cannot be overemphasized.

Recently the importance of diseased skin or long fingernails in promoting bacterial contamination of the hands of caregivers has been emphasized, especially in NICUs. Studies by Hedderwick and colleagues [87] demonstrated that potentially pathogenic micro-organisms are recovered more frequently and at higher density from artificial nails compared with short natural nails. A cluster of cases of *Pseudomonas* infection in the NICU at Babies Hospital in New York City [88] led to investigations that uncovered three nurses with *Pseudomonas* hand colonization; one with onychomycosis harbored the same strain isolated from 17 different infants. An outbreak of *Pseudomonas aeruginosa* in an Oklahoma NICU similarly identified colonization of long or artificial fingernails among nurses as an important source in a deadly epidemic [89]. In addition to long or artificial fingernails, ring wearing also contributes to hand colonization by Gram-negative bacilli. Recently Trick and colleagues [90] conducted a randomized trial comparing the efficacy of three hand hygiene agents in reducing skin bacterial counts. Regardless of the hygiene product used, ring wearing was associated with a greater risk of hand contamination by a Gram-negative bacillus, and when contamination was discovered, rings were associated with a higher density of colonization compared with a hand free of jewelry [90]. Based on these observations, banning long or artificial fingernails and ring wearing in the hospital as well as limiting patient care in personnel with damaged or diseased hands, particularly in a confined acute setting such as the NICU, has become standard in an effort to limit horizontal transmission of potentially pathogenic Gram-negative bacilli.

Epidemiology of nonoscomial Gram-negative bacteria during nonoutbreak periods

A growing body of evidence indicates that during nonoutbreak periods, both antibiotic-susceptible and resistant Gram-negative bacilli are acquired in several different fashions and from several distinct sources [91,92]. Unlike the epidemic situation, Gram-negative bacillary infection and colonization during endemic periods are usually due to multiple stains unique to each patient with little evidence of horizontal transmission within a given unit. An analysis performed in five ICUs at three Indianapolis university hospitals during the early 1990s indicated that only 13% of Gram-negative species cultured during their study period were present in more than one patient [93]. Similarly, D'Agata and colleagues [94] subjected ceftazidime-resistant organisms cultured in two Boston ICUs to molecular typing and rarely found genetic and epidemiologic evidence of horizontal spread. These findings are consistent with a model in which the critically ill patient initially is colonized by a susceptible organism as a component of his or her endogenous flora, and antibiotic resistance is induced or selected by the frequent exposure to antibiotics inherent in the care of ICU patients [94–96]. In some circumstances, the initially susceptible colonizing bacteria may acquire resistance determinants through genetic transfer from entirely unrelated species [97,98]. These observations also are consistent with acquisition of multiple new clones of Gram-negative bacilli from the ICU environment with no one clone establishing a detectable selective advantage over the others.

The picture is made yet more complicated by the recognition that a substantial proportion of resistant bacilli is imported into the unit. For example, the majority of ceftazidime resistant Gram-negative isolates in a Boston surgical ICU was isolated on admission [94,99]. In our study of Gram-negative bacillary colonization in children admitted to the PICU [45], more than half of the children found colonized with a bacillus resistant to either ceftazidime or tobramycin were identified within 72 hours of PICU admission, similarly indicating substantial importation of these resistant phenotypes into the unit. To better define the contribution of imported Gram-negative bacilli on the prevalence of these organisms in our PICU, we subsequently sought to identify the characteristics of patients who were colonized with a resistant Gram-negative bacterium at admission [100]. A strong association was found between colonization and receipt of intravenous antibiotics within the previous 12 months, with the number of intravenous antibiotics received, and with the number of lifetime ICU admissions. These findings suggested that a subpopulation of PICU patients with recurrent severe illness and multiple requirements for intensive care served to sustain the endemic presence of these resistant organisms at any given time. Additional factors reflecting the patients' pre-ICU living environment also were important, specifically, residence in a chronic care facility or household contact with a family member who had been hospitalized over the previous year.

Taken together, these findings speak to a complicated and multifaceted model accounting for the presence of resistant bacilli in the intensive care unit during nonoutbreak periods (Fig. 1) [101]. Some organisms are transmitted through the hands of caregivers from patient to patient, as in the epidemic situation, whereas others are selected from the patient's pre-existing gastrointestinal flora after exposure to antibiotics and still others are imported into the unit. Moreover, it is likely that the relative prominence of each source differs from unit to unit and probably even within the same unit over time.

In the NICU, crowded conditions and an initially sterile gut would appear to predispose to frequent sharing of gut colonizers even during nonoutbreak periods. Clearly the ontogeny of gastrointestinal colonization among NICU residents is very abnormal compared with healthy full-term infants, setting the stage for efficient patient-to-patient transmission. In healthy newborns, *Bifidobacterium* is the principal genus colonizing the gastrointestinal tract of both breast- and bottle-fed babies [102–105]. The gastrointestinal ecology of

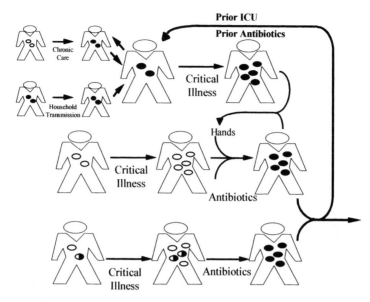

Fig. 1. A model representing the multiple sources of antibiotic-resistant Gram-negative bacilli within a hospital unit during a nonoutbreak period. Susceptible organisms are denoted by open circles, resistant organisms by closed circles, and organisms with inducible resistance by half-open circles. Resistant bacilli may be imported into the unit (*top row*), horizontally transmitted via the hands of caregivers while in the unit (*middle row*), or selected from the patient's endogenous flora (*bottom row*). (*Adapted from* Toltzis P, Blumer JL. Nosocomial acquisition and transmission of antibiotic-resistant gram-negative organisms in the pediatric intensive care unit. Pediatr Infect Dis J 2001;20(6):612–8; with permission.)

the healthy infant rapidly assumes great complexity, involving many different anaerobic and facultative species by the fifth day of life, and this ecosystem remains stable over the next several months [102–105]. The newborn admitted to the NICU does not have the opportunity to acquire normal colonizing flora from postnatal maternal contact, and acquisition is primarily influenced by the organisms resident in that environment. Goldmann and colleagues [106] were among the first to describe the ontogeny of bacterial colonization in the critically ill newborn. On admission to the NICU, approximately 50% of rectal and nasal swab specimens demonstrated no growth of any organism, and 16% to 30% of samples were still negative for growth by the third NICU day. The slow acquisition of colonizing flora appeared to be the consequence of nearly uniform exposure to antibiotics on admission to the NICU and to the relative paucity of human contact, the presumed source of the colonizing flora among normal full-term newborns [107]. When colonization ultimately did occur, normal flora frequently was mixed with organisms not normally resident. Specifically, more than half of the infants became colonized with *Klebsiella*, *Enterobacter*, or *Citrobacter* species, and once such organisms appeared they grew to high density [107]. Moreover, the incidence of colonization with these "hospital-associated" bacilli increased over time: only 2% of infants were colonized with these bacillary species at NICU admission, whereas 60% were colonized by 15 days, and more than 90% were colonized by 30 days.

The gradual acquisition of abnormal bacillary colonization in the NICU patient has since been confirmed by many other investigators [108–111]. Recently introduced techniques that measure the degree of complexity of microbiologic ecosystems based on species-specific 16s rRNA polymorphisms confirm that that gastrointestinal tract of NICU patients contain markedly fewer species than adults [112–114], denying them the colonization resistance against exogenous bacterial strains afforded by normal flora and predisposing them to colonization by facultative species not present in the normally colonized colon [115].

It is remarkable, then, that the Gram-negative bacillary flora of NICU patients, like their PICU and adult ICU counterparts, also are usually unique to each patient. Almuneef and colleagues in New Haven, Connecticut [116] and our own group in Cleveland [44,117] prospectively studied the endemic acquisition of resistant bacilli in the NICU by performing molecular typing on large numbers of isolates colonizing infants admitted to each of two tertiary care units. Although the New Haven study concentrated on gentamicin resistance whereas ours in Cleveland screened for resistance to gentamicin, ceftazidime, and piperacillin-tazobactam, both studies indicated that resistant colonizing bacteria were composed of hundreds of distinct genotypes derived from multiple genera of bacilli. Acquisition of colonization with antibiotic-resistant Gram-negative bacteria occurred very early after NICU admission, and cumulative acquisition continued over several weeks of NICU stay [44]. In our population, clones of resistant bacilli frequently cleared rapidly from the infants' flora after initial colonization, reflecting a particularly unstable gastrointestinal ecology. Both studies detected some cross-transmission of clones from infant to infant, occurring in 21% of genetically distinct isolates in New Haven and 12% in Cleveland [44,116,117]. However, the marked majority of resistant bacillary colonization in NICU residents occurred with unique isolates that established a transient presence in the newborn.

Pediatric chronic care facilities

Long-term care facilities have been identified as significant reservoirs of antibiotic-resistant organisms, including Gram-negative bacilli, among elderly adults [118–123]. In many instances, these organisms are acquired during an admission to an acute care hospital; in others, they are selected during antibiotic administration in the long-term care unit or acquired through horizontal transmission within the facility itself. Similarly, a recent study showed that a significant proportion of children colonized with a resistant Gram-negative organism on admission to our PICU in Cleveland was transferred from a chronic care unit [100]. A study therefore was undertaken in two northeastern Ohio extended-care facilities for developmentally delayed children to determine the prevalence of colonization with antibiotic-resistant Gram-negative bacteria and to define the risk factors associated with such colonization [124]. Of 116 children studied, 40.5% were colonized with a Gram-negative organism resistant to one or more of the parenteral antibiotics tested. Environmental surfaces were tested and contamination with antibiotic-resistant bacilli found in 63.9%. Hand cultures yielded only four resistant bacilli from a total of 83 samples. Colonization was strongly associated with the presence of any prosthesis but was particularly apparent among patients with tracheostomies. Cross-colonization was common, with more than two thirds of culture-positive patients sharing colonization with an antibiotic-resistant organism with one or more residents. Though children from both facilities received acute care, when required, from the same four principal pediatric acute care hospitals in the region, no genetically concordant organisms were found between the facilities, suggesting that acquisition of the resistant bacilli was originating in the chronic care facilities themselves. This study suggests that children residing in chronic care facilities may also represent a significant reservoir of colonization with antibiotic-resistant Gram-negative bacilli in the pediatric age group and that they should be considered at high risk for transmitting these organisms both within their facility and when they are admitted to an acute care unit.

Summary

Antibiotic-resistant Gram-negative bacilli are a prominent and growing problem among hospitalized children. Epidemics caused by these organisms have been implicated in many outbreaks in children's hospitals, primarily in NICUs. These epidemics are characterized by efficient patient-to-patient transmission of the outbreak clone via the hands of caregivers and through exposure to contaminated inanimate sources. The epidemiology of these resistant organisms in pediatric hospitals during endemic periods is more complex. The isolates cultured from hospitalized individuals in the absence of an outbreak usually are unique to each individual and are derived from the patient's endogenous flora or other disparate sources. As in adults, chronic care facilities for children represent significant reservoirs of antibiotic-resistant bacilli that are circulated back into the acute care hospital environment when the child becomes ill.

References

[1] Bush K, Jacoby GA, Medeiros AA. A functional classification scheme for beta-lactamases and its correlation with molecular structure. Antimicrob Agents Chemother 1995;39(6):1211–33.

[2] Heritage J, M'Zali FH, Gascoyne-Binzi D, Hawkey PM. Evolution and spread of SHV extended-spectrum beta-lactamases in gram- negative bacteria. J Antimicrob Chemother 1999;44(3):309–18.

[3] Chaibi EB, Sirot D, Paul G, Labia R. Inhibitor-resistant TEM beta-lactamases: phenotypic, genetic and biochemical characteristics. J Antimicrob Chemother 1999; 43(4):447–58.

[4] Du Bois SK, Marriott MS, Amyes SG. TEM- and SHV-derived extended-spectrum beta-lactamases: relationship between selection, structure and function. J Antimicrob Chemother 1995;35(1):7–22.

[5] Knox JR. Extended-spectrum and inhibitor-resistant TEM-type beta-lactamases: mutations, specificity, and three-dimensional structure. Antimicrob Agents Chemother 1995;39(12):2593–601.

[6] Medeiros AA. Evolution and dissemination of beta-lactamases accelerated by generations of beta-lactam antibiotics. Clin Infect Dis 1997;24(Suppl 1):S19–45.

[7] Bush K. New beta-lactamases in gram-negative bacteria: diversity and impact on the selection of antimicrobial therapy. Clin Infect Dis 2001;32(7):1085–9.

[8] Shaw KJ, Rather PN, Hare RS, Miller GH. Molecular genetics of aminoglycoside resistance genes and familial relationships of the aminoglycoside-modifying enzymes. Microbiol Rev 1993;57(1):138–63.

[9] Livermore DM. Multiple mechanisms of antimicrobial resistance in *Pseudomonas aeruginosa*: our worst nightmare? Clin Infect Dis 2002;34(5):634–40.

[10] Paterson DL, Mulazimoglu L, Casellas JM, et al. Epidemiology of ciprofloxacin resistance and its relationship to extended-spectrum beta-lactamase production in *Klebsiella pneumoniae* isolates causing bacteremia. Clin Infect Dis 2000;30(3):473–8.

[11] Martinez-Martinez L, Pascual A, Hernandez-Alles S, et al. Roles of beta-lactamases and porins in activities of carbapenems and cephalosporins against Klebsiella pneumoniae. Antimicrob Agents Chemother 1999;43(7):1669–73.

[12] Chevalier J, Pages JM, Eyraud A, Mallea M. Membrane permeability modifications are involved in antibiotic resistance in Klebsiella pneumoniae. Biochem Biophys Res Commun 2000;274(2):496–9.

[13] Nikaido H. Antibiotic resistance caused by gram-negative multidrug efflux pumps. Clin Infect Dis 1998;27(Suppl 1):S32–41.

[14] Hooper DC. Mechanisms of action of antimicrobials: focus on fluoroquinolones. Clin Infect Dis 2001;32(Suppl 1):S9–15.

[15] Sirot DL, Goldstein FW, Soussy CJ, et al. Resistance to cefotaxime and seven other beta-lactams in members of the family Enterobacteriaceae: a 3-year survey in France. Antimicrob Agents Chemother 1992;36(8):1677–81.

[16] Burwen DR, Banerjee SN, Gaynes RP. Ceftazidime resistance among selected nosocomial gram-negative bacilli in the United States. National Nosocomial Infections Surveillance System. J Infect Dis 1994;170(6):1622–5.

[17] Legakis NJ, Tzouvelekis LS, Tsakris A, Legakis JN, Vatopoulos AC. On the incidence of antibiotic resistance among aerobic gram-negative rods isolated in Greek hospitals. J Hosp Infect 1993;24(3):233–7.

[18] Dornbusch K, King A, Legakis N. Incidence of antibiotic resistance in blood and urine isolates from hospitalized patients. Report from a European collaborative study. European Study Group on Antibiotic Resistance (ESGAR). Scand J Infect Dis 1998;30(3):281–8.

[19] Flournoy DJ, Reinert RL, Bell-Dixon C, Gentry CA. Increasing antimicrobial resistance in gram-negative bacilli isolated from patients in intensive care units. Am J Infect Control 2000;28(3):244–50.

[20] Hanberger H, Garcia-Rodriguez JA, Gobernado M, Goossens H, Nilsson LE, Struelens MJ. Antibiotic susceptibility among aerobic gram-negative bacilli in intensive care units in 5 European countries. French and Portuguese ICU Study Groups. JAMA 1999;281(1): 67–71.

[21] Aksaray S, Dokuzoguz B, Guvener E, et al. Surveillance of antimicrobial resistance among gram-negative isolates from intensive care units in eight hospitals in turkey. J Antimicrob Chemother 2000;46(4):649.

[22] Itokazu GS, Quinn JP, Bell-Dixon C, Kahan FM, Weinstein RA. Antimicrobial resistance rates among aerobic gram-negative bacilli recovered from patients in intensive care units: evaluation of a national postmarketing surveillance program. Clin Infect Dis 1996;23(4):779–84.

[23] Jarlier V, Fosse T, Philippon A. Antibiotic susceptibility in aerobic gram-negative bacilli isolated in intensive care units in 39 French teaching hospitals (ICU study). Intensive Care Med 1996;22(10):1057–65.

[24] Turner PJ. MYSTIC (Meropenem Yearly Susceptibility Test Information Collection): a global overview. J Antimicrob Chemother 2000;46(Suppl B):9–23.

[25] Winokur PL, Canton R, Casellas JM, Legakis N. Variations in the prevalence of strains expressing an extended-spectrum beta-lactamase phenotype and characterization of isolates from Europe, the Americas, and the Western Pacific region. Clin Infect Dis 2001; 32(Suppl 2):S94–103.

[26] Babini GS, Livermore DM. Antimicrobial resistance amongst Klebsiella spp. collected from intensive care units in Southern and Western Europe in 1997–1998. J Antimicrob Chemother 2000;45(2):183–9.

[27] Diekema DJ, Pfaller MA, Jones RN, et al. Survey of bloodstream infections due to gram-negative bacilli: frequency of occurrence and antimicrobial susceptibility of isolates collected in the United States, Canada, and Latin America for the SENTRY Antimicrobial Surveillance Program, 1997. Clin Infect Dis 1999;29(3): 595–607.

[28] Schmitz FJ, Fluit AC, Gondolf M, et al. The prevalence of aminoglycoside resistance and corresponding resistance genes in clinical isolates of staphylococci from 19 European hospitals. J Antimicrob Chemother 1999;43(2):253–9.

[29] Fluit AC, Jones ME, Schmitz FJ, Acar J, Gupta R, Verhoef J. Antimicrobial susceptibility and frequency of occurrence of clinical blood isolates in Europe from the SENTRY antimicrobial surveillance program, 1997 and 1998. Clin Infect Dis 2000;30(3): 454–60.

[30] Goettsch W, van Pelt W, Nagelkerke N, et al. Increasing resistance to fluoroquinolones in *Escherichia coli* from urinary tract infections in the Netherlands. J Antimicrob Chemother 2000;46(2):223–8.

[31] Stoll BJ, Hansen N, Fanaroff AA, et al. Late-onset sepsis in very low birth weight neonates: the experience of the NICHD Neonatal Research Network. Pediatrics 2002; 110(2 Pt 1):285–91.

[32] Richards MJ, Edwards JR, Culver DH, Gaynes RP. Nosocomial infections in pediatric intensive care units in the United States. National Nosocomial Infections Surveillance System. Pediatrics 1999;103(4):e39.

[33] Grohskopf LA, Sinkowitz-Cochran RL, Garrett DO, et al. A national point-prevalence survey of pediatric intensive care unit-acquired infections in the United States. J Pediatr 2002;140(4):432–8.

[34] Raymond J, Aujard Y. Nosocomial infections in pediatric patients: a European, multicenter prospective study. European Study Group. Infect Control Hosp Epidemiol 2000;21(4):260–3.

[35] Wisplinghoff H, Seifert H, Tallent SM, Bischoff T, Wenzel RP, Edmond MB. Nosocomial bloodstream infections in pediatric patients in United States hospitals: epidemiology, clinical features and susceptibilities. Pediatr Infect Dis J 2003;22(8):686–91.

[36] Schrag SJ, Zywicki S, Farley MM, et al. Group B streptococcal disease in the era of intrapartum antibiotic prophylaxis. N Engl J Med 2000;342(1):15–20.

[37] Baltimore RS, Huie SM, Meek JI, Schuchat A, O'Brien KL. Early-onset neonatal sepsis in the era of group B streptococcal prevention. Pediatrics 2001;108(5):1094–8.

[38] Hyde TB, Hilger TM, Reingold A, Farley MM, O'Brien KL, Schuchat A. Trends in incidence and antimicrobial resistance of early-onset sepsis: population-based surveillance in San Francisco and Atlanta. Pediatrics 2002;110(4):690–5.

[39] Stoll BJ, Hansen N, Fanaroff AA, et al. Changes in pathogens causing early-onset sepsis in very-low-birth-weight infants. N Engl J Med 2002;347(4):240–7.

[40] Schuchat A, Zywicki SS, Dinsmoor MJ, et al. Risk factors and opportunities for prevention of early-onset neonatal sepsis: a multicenter case-control study. Pediatrics 2000;105(1 Pt 1):21–6.

[41] Shah SS, Ehrenkranz RA, Gallagher PG. Increasing incidence of gram-negative rod bacteremia in a newborn intensive care unit. Pediatr Infect Dis J 1999;18(7):591–5.

[42] Nambiar S, Singh N. Change in epidemiology of health care-associated infections in a neonatal intensive care unit. Pediatr Infect Dis J 2002;21(9):839–42.

[43] Singh N, Patel KM, Leger MM, et al. Risk of resistant infections with Enterobacteriaceae in hospitalized neonates. Pediatr Infect Dis J 2002;21(11):1029–33.

[44] Toltzis P, Dul MJ, Hoyen C, et al. Molecular epidemiology of antibiotic-resistant gram-negative bacilli in a neonatal intensive care unit during a nonoutbreak period. Pediatrics 2001;108(5):1143–8.

[45] Toltzis P, Yamashita T, Vilt L, Blumer JL. Colonization with antibiotic-resistant gram-negative organisms in a pediatric intensive care unit. Crit Care Med 1997;25(3):538–44.

[46] Celkan T, Ozkan A, Apak H, et al. Bacteremia in childhood cancer. J Trop Pediatr 2002;48(6):373–7.

[47] Aquino VM, Pappo A, Buchanan GR, Tkaczewski I, Mustafa MM. The changing epidemiology of bacteremia in neutropenic children with cancer. Pediatr Infect Dis J 1995;14(2):140–3.

[48] Aledo A, Heller G, Ren L, et al. Septicemia and septic shock in pediatric patients: 140 consecutive cases on a pediatric hematology-oncology service. J Pediatr Hematol Oncol 1998;20(3):215–21.

[49] Krupova I, Kaiserova E, Foltinova A, et al. Bacteremia and fungemia in pediatric versus adult cancer patients after chemotherapy: comparison of etiology, risk factors and outcome. J Chemother 1998;10(3):236–42.

[50] Cosgrove SE, Carmeli Y. The impact of antimicrobial resistance on health and economic outcomes. Clin Infect Dis 2003;36(11):1433–7.

[51] Osmon S, Warren D, Seiler SM, Shannon W, Fraser VJ, Kollef MH. The influence of infection on hospital mortality for patients requiring >48 h of intensive care. Chest 2003;124(3):1021–9.

[52] Digiovine B, Chenoweth C, Watts C, Higgins M. The attributable mortality and costs of primary nosocomial bloodstream infections in the intensive care unit. Am J Respir Crit Care Med 1999;160(3):976–81.

[53] Ibrahim EH, Sherman G, Ward S, Fraser VJ, Kollef MH. The influence of inadequate antimicrobial treatment of bloodstream infections on patient outcomes in the ICU setting. Chest 2000;118(1):146–55.

[54] Carmeli Y, Troillet N, Karchmer AW, Samore MH. Health and economic outcomes of antibiotic resistance in Pseudomonas aeruginosa. Arch Intern Med 1999;159(10):1127–32.

[55] Cosgrove SE, Kaye KS, Eliopoulous GM, Carmeli Y. Health and economic outcomes of the emergence of third-generation cephalosporin resistance in Enterobacter species. Arch Intern Med 2002;162(2):185–90.

[56] Harbarth S, Rohner P, Auckenthaler R, Safran E, Sudre P, Pittet D. Impact and pattern of gram-negative bacteraemia during 6 y at a large university hospital. Scand J Infect Dis 1999;31(2):163–8.

[57] Blot S, Vandewoude K, De Bacquer D, Colardyn F. Nosocomial bacteremia caused by antibiotic-resistant gram-negative bacteria in critically ill patients: clinical outcome and length of hospitalization. Clin Infect Dis 2002;34(12):1600–6.

[58] Levy I, Leibovici L, Drucker M, Samra Z, Konisberger H, Ashkenazi S. A prospective study of Gram-negative bacteremia in children. Pediatr Infect Dis J 1996;15(2):117–22.

[59] Kartali G, Tzelepi E, Pournaras S, et al. Outbreak of infections caused by Enterobacter cloacae producing the integron-associated beta-lactamase IBC-1 in a neonatal intensive care unit of a Greek hospital. Antimicrob Agents Chemother 2002;46(5):1577–80.

[60] v Dijk Y, Bik EM, Hochstenbach-Vernooij S, et al. Management of an outbreak of Enterobacter cloacae in a neonatal unit using simple preventive measures. J Hosp Infect 2002;51(1):21–6.

[61] van Acker J, de Smet F, Muyldermans G, Bougatef A, Naessens A, Lauwers S. Outbreak of necrotizing enterocolitis associated with Enterobacter sakazakii in powdered milk formula. J Clin Microbiol 2001;39(1):293–7.

[62] van den Berg RW, Claahsen HL, Niessen M, Muytjens HL, Liem K, Voss A. Enterobacter cloacae outbreak in the NICU related to disinfected thermometers. J Hosp Infect 2000;45(1):29–34.

[63] Tresoldi AT, Padoveze MC, Trabasso P, et al. Enterobacter cloacae sepsis outbreak in a newborn unit caused by contaminated total parenteral nutrition solution. Am J Infect Control 2000;28(3):258–61.

[64] Yu WL, Cheng HS, Lin HC, Peng CT, Tsai CH. Outbreak investigation of nosocomial Enterobacter cloacae bacteraemia in a neonatal intensive care unit. Scand J Infect Dis 2000;32(3):293–8.

[65] Liu SC, Leu HS, Yen MY, Lee PI, Chou MC. Study of an outbreak of Enterobacter cloacae sepsis in a neonatal intensive care unit: the application of epidemiologic chromosome profiling by pulsed-field gel electrophoresis. Am J Infect Control 2002;30(7):381–5.

[66] Fernandez-Baca V, Ballesteros F, Hervas JA, et al. Molecular epidemiological typing of Enterobacter cloacae isolates from a neonatal intensive care unit: three-year prospective study. J Hosp Infect 2001;49(3):173–82.

[67] Peters SM, Bryan J, Cole MF. Enterobacterial repetitive intergenic consensus polymerase chain reaction typing of isolates of Enterobacter cloacae from an outbreak of infection in a neonatal intensive care unit. Am J Infect Control 2000;28(2):123–9.

[68] Cotton MF, Wasserman E, Pieper CH, et al. Invasive disease due to extended spectrum beta-lactamase-producing Klebsiella pneumoniae in a neonatal unit: the possible role of cockroaches. J Hosp Infect 2000;44(1):13–7.

[69] Gonzalez-Vertiz A, Alcantar-Curiel D, Cuauhtli M, et al. Multiresistant extended-spectrum beta-lactamase-producing Klebsiella pneumoniae causing an outbreak of nosocomial bloodstream infection. Infect Control Hosp Epidemiol 2001;22(11):723–5.

[70] Berthelot P, Grattard F, Patural H, et al. Nosocomial colonization of premature babies with Klebsiella oxytoca: probable role of enteral feeding procedure in transmission and control of the outbreak with the use of gloves. Infect Control Hosp Epidemiol 2001;22(3):148–51.

[71] Jeong SH, Kim WM, Chang CL, et al. Neonatal intensive care unit outbreak caused by a strain of Klebsiella oxytoca resistant to aztreonam due to overproduction of chromosomal beta-lactamase. J Hosp Infect 2001;48(4):281–8.

[72] Lebessi E, Dellagrammaticas H, Tassios PT, et al. Extended-spectrum beta-lactamase-producing Klebsiella pneumoniae in a neonatal intensive care unit in the high-prevalence area of Athens, Greece. J Clin Microbiol 2002;40(3):799–804.

[73] Macrae MB, Shannon KP, Rayner DM, Kaiser AM, Hoffman PN, French GL. A simultaneous outbreak on a neonatal unit of two strains of multiply antibiotic resistant Klebsiella pneumoniae controllable only by ward closure. J Hosp Infect 2001;49(3):183–92.

[74] Otman J, Cavassin ED, Perugini ME, Vidotto MC. An outbreak of extended-spectrum beta-lactamase-producing Klebsiella species in a neonatal intensive care unit in Brazil. Infect Control Hosp Epidemiol 2002;23(1):8–9.

[75] Jang TN, Fung CP, Yang TL, Shen SH, Huang CS, Lee SH. Use of pulsed-field gel electrophoresis to investigate an outbreak of Serratia marcescens infection in a neonatal intensive care unit. J Hosp Infect 2001;48(1):13–9.

[76] Jones BL, Gorman LJ, Simpson J, et al. An outbreak of Serratia marcescens in two neonatal intensive care units. J Hosp Infect 2000;46(4):314–9.

[77] Assadian O, Berger A, Aspock C, Mustafa S, Kohlhauser C, Hirschl AM. Nosocomial outbreak of Serratia marcescens in a neonatal intensive care unit. Infect Control Hosp Epidemiol 2002;23(8):457–61.

[78] Fleisch F, Zimmermann-Baer U, Zbinden R, et al. Three consecutive outbreaks of Serratia marcescens in a neonatal intensive care unit. Clin Infect Dis 2002;34(6):767–73.

[79] Prasad GA, Jones PG, Michaels J, Garland JS, Shivpuri CR. Outbreak of Serratia marcescens infection in a neonatal intensive care unit. Infect Control Hosp Epidemiol 2001;22(5):303–5.

[80] Villari P, Crispino M, Salvadori A, Scarcella A. Molecular epidemiology of an outbreak of Serratia marcescens in a neonatal intensive care unit. Infect Control Hosp Epidemiol 2001;22(10):630–4.

[81] Pillay T, Pillay DG, Adhikari M, Pillay A, Sturm AW. An outbreak of neonatal infection with Acinetobacter linked to contaminated suction catheters. J Hosp Infect 1999;43(4): 299–304.

[82] Casewell M, Phillips I. Hands as route of transmission for Klebsiella species. BMJ 1977; 2(6098):1315–7.

[83] Knittle MA, Eitzman DV, Baer H. Role of hand contamination of personnel in the epidemiology of gram- negative nosocomial infections. J Pediatr 1975;86(3):433–7.

[84] Guenthner SH, Hendley JO, Wenzel RP. Gram-negative bacilli as nontransient flora on the hands of hospital personnel. J Clin Microbiol 1987;25(3):488–90.

[85] Pittet D, Dharan S, Touveneau S, Sauvan V, Perneger TV. Bacterial contamination of the hands of hospital staff during routine patient care. Arch Intern Med 1999;159(8): 821–6.

[86] Pittet D, Hugonnet S, Harbarth S, et al. Effectiveness of a hospital-wide programme to improve compliance with hand hygiene. Infection Control Programme. Lancet 2000; 356(9238):1307–12.

[87] Hedderwick SA, McNeil SA, Lyons MJ, Kauffman CA. Pathogenic organisms associated with artificial fingernails worn by healthcare workers. Infect Control Hosp Epidemiol 2000;21(8):505–9.

[88] Foca M, Jakob K, Whittier S, et al. Endemic Pseudomonas aeruginosa infection in a neonatal intensive care unit. N Engl J Med 2000;343(10):695–700.

[89] Moolenaar RL, Crutcher JM, San Joaquin VH, et al. A prolonged outbreak of Pseudomonas aeruginosa in a neonatal intensive care unit: did staff fingernails play a role in disease transmission?. [see comments] Infect Control Hosp Epidemiol 2000;21(2):80–5.

[90] Trick WE, Vernon MO, Hayes RA, et al. Impact of ring wearing on hand contamination and comparison of hand hygiene agents in a hospital. Clin Infect Dis 2003;36(11):1383–90.

[91] Davin-Regli A, Monnet D, Saux P, et al. Molecular epidemiology of Enterobacter aerogenes acquisition: one-year prospective study in two intensive care units. J Clin Microbiol 1996;34(6):1474–80.

[92] Yuan M, Aucken H, Hall LM, Pitt TL, Livermore DM. Epidemiological typing of klebsiellae with extended-spectrum beta-lactamases from European intensive care units. J Antimicrob Chemother 1998;41(5):527–39.

[93] Chetchotisakd P, Phelps CL, Hartstein AI. Assessment of bacterial cross-transmission as a cause of infections in patients in intensive care units. Clin Infect Dis 1994;18(6): 929–37.

[94] D'Agata E, Venkataraman L, DeGirolami P, Samore M. Molecular epidemiology of acquisition of ceftazidime-resistant gram-negative bacilli in a nonoutbreak setting. J Clin Microbiol 1997;35(10):2602–5.

[95] Flynn DM, Weinstein RA, Nathan C, Gaston MA, Kabins SA. Patients' endogenous flora as the source of "nosocomial" Enterobacter in cardiac surgery. J Infect Dis 1987; 156(2):363–8.

[96] Olson B, Weinstein RA, Nathan C, Chamberlin W, Kabins SA. Epidemiology of endemic Pseudomonas aeruginosa: why infection control efforts have failed. J Infect Dis 1984; 150(6):808–16.

[97] Leverstein-van Hall MA, Box AT, Blok HE, Paauw A, Fluit AC, Verhoef J. Evidence of extensive interspecies transfer of integron-mediated antimicrobial resistance genes among multidrug-resistant Enterobacteriaceae in a clinical setting. J Infect Dis 2002;186(1):49–56.

[98] Wu TL, Chia JH, Su LH, Kuo AJ, Chu C, Chiu CH. Dissemination of extended-spectrum beta-lactamase-producing Enterobacteriaceae in pediatric intensive care units. J Clin Microbiol 2003;41(10):4836–8.

[99] D'Agata EM, Venkataraman L, DeGirolami P, et al. Colonization with broad-spectrum cephalosporin-resistant gram-negative bacilli in intensive care units during a nonoutbreak period: prevalence, risk factors, and rate of infection. [see comments] Crit Care Med 1999; 27(6):1090–5.

[100] Toltzis P, Hoyen C, Spinner-Block S, Salvator AE, Rice LB. Factors that predict preexisting colonization with antibiotic-resistant gram-negative bacilli in patients admitted to a pediatric intensive care unit. Pediatrics 1999;103(4 Pt 1):719–23.

[101] Toltzis P, Blumer JL. Nosocomial acquisition and transmission of antibiotic-resistant gram-negative organisms in the pediatric intensive care unit. Pediatr Infect Dis J 2001; 20(6):612–8.

[102] Benno Y, Sawada K, Mitsuoka T. The intestinal microflora of infants: composition of fecal flora in breast-fed and bottle-fed infants. Microbiol Immunol 1984;28:975–86.

[103] Balmer SE, Scott PH, Wharton BA. Diet and faecal flora in the newborn: lactoferrin. Arch Dis Child 1989;64(12):1685–90.

[104] Balmer SE, Wharton BA. Diet and faecal flora in the newborn: breast milk and infant formula. Arch Dis Child 1989;64(12):1672–7.

[105] Hokama T, Imamura T. Members of the throat microflora among infants with different feeding methods. J Trop Pediatr 1998;44(2):84–6.

[106] Goldmann DA, Leclair J, Macone A. Bacterial colonization of neonates admitted to an intensive care environment. J Pediatr 1978;93(2):288–93.

[107] Goldmann DA. Bacterial colonization and infection in the neonate. Am J Med 1981;70: 417–22.

[108] Finelli L, Livengood JR, Saiman L. Surveillance of pharyngeal colonization: detection and control of serious bacterial illness in low birth weight infants. Pediatr Infect Dis J 1994;13(10):854–9.

[109] Eriksson M, Melen B, Myrback KE, Winbladh B, Zetterstrom R. Bacterial colonization of newborn infants in a neonatal intensive care unit. Acta Paediatr Scand 1982;71(5):779–83.

[110] Savey A, Fleurette J, Salle BL. An analysis of the microbial flora of premature neonates. J Hosp Infect 1992;21(4):275–89.

[111] Tullus K, Fryklund B, Berglund B, Kallenius G, Burman LG. Influence of age on faecal carriage of P-fimbriated *Escherichia coli* and other gram-negative bacteria in hospitalized neonates. J Hosp Infect 1988;11(4):349–56.

[112] Schwiertz A, Gruhl B, Lobnitz M, Michel P, Radke M, Blaut M. Development of the intestinal bacterial composition in hospitalized preterm infants in comparison with breast-fed, full-term infants. Pediatr Res 2003;54(3):393–9.

[113] Millar MR, Linton CJ, Cade A, Glancy D, Hall M, Jalal H. Application of 16S rRNA gene PCR to study bowel flora of preterm infants with and without necrotizing enterocolitis. J Clin Microbiol 1996;34(10):2506–10.

[114] Favier CF, Vaughan EE, De Vos WM, Akkermans AD. Molecular monitoring of succession of bacterial communities in human neonates. Appl Environ Microbiol 2002; 68(1):219–26.

[115] Vollaard EJ, Clasener HA. Colonization resistance. Antimicrob Agents Chemother 1994; 38(3):409–14.

[116] Almuneef MA, Baltimore RS, Farrel PA, Reagan-Cirincione P, Dembry LM. Molecular typing demonstrating transmission of gram-negative rods in a neonatal intensive care unit in the absence of a recognized epidemic. Clin Infect Dis 2001;32(2):220–7.

[117] Toltzis P, Dul MJ, Hoyen C, et al. The effect of antibiotic rotation on colonization with antibiotic-resistant bacilli in a neonatal intensive care unit. Pediatrics 2002;110(4):707–11.

[118] Crossley K. Long-term care facilities as sources of antibiotic-resistant nosocomial pathogens. Curr Opin Infect Dis 2001;14(4):455–9.

[119] Bonomo RA. Multiple antibiotic-resistant bacteria in long-term-care facilities: an emerging problem in the practice of infectious diseases. Clin Infect Dis 2000;31(6): 1414–22.

[120] Muder RR, Brennen C, Drenning SD, Stout JE, Wagener MM. Multiply antibiotic-resistant gram-negative bacilli in a long-term-care facility: a case-control study of patient risk factors and prior antibiotic use. Infect Control Hosp Epidemiol 1997;18(12):809–13.

[121] Strausbaugh LJ, Crossley KB, Nurse BA, Thrupp LD. Antimicrobial resistance in long-term-care facilities. Infect Control Hosp Epidemiol 1996;17(2):129–40.

[122] Wiener J, Quinn JP, Bradford PA, et al. Multiple antibiotic-resistant Klebsiella and *Escherichia coli* in nursing homes. JAMA 1999;281(6):517–23.

[123] Mylotte JM, Goodnough S, Tayara A. Antibiotic-resistant organisms among long-term care facility residents on admission to an inpatient geriatrics unit: tetrospective and prospective surveillance. Am J Infect Control 2001;29(3):139–44.

[124] Lidsky K, Hoyen C, Salvator A, Rice LB, Toltzis P. Antibiotic-resistant gram-negative organisms in pediatric chronic-care facilities. Clin Infect Dis 2002;34(6):760–6.

ELSEVIER
SAUNDERS

CLINICS IN
LABORATORY
MEDICINE

Clin Lab Med 24 (2004) 381–402

Vancomycin resistance in *Staphylococcus aureus*

Peter C. Appelbaum, MD, PhD*,
Bülent Bozdogan, MD, PhD

*Department of Pathology, Hershey Medical Center, 500 University Drive,
Hershey, PA 17033, USA*

Staphylococcus aureus is a common cause of both community- and hospital-acquired infections, ranging from simple skin pustules to wound abscesses, systemic infection with toxic shock, and death [1]. Resistance to penicillin G developed soon after its introduction due to staphylococcal β-lactamase production. This was followed by development of resistance in the 1960s to all currently available β-lactams through altered penicillin binding protein (PBP) 2a encoded by the *mec*A gene [2–4]. Such strains are referred to as methicillin-resistant *S aureus* (MRSA) based on resistance to methicillin, the first β-lactamase stable penicillin derivative introduced into clinical use. Current estimates are that up to 50% of *S aureus* in the United States are MRSA [5]. Until recently, MRSA was predominantly a problem of institutions such as acute and chronic care hospitals, but it is now also a problem in other institutions, such as jails and child care centers, and is increasingly community acquired, for example by competitive contact sports participants [6].

β-Lactam antibiotics are enzyme inhibitors, and their mechanism of action involves inhibition of bacterial transpeptidases (also called penicillin binding proteins) that catalyze cell wall assembly. In contrast, glycopeptide antibiotics like vancomycin act on an earlier stage of cell wall synthesis by binding to the C-terminal of the cell wall precursor pentapeptide (Lipid II) complex and preventing it from being used for cell wall synthesis. The mechanisms of PBP-mediated β-lactam and of glycopeptide resistance match the mode of action of these antibiotics: methicillin-resistant staphylococci produce a surrogate transpeptidase with low affinity for β-lactams that has not been overcome with any β-lactam in clinical use. Vancomycin-resistant enterococci (VRE)

---

* Corresponding author.
E-mail address: pappelbaum@psu.edu

0272-2712/04/$ - see front matter © 2004 Elsevier Inc. All rights reserved.
doi:10.1016/j.cll.2004.03.004

contain a cell wall precursor with an altered C-terminal pentapeptide residue as a result of substitution of the terminal D-alanine with D-lactate, referred to as a depsipeptide, the bactoprenyl derivative of which (Lipid II) is only poorly bound by the antibiotic.

S aureus had, until recently, retained its susceptibility to glyco-peptides such as vancomycin. Minimum inhibitory concentrations (MICs) of vancomycin against susceptible isolates of *S aureus* range from ≤ 0.25 to 2 μg/mL, with MIC_{50} and MIC_{90} values of 1 μg/mL [7,8]. Current sus-ceptibility breakpoints for vancomycin are as follows: MICs of ≤ 4 μg/mL, susceptible; 8 to 16 μg/mL, intermediate; and ≥ 32 μg/mL, resistant [9].

Development of vancomycin-resistant enterococci

High-level vancomycin resistance in enterococci (VanA or VanB type) is associated with the acquisition of around 10 kb of DNA-encoding polypeptides that perform various different functions in cell wall synthesis, such as transposition, regulation, or synthesis of abnormal pentapeptide peptidoglycan precursors to which neither vancomycin nor teicoplanin bind with high affinity and hydrolysis of precursors of normal peptidoglycan [10]. Environmental organisms are thought to be the source of these genes. Vancomycin has been in use since 1958, and high-level vancomycin resistance emerged in enterococci in 1986 [11]. Increased use of vancomycin in the 1980s because of the increased prevalence of MRSA and the recognition of *Clostridium difficile*–associated diarrhea probably contributed to the development of VRE. VRE are usually *E faecium*, and strains are usually also highly resistant to ampicillin and aminoglycosides.

Mechanism of vancomycin resistance in vancomycin-resistant enterococci

Various types of VRE have been characterized on phenotypic and geno-typic bases [12]. VanA enterococci are resistant to high levels of vancomycin (MIC ≥ 64 μg/mL) and teicoplanin (MIC ≥ 8 μg/mL), and resistance is induced by the presence of either drug. VanB organisms are resistant to a range of vancomycin concentrations, from 4 to >1024 μg/mL, but typically retain susceptibility to teicoplanin, which does not induce resistance.

The mechanism of glycopeptide resistance in VanA and VanB enterococci is highly complex and involves a cluster of genes encoding an alternate biosynthetic pathway for the production of cell wall precursors that bind vancomycin poorly (Fig. 1) [12]. Unlike the normal peptidoglycan (PG) precursors, which have D-alanyl D-alanine (D-Ala D-Ala) dipeptide termini, those of VRE end with the depsipeptide D-alanyl D-lactate (D-Ala D-Lac). The affinity of vancomycin for these altered molecules is 1000 times lower than its affinity for the native PG precursor. This alteration of the target site for glycopeptide antibiotics is accomplished by several proteins, which sense

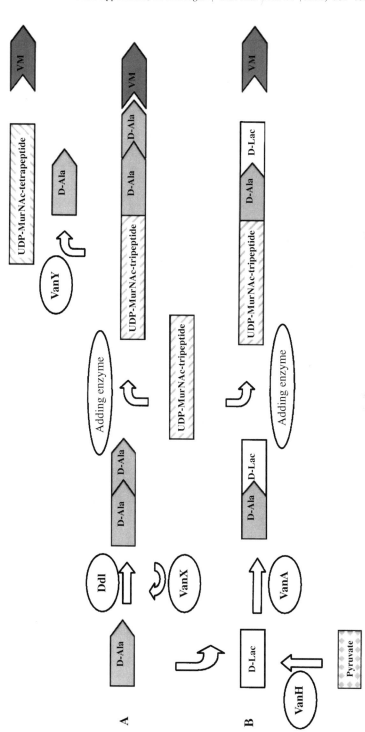

Fig. 1. Simplified schematic representation of the two pathways for synthesis of peptidoglycan (PG) precursors present in a VanA enterococcus. The upper pathway (*A*) produces the native PG precursor that is the target for vancomycin. The altered PG precursor produced by the lower pathway (*B*) binds vancomycin poorly. VanY, encoded by the vanA gene cluster, modifies the finished native PG precursor. D-Ala, D-alanine; D-Ala D-Ala, D-alanyl D-alanine; D-Ala D-Lac, D-alanyl D-lactate; Ddl, D-Ala:D-Ala ligase; D-Lac, D-lactate; UDP-MurNAc, uridine diphosphate-N-acetyl muramyl; VM, vancomycin. (*From* Gold HS. Vancomycin-resistant enterococci: mechanisms and clinical observations. Clin Infect Dis 2001;33:210–9; with permission.)

the presence of the drug, produce a drug-resistant target, and eliminate the drug-susceptible target in a coordinated manner. In VanA enterococci, for example, the VanR protein (the response regulator) and the VanS protein (a histidine kinase sensor) form a two-component regulatory system. The presence of vancomycin or teicoplanin causes the VanS protein to auto-phosphorylate, then in turn to phosphorylate VanR. In addition to in-creasing expression of vanR and vanS, phosphorylated VanR protein binds to the promoter region for vanHAX, driving transcription of the genes that encode the essential structural molecules of the gene cluster. The VanH protein converts pyruvate into D-lactate, which is combined with D-alanine by the VanA ligase to create D-Ala D-Lac. The VanX dipeptidase hydrolyzes D-Ala D-Ala (the product of the native D-Ala:D-Ala ligase), thereby reducing the pool of D-Ala D-Ala available to make the vancomycin-susceptible PG precursor. VanY is an accessory structural protein that removes the terminal D-Ala residue from the PG precursor. This carboxy-peptidase augments glycopeptide resistance by removing residual vancomy-cin binding sites. The function of the VanZ protein is not understood, but it contributes to teicoplanin resistance. These modified precursors are then polymerized into the functional cell wall in place of the native PG precursors.

Experimental transfer of vancomycin resistance from *Enterococcus* to *S aureus*

Transfer of resistance genes from *Enterococcus faecalis* NCTC 12201, which is resistant to vancomycin, penicillin, tetracycline, erythromycin, chloramphenicol, gentamicin, streptomycin, and mupirocin, to *S aureus* B111 with chromosomal resistance to rifampin was reported by Noble et al [13] in 1992. Resistance transfer was attempted in vitro on filters and in vivo on the occluded skin of mice and was detected by attempting to recover resistant transconjugants on media containing rifampin and either erythro-mycin, chloramphenicol, or vancomycin. Resistant transconjugants were rarely detected from in vitro experiments (<1 in 10^6 recipients), but occurred at a frequency of 10^0 to 10^3 per 10^6 recipients from in vivo experiments. Transfer of resistance to erythromycin, chloramphenicol, and streptomycin was detected in many transconjugants, with transfer of resistance to vancomycin in the majority of instances (87%). Resistance to gentamicin was only transferred in 0.5% of transconjugants, and no transfer of resistance to tetracycline or mupirocin occurred. Transfer of resistance to each agent occurred independently as shown by recovery of transconjugants with a variety of resistance patterns, and resistance appeared to be transposon mediated. The investigators of this study concluded that as high-level vancomycin resistance can be transferred from an enterococcus to a staphylococcus under conditions similar to those that exist in nature, no doubt wild-type *S aureus* will acquire vancomycin resistance in time.

Development of vancomycin-intermediate *S aureus*

The first report of *S aureus* with reduced susceptibility to vancomycin (MIC of 8 µg/mL) was from Japan [14]. Subsequently, eight isolates of vancomycin-intermediate *S aureus* (VISA) have been documented in the United States from patients with clinical infections [15–20]. The first United States case was seen in Michigan in a patient on long-term ambulatory peritoneal dialysis. The patient had been treated with vancomycin repeatedly for MRSA-associated peritonitis. Susceptibility testing showed vancomycin MIC of 8 µg/mL [15]. A month later another patient in New Jersey, also with chronic, repeated MRSA infections, presented with bacteremia caused by a VISA strain with a vancomycin MIC of 8 µg/mL. This patient also was known to be colonized with VRE [16]. Development of resistance during vancomycin treatment of a multiply resistant MRSA infection occurred in 1997 in an elderly hemodialysis patient with multiple thrombi and arterial grafts, who was treated with intravenous vancomycin. The strain was initially susceptible to vancomycin (MIC of 2 µg/mL) in two blood specimens taken 10 days apart. Treatment continued with intravenous vancomycin for a month following the second culture. Within a month of discontinuation of therapy, the patient presented in septic shock and died. A blood culture grew MRSA, which was now vancomycin intermediate (MIC 8 µg/mL) and had the identical DNA fingerprint pattern of the initial isolates [21].

Mechanisms of resistance of vancomycin-intermediate *S aureus*

Two mechanisms of resistance have been described in VISA strains [22,23]. The effect of reduced vancomycin susceptibility with both mechanisms is abnormal, thickened cell walls (Fig. 2) [22].

The mechanism of resistance in *S aureus* Mu50 was associated with an increased proportion of glutamine nonamidated muropeptides, and enhanced glutamine synthetase and L-glutamine D-fructose-6-phosphate aminotransferase activities, which are involved in the cell-wall peptidoglycan synthesis pathway. Increased levels of incorporation of ^{14}C-labeled D-glucose into the cell wall were also observed. Cells allowed to synthesize cell wall in the absence or presence of glucose and glutamine resulted in cells with different cell-wall thicknesses and different levels of cross-linking. Susceptibility testing of these cells demonstrated a strong correlation between the cell-wall thickness and the degree of vancomycin resistance. Affinity trapping of vancomycin molecules by cell wall monomers and clogging of the outer layers of peptidoglycan by bound vancomycin molecules were considered to be the mechanism of vancomycin resistance of *S aureus* Mu50.

The second mechanism of resistance was described in a strain of *S aureus* that developed reduced vancomycin susceptibility during vancomycin therapy. A series of isogenic MRSA isolates recovered from a bacteremic patient were shown to acquire gradually increasing levels of resistance to

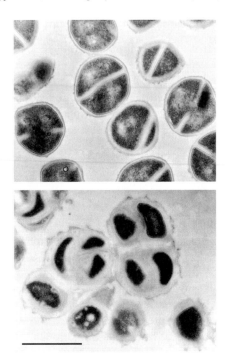

Fig. 2. Transmission electron microscopy of cell wall thickening of vancomycin-intermediate *Staphylococcus aureus* grown in tryptic soy broth in the absence (*top*) and presence (*bottom*) of 8 μg/mL vancomycin and harvested in the midexponential growth phase. The black bar represents 1 μm. (*From* Sieradzki K, Roberts RB, Haber SW, Tomasz A. The development of vancomycin resistance in a patient with methicillin-resistant Staphylococcus aureus infection. N Engl J Med 1999;340:517–23; with permission.)

vancomycin during chemotherapy with the drug. MICs rose from 1 μg/mL to 4 and 8 μg/mL [23]. The resistant isolates produced abnormally thick cell walls and poorly separated cells when grown in antibiotic-free medium. Chemical analysis of the resistant isolates showed decreased cross-linkage of the peptidoglycan and drastically reduced levels of PBP4. Resistant isolates showed reduced rates of cell wall turnover and autolysis. In vitro hydrolysis of resistant cell walls by autolytic extracts prepared from either susceptible or resistant strains was also slow, and this abnormality could be traced to a change in the cell wall teichoic acid component of resistant isolates. Some change in the structure and/or metabolism of teichoic acids appears to be an important component of the mechanism of decreased susceptibility to vancomycin in these isolates of *S aureus*.

Development of vancomycin-resistant *S aureus*

The first isolates of vancomycin-resistant *S aureus* (VRSA) occurred in June and September of 2002 in Michigan [24,25] and Pennsylvania [26–28].

The patient in the first case was a Michigan resident aged 40 years with diabetes, peripheral vascular disease, and chronic renal failure. In June 2002, VRSA (referred to as MI-VRSA in this article) was isolated from a swab obtained from a hemodialysis catheter exit site from this patient, who had also been treated for chronic foot ulcerations with multiple courses of antimicrobial therapy, some of which included vancomycin, over the course of a year. In April 2002, the patient underwent amputation of a gangrenous toe and subsequently developed MRSA bacteremia caused by an infected arteriovenous hemodialysis graft. The infection was treated with vancomycin, rifampin, and removal of the infected graft. In June, the patient developed a suspected catheter exit-site infection, and the temporary hemodialysis catheter was removed; cultures of the exit site and catheter tip subsequently grew *S aureus* resistant to oxacillin (MIC > 16 µg/mL) and vancomycin (MIC > 128 µg/mL). A week after catheter removal, the exit site appeared healed; however, the patient's chronic foot ulcer appeared infected. VRSA, vancomycin-resistant *E faecalis*, and *Klebsiella oxytoca* were recovered from the ulcer. The infection was treated with aggressive wound care and systemic antimicrobial therapy with trimethroprim/sulfamethoxazole, to which the VRSA isolate was susceptible.

The second VRSA isolate from the United States was obtained from a 70-year-old morbidly obese patient who presented in September 2002 with a several week history of increased somnolence, intermittent fever, chills, malaise, night sweats, shortness of breath, and dyspnea on exertion [28]. He was admitted to the hospital and found to have a chronic heel ulcer producing purulent drainage. Multiple organisms were grown from swab specimens taken from the ulcer, including *Streptococcus agalactiae, Pseudomonas aeruginosa, Stenotrophomonas maltophilia,* and *S aureus.* The *S aureus* was resistant to vancomycin (MIC 32–64 µg/mL) (referred to as PA-VRSA in this article) and oxacillin and contained both the *mec*A and *van*A genes. The isolate was susceptible to chloramphenicol, linezolid, minocycline, quinupristin-dalfopristin, rifampin, and trimethoprim-sulfamethoxazole. The patient was discharged from the hospital and responded to antimicrobial treatment.

Antimicrobial susceptibility of vancomycin-resistant *S aureus*

The MI-VRSA was highly resistant to vancomycin, with MICs of 1024 µg/mL by broth microdilution and >256 µg/mL by E-test [25]. The isolate was susceptible to chloramphenicol, linezolid, minocycline, quinupristin-dalfopristin, and trimethoprim-sulfamethoxazole.

On initial testing of the PA-VRSA isolate, a small area of clearing was noted within a zone of reduced growth around a 30-µg vancomycin disk, suggesting possible resistance (Fig. 3) [28]. Growth was also observed on a BHI agar screen plate containing 6 µg/mL of vancomycin. The

Fig. 3. Disk diffusion and E-test analysis of Pennsylvania vancomycin-resistant *Staphylococcus aureus* isolate on MuellerHinton agar. A zone of complete growth inhibition can be observed within a wider zone of reduced growth around both the E-test strip and the 30-μg vancomycin disk. (*From* Tenover FC, Weigel LM, Appelbaum PC, et al. Vancomycin-resistant *Staphylococcus aureus* isolate from a patient in Pennsylvania. Antimicrob Agents Chemother 2004;48:275–80; with permission.)

vancomycin MIC was 64 μg/mL using the E-test method and 32 μg/mL by the National Committee for Clinical Laboratory Standards (NCCLS) broth microdilution method, and the teicoplanin MIC was 8 μg/mL by broth microdilution. MICs of other antimicrobial agents are shown in Table 1. The isolate was resistant to aminoglycosides, macrolides, oxacillin, rifampin, and tetracycline but susceptible to chloramphenicol, linezolid, minocycline, quinuprostin-dalfopristin, rifampin, and trimethoprim-sulfamethoxazole. Vancomycin susceptibility was tested by three automated methods: Micro-Scan conventional MIC plates, Vitek cards, and Vitek 2 cards, and each method was tested on 3 separate days (Table 2). None of the vancomycin MIC results were in the resistant range based on NCCLS interpretive criteria (ie, MIC ≥ 32 μg/mL). However, after overnight growth on BHI agar containing 6 μg/mL of vancomycin, the vancomycin MICs tended to be higher when tested by Vitek and Vitek2 than when propagated on nonselective media (see Table 2). The disconcerting finding of the study was that the automated suscepti-bility testing systems, Microscan, Vitek, and Vitek2, did not identify the PA-VRSA isolate as resistant to vancomycin. Even after overnight growth on vancomycin-containing media, the organism was not identified as fully resistant to vancomycin. Thus, when performing automated susceptibility testing of *S aureus* strains, and particularly oxacillin-resistant *S aureus*, microbiologists should consider including a vancomycin agar screen plate (BHI containing 6 μg/mL vancomycin) in the testing battery, or performing

Table 1
Minimum inhibitory concentrations of antimicrobial agents against Pennsylvania vancomycin-resistant *Staphylococcus aureus* isolate

Target	Class	Antibacterial	MIC (µg/mL)
Cell wall	Glycopeptides	Vancomycin	32
		Teicoplanin	8
		Oritavancin	0.25
		TD-6424	0.5
	β-lactams	Penicillin G	32
		Oxacillin	> 64
		Imipenem	4
		Meropenem	16
		Ertapenem	32
		Faropenem	16
		RWJ54428	0.5
Cell membrane	Lipopeptide	Daptomycin	0.5
Ribosome	Macrolides	Erythromycin	> 64
		Azithromycin	> 64
		Clarithromycin	> 64
	Ketolides	Telithromycin	> 64
	Lincosamides	Clindamycin	> 64
	Streptogramins	Quinupristin-Dalfopristin	1
	Aminoglycosides	Kanamycin	> 64
		Gentamicin	64
		Tobramycin	> 64
		Amikacin	32
	Tetracyclines	Tetracycline	64
		Minocycline	0.12
	Glycylcyclines	Tigecycline	0.12
	Oxazolidinones	Linezolid	1
		Ranbezolid	1
Topoisomerase	Quinolones	Ciprofloxacin	> 64
		Levofloxacin	32
		Gatifloxacin	8
		Moxifloxacin	4
		Clinafloxacin	2
		Sitafloxacin	1
		Garenoxacin	2
RNA polymerase	Rifampicin	Rifampicin	<0.06
Folic acid metabolism		Trimethoprim-sulfamethoxazole	0.25
	Diaminoprymidine	Iclaprim	0.25

Data from Tenover FC, Weigel LM, Appelbaum PC, et al. Vancomycin-resistant *Staphylococcus aureus* isolate from a patient in Pennsylvania. Antimicrob Agents Chemother 2004;48:275–80.

nonautomated broth- or agar-based MIC tests to insure that vancomycin-resistant strains do not go undetected.

Time-kill studies and population analysis showed that, although daptomycin was rapidly bactericidal for the PA-VRSA strain (Fig. 4), linezolid and quinupristin-dalfopristin were only bacteriostatic (Table 3) [28]. By population analysis, the organism appeared to be homogeneously resistant

Table 2
Results of automated susceptibility testing of Pennsylvania vancomycin-resistant *Staphylococcus aureus* (PA-VRSA) isolate

	MIC range[a] (in µg/mL) by method		
S aureus strain	MicroScan	Vitek	Vitek2
PA-VRSA (uninduced)	4, <2, <2	2, 1, 4	2, 2, 2
PA-VRSA (induced)[b]	<2, <2, 4	1, 16, 16	8, 8, 8
ATCC 29213	<2	<0.5–1	<1

[a] Tests were run in triplicate.

[b] Organisms were grown overnight on BHI agar containing 6 µg/mL of vancomycin prior to testing (induced). Uninduced strains were grown on sheep blood agar overnight.

Data from Tenover FC, Weigel LM, Appelbaum PC, et al. Vancomycin-resistant *Staphylococcus aureus* isolate from a patient in Pennsylvania. Antimicrob Agents Chemother 2004;48:275–80.

to vancomycin (Fig. 5) with no apparent shoulder in the curve that would indicate a heterogeneously resistant subpopulation.

Two experimental anti-MRSA cephalosporins, BAL9141 and RWJ-54428, had low MICs against the VRSA strain and were bactericidal at 2×MIC after 6 hours and 12 hours, respectively [27]. The PA-VRSA was susceptible to quinupristin/dalfopristin; however, quinupristin/dalfopristin was bacteriostatic. The MICs of oxazolidinones linezolid and ranbezolid were 1 mg/L, and

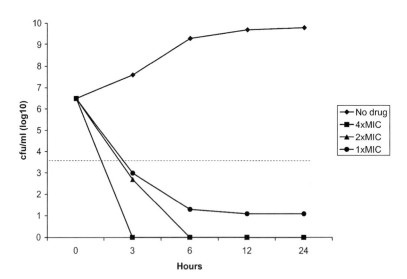

Fig. 4. Time-kill studies with Pennsylvania vancomycin-resistant *Staphylococcus aureus* isolate and daptomycin. The organism was grown in the absence of drug (growth control) at the minimum inhibitory concentration of the organism, and at twice (2×) and four times (4×) the concentration of daptomycin required to inhibit the growth of the organism. The decrease in viable counts of > 3 logs indicates that daptomycin is bactericidal for this organism. (*From* Tenover FC, Weigel LM, Appelbaum PC, et al. Vancomycin-resistant *Staphylococcus aureus* isolate from a patient in Pennsylvania. Antimicrob Agents Chemother 2004;48:275–80; with permission.)

Table 3
Time-kill studies with Pennsylvania vancomycin-resistant *Staphylococcus aureus* isolate

Drug and concentration[a]	Viability counts[b]			
	3h	6h	12h	24h
Daptomycin				
4×MIC	>−3	>−3	>−3	>−3
2×MIC	>−3	>−3	>−3	>−3
MIC (0.5 µg/mL)	>−3	>−3	>−3	>−3
Linezolid				
4×MIC	<−1	−1	−2	−2
2×MIC	<−1	<−1	<−1	−1
MIC (1 µg/mL)	<−1	<−1	<−1	<−1
Quinupristin-Dalfopristin				
4×MIC	<−1	<−1	−1	−2
2×MIC	<−1	<−1	−1	−2
MIC (1 µg/mL)	<−1	<−1	−1	−2
Trimethoprim/sulfamethoxazole				
4×MIC	>−1	−2	>−3	>−3
2×MIC	>−1	−2	>−3	−2
MIC (0.25 µg/mL, trimethoprim component)	<−1	−1	>−3	<−1

[a] 4×MIC, four times the MIC; 2×MIC, two times the MIC.
[b] −1, 90% killing; −2, 99% killing; −3, 99.9% killing.
Data from Bozdogan B, Esel D, Whitener C, Browne FA, Appelbaum PC, Antibacterial susceptibility of a vancomycin-resistant *Staphylococcus aureus* strain isolated at the Hershey Medical Center. J Antimicrob Chemother 2003;52:864–8.

they were bacteriostatic. Though marketed fluoroquinolones were not active against the PA-VRSA strain, experimental quinolones sitafloxacin, WCK 771, WCK 1153, and DK-507K each had MICs of 0.5 to 1 mg/L and were bactericidal at 1 to 2×MIC after 3 to 6 hours. DNA nanobinders, a new class of antibiotics that bind to the minor groove of DNA and inhibit DNA function and transcription, GS02-02, GS02-47, and GS02-104, all had low MICs against the PA-VRSA strain, and GS02-02 was bactericidal. Peptide deformylase inhibitors, which interfere with removal of the formyl moiety of nascent polypeptides by peptide deformylase, NVP-PDF713 and GS02-12, had low MICs against the PA-VRSA strain but were bacteriostatic. Tigecycline, mupirocin, fusidic acid, and iclaprim were all bacteriostatic. Trimethoprim/sulfamethoxazole had a low MIC (0.25 mg/L) and was bactericidal at 4×MIC after 12 hours (see Tables 1 and 3).

Genetic basis of vancomycin-resistant *S aureus*

Michigan isolate

The MI-VRSA isolate contained the vanA gene, the sequences of which were identical to those of transposon Tn1546 and of the patients vancomysin-resistant *E faecalis* isolate [25]. Additionally, this isolate was indistinguishable

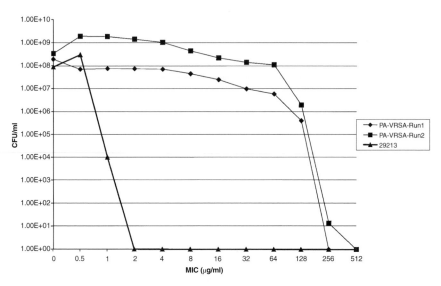

Fig. 5. Population analysis of Pennsylvania vancomycin-resistant *Staphylococcus aureus* (PA-VRSA) isolate. Serial dilutions of the organism were plated on increasing concentrations of vancomycin. The PA-VRSA isolate was tested on two separate occasions (replicates 1 and 2). *S aureus* ATCC 29213 was used as a vancomycin-susceptible control. (*From* Tenover FC, Weigel LM, Appelbaum PC, et al. Vancomycin-resistant *Staphylococcus aureus* isolate from a patient in Pennsylvania. Antimicrob Agents Chemother 2004;48:275–80; with permission.)

by pulsed field gel electrophoresis (PFGE) after digestion of DNA with SmaI, from the patient's vancomycin-susceptible isolate isolated from the nares, as well as from a vancomycin-susceptible isolate recovered from a friend of the patient [25]. The MI-VRSA isolate harbored a 57.9-kilobase multiresistance conjugative plasmid within which the van A transposon, Tn1546, was integrated. Additional elements on the plasmid encoded resistance to tri-methoprim (dfrA), β-lactams (blaZ), aminoglycosides (aacA-aphD), and disinfectants (qacC). Genetic analyses suggest that the long-anticipated transfer of vancomycin resistance to a methicillin-resistant *S aureus* occurred in vivo by interspecies transfer of Tn1546 from a co-isolate of *Enterococcus faecalis* [29]. The SmaI digestion PFGE pattern of the MI-VRSA isolate showed that it was within the USA100 lineage (also known as the New York/Japan clone) [28].

Pennsylvania isolate

The organism was positive by polymerase chain reaction (PCR) for the mecA, vanA, erm(A), and aac(6')-aph(2'') determinants [28]. Additional PCR primers specific for the components of the vanA transposon, Tn1546, confirmed the presence of vanR, vanS, vanX, vanY, and vanH, suggesting that a significant portion of the Tn1546 was present. However, two primer sets directed to regions of orf1 and orf2 at the 5'end of Tn1546 failed to amplify the expected products, suggesting that these sequences may be absent or truncated. Two other primer sets directed to the regions between orf1 and orf2, and vanS and vanH, yielded products larger than the predicted sizes of 1299 and 593 bp, suggesting the presence of insertion sequences in these areas. DNA sequence analysis of the vanA gene was consistent with the prototype vanA sequence of *E faecalis* A256. Plasmid analysis revealed two plasmids of 120 kb and 4 kb. The vanA gene was localized to the 120-kb plasmid by Southern hybridization. The tetK gene, which mediates resistance to tetracycline but not minocycline, was present on the 4-kb plasmid. The SmaI digestion PFGE pattern of the PA-VRSA isolate fell within the USA100 lineage, but its pattern was readily distinguishable from the MI-VRSA, indicating that the these isolates are not epidemiologically linked (Fig. 6). However, both isolates show PFGE patterns that are consistent with the most common PFGE types of hospital-acquired staphylococcal infections in the United States.

Although the PA-VRSA isolate contained vanA, the isolate demonstrated only moderate resistance to vancomycin (MIC range 16 to 64 μg/mL). In addition, the teicoplanin MIC (range 4 to 8 μg/mL) for the PA-VRSA was in the susceptible range as defined by NCCLS. This is inconsistent with the VanA phenotype typically observed in enterococci. The reason for the

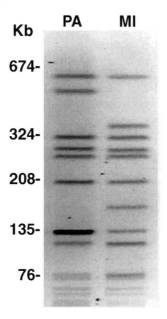

Fig. 6. Pulsed field gel electrophoresis of *Sma*I macrorestriction fragments of the Pennsylvania (PA) and Michigan (MI) vancomycin-resistant *Staphylococcus aureus* (VRSA) strains. The *Sma*I macroresistrction fragments for the two VRSA isolates indicate that both are related to the USA100 pulsed-field type, also known as the New York/Japan clone. (*From* Tenover FC, Weigel LM, Appelbaum PC, et al. Vancomycin-resistant *Staphylococcus aureus* isolate from a patient in Pennsylvania. Antimicrob Agents Chemother 2004;48:275–80; with permission.)

low vancomycin MIC may be related to the level of expression of the vanA gene that is present on a large, 120-kb plasmid. Plasmids of this size are not typical of S aureus. Thus, this plasmid may represent either an enterococcal plasmid or a cointegrate plasmid composed of enterococcal and staphylococcal plasmid sequences. This suggests that sequences corresponding to the vanR, vanS, vanX, vanY, and vanH of the Tn1546 genetic element are present on the 120-kb plasmid, although the 5′end of the transposon may be truncated. It would also appear that there are insertion sequences in two regions of the transposon. Thus, the plasmids in the PA-VRSA and the MI-VRSA are significantly different, indicating two independent events of interspecies transfer, most likely from enterococci.

Physiologic basis of vancomycin-resistant S aureus

This has been studied by construction of strain COLVA by filter mating of the MI-VRSA strain with the well-characterized MRSA strain COL [24]. The donor was the clinical MI-VRSA isolate, which carried transposon Tn1546 on plasmid pLW1043. COLVA grown overnight in broth alone or supplemented with 100 µg/mL vancomycin showed the following susceptibility to oxacillin and vancomycin by the E-test. The cultures grown in broth showed high-level resistance to oxacillin (MIC: 800 µg/mL) (Fig. 7A), and the culture grown in broth with vancomycin showed high-level vancomycin resistance (MIC: 512 µg/mL) (Fig. 7B).

Cell wall peptidoglycan prepared, purified, and solubilized by enzymatic hydrolysis, UDP-linked peptidoglycan precursors prepared and analyzed by high-performance liquid chromatography (HPLC) with muropeptides separated by mass spectrometry analysis showed that the composition of the cell wall peptidoglycan profiles of strain COLVA grown in antibiotic-free and antibiotic-containing media were virtually identical, except that in strain COLVA beside many of the familiar muropeptide peaks of strain COL there was often a small secondary peak. In COLVA grown in the presence of vancomycin, these novel peaks became the dominant muropeptide species of the peptidoglycan. Growth of COLVA in the presence of oxacillin (10 µg/mL) caused a virtual disappearance of all but one of the novel peaks, and the peptidoglycan composition changed to a profile characteristic of strain COL grown in the presence of β-lactam antibiotics.

Structures of the novel muropeptide components in strain COLVA grown in vancomycin-containing medium showed (1) the complete replacement of pentapeptides by tetrapeptides and (2) the frequent deficit or complete lack of pentaglycine branches in muropeptides particularly in muropeptide monomers and in the biosynthetically "first" donor components of oligomeric muropeptides. Also apparent were structural modifications in some muropeptides that were interpreted as evidence for lack of amidation of the stem peptide glutamic acid residues (muropeptide 4v) and

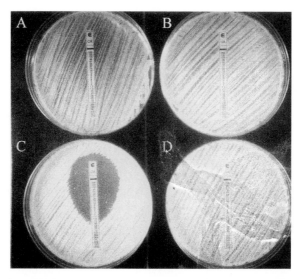

Fig. 7. Expression of high-level oxacillin and vancomycin resistance in *Staphylococcus aureus*. *S aureus* strain COLVA carrying both *mecA* and *vanA* (*A, B*) and a mutant derivative COLVA-Δ*mecA* with a *Tn551*-inactivated *mecA* (*C, D*) were assayed for the level of resistance to oxacillin and vancomycin. Overnight cultures of bacterial strains grown in trypticase soy broth (TSB) (*A, C*) or in TSB containing 100 µg/mL vancomycin (*B, D*) were diluted and spread on trypticase soy agar (TSA) after which the antibiotic-containing paper strips (oxacillin strips in *A* and *C* and vancomycin strips in *B* and *D*) were deposited on the agar surface. (*From* Severin A, Tabei K, Tenover F, Chung M, Clarke N, Tomasz A. High level oxacillin and vancomycin resistance and altered cell wall composition in *Staphylococcus aureus* carrying the staphylococcal mecA and the enterococcal vanA gene complex. J Biol Chem 2003;279:3398–407; with permission.)

the presence of deacetylated (16v and 17v) and O-acetylated (6v) hexosamines. The percentage representation of various muropeptide peaks in bacteria grown under different conditions is illustrated in Table 4. The effect of inactivation of *mec*A on vancomycin resistance and cell wall composition of strain COLVA was studied by transducing Tn551-inactivated *mec*A into strain COLVA to generate mutant COLVA-'mecA. COLVA-'mecA retained unaltered high level resistance to vancomycin, but resistance to oxacillin was reduced to 10 µg/mL. Strain COLVA-'mecA grown in broth containing 250 µg/mL vancomycin showed the cell wall precursor pool had a composition very similar to that of COLVA grown in vancomycin containing medium (Table 5). The composition of the cell wall peptidoglycan is shown in Table 4. COLVA with an inactivated *mec*A produced a muropeptide profile that was very similar to the muropeptide profile of strain COLVA that carried an intact *mec*A.

Study of the composition of the cell wall precursor pool showed that six components in the precursor pool were common and were present in comparable amounts in both strains. An additional minor component (peak 8) was only detected in strain COLVA. Peaks 1 through 4 and peak 6 were

Table 4
Proportion of major muropeptides in the peptidoglycan of vancomycin-susceptible strain COL and vancomycin-resistant strain COLVA

Major peak	Relative amounts of muropeptides[a]				
	COL No antibiotics	COLVA No antibiotics	COLVA +vancomycin	COLVA +oxacillin	COLVA–'mecA +vancomycin
1	1.4	1.7	0.0	1.6	0.0
5	3.7	2.9	0.0	15.8	0.0
11	5.4	4.3	0.0	12.6	0.0
15	5.3	4.2	0.0	7.2	0.0
16	3.7	3.2	0.0	3.8	0.0
17	3.7	3.0	0.0	2.6	0.0
3v	0.0	0.5	12.4	4.7	12.4
8v	0.0	1.7	2.4	0.0	8.9
11v	0.0	0.5	2.5	0.0	3.1
13v	0.0	1.7	3.9	0.0	7.7
14v	0.0	0.0	2.2	0.0	2.7
15v	0.0	1.2	3.6	0.0	5.7
16v	0.0	0.0	1.5	0.0	1.3
17v	0.0	0.8	2.7	0.0	2.8
19v	0.0	0.0	1.5	0.0	1.8
Monomers	13.2	13.9	24.4	35.2	35.3
Oligomers	48.8	47.6	38.2	53.7	48.8
Hump	38.0	38.5	37.4	11.1	15.8

[a] Relative amounts of muropeptide species are expressed as the percent of total UV-absorbing material recovered from the high-performance liquid chromatography column.

Data from Severin A, Tabei K, Tenover F, Chung M, Clarke N, Tomasz A. High level oxacillin and vanocmycin resistance and altered cell wall composition in *Staphylococcus aureus* carrying the Staphylococcal mecA and the enterococcal vanA gene complex. J Bid Chem 2003;279:3398–407.

identified as the well-known cell wall muropeptide precursors: UDP-MurNAc (peak 1), UDP-MurNAc-L-Ala (peak 2), UDP-MurNAc-L-Ala-DGlu-L-Lys (peak 3), UDP-MurNAc-L-Ala-D-Glu (peak 4), and the pentapeptide derivative of UDP-MurNAc–UDP-MurNAc-L-Ala-D-Glu-L-Lys-D-Ala-D-Ala (peak 6), the latter representing close to 80% of the precursor material. An additional minor peak 7 was identified in both COL and COLVA as a derivative of the UDP-MurNAc-pentapeptide carrying a single glycin substitute on the ε-amino group of the lysine residue. The precursor pool of COLVA (but not COL) also contained an additional minor component (peak 8), which had HPLC retention time and molecular mass characteristic of the UDP-MurNAc-depsipeptide (UDP-MurNAc-LAla-D-Glu-L-Lys-D-Ala-D-Lac) described in vancomycin-resistant enterococci. These compositional shifts and the appearance of tetra and depsipeptide compounds are similar to the altered chemical composition of the cell wall precursors described in vancomycin-resistant enterococci.

Radically different results were obtained when the cell wall precursor pool was analyzed from COLVA grown in vancomycin-containing medium.

Table 5
Composition of cell wall precursor pool in the vancomycin-susceptible strain COL and vancomycin-resistant strain COLVA

Peak number	Precursor	Relative amounts of precursor				
		COL[a] No antibiotics	COLVA[a] No antibiotics	COLVA +vancomycin	COLVA +oxacillin[a]	COLVA 'mecA +vancomycin
1	UDP-MurNAc	16.7	13.8	7.6	14.6	13.5
2	UDP-MurNAc-Ala	21.1	17.7	7.9	19.1	8.8
3, 4[b]	UDP-MurNAc-Ala-Glu-Lys + UDP-MurNAc-Ala-Glu	1.7	2.6	0.3	2.9	3.1
5	UDP-MurNAc-Ala-Glu-Lys-Ala	0.0	0.0	27.0	0.0	28.9
6	UDP-MurNAc-Ala-Glu-Lys-Ala-Ala	57.0	61.5	1.3	58.6	1.4
7	UDP-MurNAc-Ala-Glu-Lys(Gly)-Ala-Ala	1.3	1.3	0.0	1.4	0.0
8	UDP-MurNAc-Ala-Glu-Lys-Ala-Lac	0.0	1.0	34.6	1.8	39.0
9	UDP-MurNAc-Ala-Glu-Lys(Gly)-Ala-Lac	0.0	0.0	<1	0.0	0.0
	Total	98	98	79	98	95

[a] To accumulate cytoplasmic precursor, cells were exposed for the last 30 min of growth to 100 μg/mL of bacitracin.

[b] Peaks 3 and 4 were integrated together.

Data from Severin A, Tabei K, Tenover F, Chung M, Clarke N, Tomasz A. High level oxacillin and vancomycin resistance and altered cell wall composition in Staphylococcus aureus carrying the staphylococcal mecA and the enterococcal vanA gene complex. J Biol Chem 2003;279:3398–407.

Although peaks 1 through 4 appeared to be unchanged, peak 6, the major component in the bacteria grown without vancomycin, was diminished and was replaced by two new major components (peaks 5 and 8). Analysis of peak 5 identified it as the UDP-MurNAc-L-Ala-D-Glu-L-Lys-D-Ala tetrapeptide. Peak 8 had a retention time of 21 minutes on the HPLC elution profile and a molecular mass that differed by 1 mass unit from that of the UDP-MurNAc-pentapeptide.

The composition of the cell wall precursor pool in strain COLVA grown in the presence of 10 µg/mL oxacillin was indistinguishable from the precursor profile of COLVA grown in drug-free medium, including even the presence of small amounts of the UDP-MurNAc-depsipeptide (peak 8). The percentage representation of various compounds in the cytoplasmic cell wall precursor pool in COL and COLVA grown under different conditions is shown in Table 5.

Subinhibitory concentrations of oxacillin have been shown to inhibit the expression of vancomycin resistance. Although strain COLVA was clearly capable of expressing high-level resistance to both oxacillin and vancomycin, these two agents had strong and mutually antagonist effects on the expression of the drug-resistant phenotypes. As little as 40 µg/mL oxacillin reduced the vancomycin MIC value of strain COLVA from 512 to 12 µg/mL (Fig. 8A). Similarly, as little as 50 µg/mL vancomycin reduced the oxacillin MIC of COLVA from 800 to 10 µg/mL (Fig. 8B). In both cases the homogeneous phenotypes were also converted to heterogeneous ones. These experiments provide important insights into differences in the mechanism of cell wall synthesis in bacteria expressing either the β-lactam or the vancomycin-resistance genes (Fig. 9). In COL the assembly of peptidoglycan in the presence of oxacillin is catalyzed by two PBPs: the transpeptidase activity of PBP2A and the transglycosylase activity of PBP2. The inhibition of expression of vancomycin resistance by oxacillin in strain COLVA suggests that the low affinity PBP2A, which is the only transpeptidase that remains active in the presence of oxacillin, is not able to use the depsipeptide cell wall precursors. The inhibition of vancomycin resistance by penicillin in enterococci has been interpreted in a similar manner. It was proposed that PBP5, which has low affinity to β-lactams, is unable to use depsipeptide wall precursors. Thus, the polymerization of UDP-MurNAc-depsipeptide precursor and its cross-linking in the peptidoglycan of strain COLVA must be catalyzed by one of the highly oxacillin-sensitive native PBPs. This interpretation is consistent with the composition of peptidoglycan of COLVA grown in the presence of oxacillin. Direct experimental evidence for this interpretation came from the insertional inactivation of mecA in strain COLVA, which had no effect on the vancomycin MIC while it completely reversed resistance to oxacillin. The two major antibiotic resistance mechanisms encoded by mecA and vanA residing in the same S aureus appear to use different sets of enzymes for the assembly of cell walls.

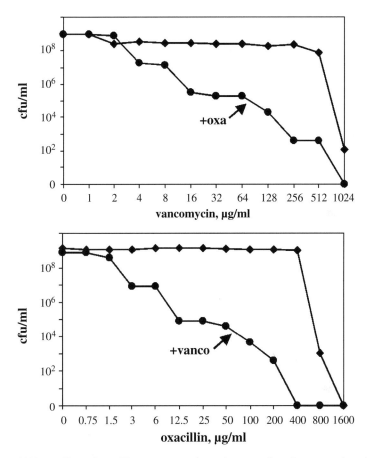

Fig. 8. Inhibitory effects of oxacillin or vancomycin on the expression of vancomycin resistance or oxacillin resistance in strain COLVA. Cultures of strain COLVA grown in vancomycin-containing TSB or antibiotic-free TSB were assayed for antibiotic resistance, using the method of population analysis. (♦) Population analysis profile of strain COLVA assayed on vancomycin-containing (*top panel*) or oxacillin-containing (*bottom panel*) agar; (•) population analysis profile of the same strain performed in the presence of a constant concentration of oxacillin (40 µg/mL) (*top panel*) or vancomycin (50 µg/mL) (*bottom panel*) added to each agar plate. (*From* Severin A, Tabei K, Tenover F, Chung M, Clarke N, Tomasz A. High level oxacillin and vancomycin resistance and altered cell wall composition in *Staphylococcus aureus* carrying the staphylococcal mecA and the enterococcal vanA gene complex. J Biol Chem 2003;279:3398–407; with permission.)

Summary

Vancomycin resistance in enterococci, predominantly *Enterococcus faecium*, developed in the latter half of the 1980s and was associated with a complex mechanism encoded by a series of genes carried on a transposon. These changes resulted in remodeling of the cell wall glycopeptide, with replacement of the terminal D-alanime molecule in the pentapeptide

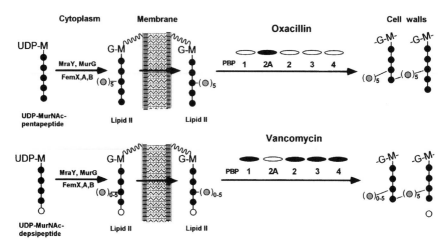

Fig. 9. Model for the synthesis of peptidoglycan in strain COLVA with or without induction of the *van*A operon. The UDP-MurNAc-linked pentapeptide cell wall precursor undergoes modifications: UDP is replaced by the undercaprenyl-pyrophosphate carrier lipid (wavy lines), catalyzed by MraY, followed by the attachment of N-acetyl glucosamine (G) catalyzed by MurG to form Lipid II. After attachment of pentaglycine branches (FemX, FemA, FemB), Lipid II is translocated to the outer surface of the plasma membrane where PBPs use it for cell wall assembly. (*Top panel*): In the absence of the expression of *van*A gene complex, strain COLVA produces a peptidoglycan built primarily of the normal UDP-MurNAc-linked pentapeptide cell wall precursors. In the presence of oxacillin, the penicillin binding protein responsible for the polymerization of cell wall is PBP2A, and the peptidoglycan contains muropeptides that carry the C-terminal D-alanyl-D-alanine residues. (⊙) oligoglycine branches and glycine. (*Bottom panel*): Upon expression of the *van*A gene complex, the normal pentapeptide precursor is replaced by the D-lactate (○)- containing depsipeptide. Derivatization of this precursor by FemX, A, B is incomplete, resulting in Lipid II molecules defective in oligoglycine branches (•). PBP2A is unable to handle these D-lactate-containing precursors, which are polymerized and incorporated to the cell wall peptidoglycan by some of the normal PBPs of *Staphylococcus aureus*. The peptidoglycan produced under these conditions contains only tetrapeptides in both monomeric and oligomeric muropeptide species. Symbols: N-acetylmuramic acid (M); N-acetyl-glucosamine (G); carrier lipid (wavy line); regular stem peptide residues (•); D-lactate residue (○); glycine (•). Open ellipsoid symbols: functionally inactive PBPs; solid ellipsoid symbols: functionally active PBPs. (*From* Severin A, Tabei K, Tenover F, Chung M, Clarke N, Tomasz A. High level oxacillin and vancomycin resistance and altered cell wall composition in *Staphylococcus aureus* carrying the staphylococcal mecA and the enterococcal vanA gene complex. J Biol Chem 2003;279:3398–407; with permission.)

component with D-lactose. This was followed by a report in 1992 of the successful experimental transfer of vancomycin resistance from an entero-coccus to *Staphylococcus aureus* both in vitro and in vivo, with the frequency of transfer being considerably higher in the in vivo model. The long anticipated development of vancomycin resistance in *S aureus* has now occurred. A number of vancomycin-intermediate strains have been de-scribed, and these strains have abnormal, thickened cells walls in the presence of vancomycin. Two mechanisms of resistance have been described in the strains: affinity trapping of vancomycin molecules by cell wall monomers and clogging of the outer layers of peptidoglycan by bound vancomycin molecules, and change in the structure or metabolism of teichoic acids. Of more serious concern has been the description in 2002 of two patients with vancomycin-resistant *S aureus* infections. In one instance, the patients had skin lesions coinfected with vancomycin-resistant, vanA genotype, *E faecalis*, and the vanA resistance genes were shown to have been transferred to the *S aureus* strains. Expression of resistance was high in one *S aureus* strain and low in the other, making detection more challenging in the latter instance. These developments are of great concern, and every effort should be made to prevent further development and spread of vancomycin resistance in staphylococci.

References

[1] Staphylococcal diseases. In: Benenson AS, editor. Control of communicable diseases manual. 16th edition. Washington, DC: American Public Health Association; 1995. p. 428–38.

[2] Hartman BJ, Tomasz A. Low-affinity penicillin-binding protein associated with beta-lactam resistance in *Staphylococcus aureus*. J Bacteriol 1984;158:513–6.

[3] Reynolds PE, Brown DF. Penicillin-binding proteins of beta-lactam-resistant strains of *Staphylococcus aureus*. Effect of growth conditions. FEBS Lett 1985;192:28–32.

[4] Utsui Y, Yokota T. Role of an altered penicillin-binding protein in methicillin- and cephem-resistant *Staphylococcus aureus*. Antimicrob Agents Chemother 1985;28:397–403.

[5] Chambers HF. The changing epidemiology of *Staphylococcus aureus*? Emerg Infect Dis 2001;7:178–82.

[6] CDC. Methicillin-resistant *Staphylococcus aureus* infections among competitive sports participants–Colorado, Indiana, Pennsylvania, and Los Angeles County, 2000–2003. Morbid Mortal Wkly Report 2003;52:793–5.

[7] Canton R, Loza E, Morosini MI, Baquero F. Antimicrobial resistance amongst isolates of *Streptococcus pyogenes* and *Staphylococcus aureus* in the PROTEKT antimicrobial surveillance programme during 1999–2000. J Antimicrob Chemother 2002;(50 Suppl S1): 9–24.

[8] Critchley IA, Draghi DC, Sahm DF, Thornsberry C, Jones ME, Karlowsky JA. Activity of daptomycin against susceptible and multidrug-resistant Gram-positive pathogens collected in the SECURE study (Europe) during 2000–2001. J Antimicrob Chemother 2003;51: 639–49.

[9] NCCLS. Performance standards for antimicrobial susceptibility testing; twelfth informational supplement. M100–S12. Wayne, PA: NCCLS; 2002.

[10] Patel R. Clinical impact of vancomycin-resistant enterococci. J Antimicrob Chemother 2003;51(Suppl 3):13–21.

[11] Uttley AH, George RC, Naidoo J, et al. High-level vancomycin-resistant enterococci causing hospital infections. Epidemiol Infect 1989;103:173–81.

[12] Gold HS. Vancomycin-resistant enterococci: mechanisms and clinical observations. Clin Infect Dis 2001;33:210–9.

[13] Noble WC, Virani Z, Cree RG. Co-transfer of vancomycin and other resistance genes from *Enterococcus faecalis* NCTC 12201 to *Staphylococcus aureus*. FEMS Microbiol Lett 1992; 72:195–8.

[14] Hiramatsu K, Hanaki H, Ino T, Yabuta K, Oguri T, Tenover FC. Methicillin-resistant *Staphylococcus aureus* clinical strain with reduced vancomycin susceptibility. J Antimicrob Chemother 1997;40:135–6.

[15] *Staphylococcus aureus* with reduced susceptibility to vancomycin–United States, 1997. MMWR Morb Mortal Wkly Rep 1997;46:765–6.

[16] Update. *Staphylococcus aureus* with reduced susceptibility to vancomycin–United States, 1997. MMWR Morb Mortal Wkly Rep 1997;46:813–5.

[17] Smith TL, Pearson ML, Wilcox KR, et al. Emergence of vancomycin resistance in *Staphylococcus aureus*. Glycopeptide-Intermediate *Staphylococcus aureus* Working Group. N Engl J Med 1999;340:493–501.

[18] Fridkin SK. Vancomycin-intermediate and -resistant *Staphylococcus aureus*: what the infectious disease specialist needs to know. Clin Infect Dis 2001;32:108–15.

[19] Walsh TR, Howe RA. The prevalence and mechanisms of vancomycin resistance in *Staphylococcus aureus*. Annu Rev Microbiol 2002;56:657–75.

[20] Hageman JC, Pegues DA, Jepson C, et al. Vancomycin-intermediate *Staphylococcus aureus* in a home health-care patient. Emerg Infect Dis 2001;7:1023–5.

[21] Sieradzki K, Roberts RB, Haber SW, Tomasz A. The development of vancomycin resistance in a patient with methicillin-resistant *Staphylococcus aureus* infection. N Engl J Med 1999;340:517–23.

[22] Cui L, Murakami H, Kuwahara-Arai K, Hanaki H, Hiramatsu K. Contribution of a thickened cell wall and its glutamine nonamidated component to the vancomycin resistance expressed by *Staphylococcus aureus* Mu50. Antimicrob Agents Chemother 2000; 44:2276–85.

[23] Sieradzki K, Leski T, Dick J, Borio L, Tomasz A. Evolution of a vancomycin-intermediate *Staphylococcus aureus* strain in vivo: multiple changes in the antibiotic resistance phenotypes of a single lineage of methicillin-resistant *S. aureus* under the impact of antibiotics administered for chemotherapy. J Clin Microbiol 2003;41:1687–93.

[24] Severin A, Tabei K, Tenover F, Chung M, Clarke N, Tomasz A. High level oxacillin and vancomycin resistance and altered cell wall composition in *Staphylococcus aureus* carrying the Staphylococcal mecA and the enterococcal vanA gene complex. J Biol Chem 2003;279: 3398–407.

[25] Chang S, Sievert DM, Hageman JC, et al. Infection with vancomycin-resistant *Staphylococcus aureus* containing the vanA resistance gene. N Engl J Med 2003;348: 1342–7.

[26] Vancomycin-resistant *Staphylococcus aureus*–Pennsylvania, 2002. MMWR Morb Mortal Wkly Rep 2002;51:902.

[27] Bozdogan B, Esel D, Whitener C, Browne FA, Appelbaum PC. Antibacterial susceptibility of a vancomycin-resistant *Staphylococcus aureus* strain isolated at the Hershey Medical Center. J Antimicrob Chemother 2003;52:864–8.

[28] Tenover FC, Weigel LM, Appelbaum PC, et al. Vancomycin-resistant *Staphylococcus aureus* isolate from a patient in Pennsylvania. Antimicrob Agents Chemother 2004;48: 275–80.

[29] Weigel LM, Clewell DB, Gill SR, et al. Genetic analysis of a high-level vancomycin-resistant isolate of *Staphylococcus aureus*. Science 2003;302:1569–71.

ELSEVIER
SAUNDERS

CLINICS IN
LABORATORY
MEDICINE

Clin Lab Med 24 (2004) 403–418

Community-acquired methicillin-resistant *Staphylococcus aureus* infections

Elizabeth Palavecino, MD

*Department of Pathology, Wake Forest University Health Sciences,
Medical Center Boulevard, Winston-Salem, NC 27157-1072, USA*

Staphylococcus aureus has been responsible for a great deal of human morbidity and mortality throughout history. It causes a variety of minor diseases, such as localized skin lesions, abscesses, laceration infections, and impetigo, but also is responsible for staphylococcal pneumonia and sepsis, both of which can be fatal. It is thought to be responsible for many of the pneumonia deaths associated with the influenza pandemics of the 20th century, including the "Spanish" flu of 1918, the "Asian" flu of 1957–58, and the "Hong Kong" flu of 1968–69 [1–3].

The introduction of penicillin in the 1940s greatly improved the prognosis for patients with severe staphylococcal infections. However, after a few years of clinical use, most staphylococcal strains were able to hydrolyze penicillin by producing β-lactamases, making penicillin a useless antibiotic to treat staphylococcal infections caused by β-lactamase–producing *S aureus*. Methicillin, a semisynthetic penicillin introduced in 1959, was specifically designed to be resistant to β-lactamase degradation, but resistance developed soon after its introduction into clinical practice. Methicillin-resistant *S aureus* (MRSA) was first reported in the United Kingdom in 1961, followed by reports from other European countries, Japan, and Australia [4]. The first reported case of MRSA in the United States was in 1968 [5]. Sporadic cases were reported through the 1970s with occasional outbreaks reported in intensive care facilities with high antibiotic use [6]. In the subsequent 20 years, the prevalence of MRSA increased, though it was largely localized in acute and chronic care facilities. Occasionally, outbreaks would occur in the community, but these were generally assumed to have been associated with contemporaneous hospital outbreaks. Currently, MRSA is an important pathogen in nosocomial infections and is a problem in hospitals worldwide, and it is increasingly recovered from nursing home residents with established risk factors. More

E-mail address: epalave@wfubmc.edu

recently, community-acquired MRSA infections have been documented among healthy individuals with no recognizable risk factors, and it seems clear that community-acquired MRSA (CA-MRSA) strains are epidemiologically and clonally unrelated to hospital-acquired strains.

This article focuses on the epidemiology, clinical significance, and virulence markers of CA-MRSA infections.

Epidemiology

Infections caused by community-acquired methicillin-resistant strains have been reported worldwide. The actual prevalence of CA-MRSA in the communities in the United States is unknown, and the lack of standardized criteria for classifying a MRSA infection as community acquired makes it difficult to compare published studies. The prevalence of CA-MRSA varies depending on geographic location as well as patient population. Overall, patients with CA-MRSA infections are usually children and young adults who lack risk factors associated with health care MRSA infections.

A prospective medical record review of CA-MRSA hospital admissions in children was done at a Chicago hospital to determine whether the prevalence of CA-MRSA without identified predisposing risk factors, such as recent contact with a health care environment, had increased [7]. Two 3-year periods, 1988–90 and 1993–95, were compared and showed a large increase in children hospitalized with community-acquired MRSA (eight versus 35). The proportions of CA-MRSA admissions in those periods were 10 per 100,000 admissions in the earlier period, compared with 259 per 100,000 in 1993–95 ($P < 0.001$). In contrast, the prevalence of CA-MRSA in adults attending a University Hospital also in Chicago during 1998 to 1999 was low, with only two cases confirmed as having CA-MRSA [8].

It is impossible to determine the true background rate of MRSA carriage in the community. Barring the swabbing of random people on the street, large-scale surveillance is not feasible. It is generally through outbreaks and the subsequent investigations that a picture of the problem can begin to be created.

To assess whether children in the community were colonized with MRSA, a 1996 study used nares and perineum culture of 500 children attending a pediatric emergency room, combined with a questionnaire to determine the presence of risk factors in both the children and their household contacts for non-community acquisition [9]. Risk factors assessed included recent hospitalizations or visits to the emergency room in the previous year, residence in a chronic care facility, antibiotic therapy within the prior 6 months, HIV infection or any chronic disorder, history of endotracheal intubation, or intravenous drug use. Among the 500 children tested, 132 (26.4%) were found to be colonized with S aureus; of these, 11 (8.3%) were MRSA. Of the 11 children colonized with MRSA, seven had risk factors for nosocomial acquisition, whereas four (36%) had no identified risk factors.

More recently, investigators evaluated the prevalence of MRSA nasal colonization in children and their guardians in New York City and found that MRSA colonization is not ubiquitous in people without predisposing risk outside of the health care environment [10]. Similar findings were reported among the urban poor in San Francisco [11].

Genetics of methicillin resistance

There are three known mechanisms by which *S aureus* becomes resistant to methicillin: hyperproduction of β-lactamases, modification of normal penicillin-binding protein (PBPs), and the presence of an acquired PBP, PBP 2a, which is encoded by the *mec*A gene [12,13]. The latter is the most prevalent mechanism among clinical isolates, and these strains have heterogeneous drug resistance (only a small number of cells express resistance), making susceptibility testing of MRSA a challenge for the clinical microbiology laboratory. The methicillin-resistance gene (*mec*A) is not present in methicillin-susceptible strains and is believed to have been acquired from a distantly related species [4]. The *mec*A is carried on a mobile genetic element, the staphylococcal cassette chromosome *mec* (SCC*mec*), of which four forms have been described that differ in size and genetic composition. Isolates containing this resistance mechanism are clinically resistant to all available β-lactams, including penicillins, cephalosporins, β-lactam/β-lactamase inhibitor combinations, monobactams, and carbapenems. Although additional antimicrobial agents active against MRSA have been developed in the last few years, vancomycin has been the agent of choice to treat serious infections caused by MRSA strains. The recent emergence of CA-MRSA raised considerable concern that treatment of infections caused by CA-MRSA would markedly increase the need for vancomycin therapy in the outpatient setting.

Mechanism of resistance associated with community-acquired methicillin-resistant *S aureus*

Unlike hospital strains of MRSA, most of the CA-MRSA strains are susceptible to most or all other drug classes [14]. This phenomenon has led to research to determine whether there was something different about the resistance mechanism in these strains compared with their nosocomially spread cousins. Although all MRSA strains have the same *mec*A gene, there are differences in the staphylococcal cassette chromosome *mec* (SCC*mec*), the large, mobile genetic element that carries the gene. In the CA-MRSA strains, the SCC*mec* is different from the three types previously identified in hospital strains [15], demonstrating that the community-circulating clones are not originating in hospital settings [15,16]. In addition, the newly identified SCCmec type IV is significantly (by 10–46 kbp) smaller than the three previously described cassettes, suggesting the possibility of increased mobility and easier transfer on a plasmid or bacteriophage to a susceptible recipient strain [15]. Although there is no clear correlation between antibiogram and the SCCmec type, most CA-MRSA appear to be resistant to β-lactams only. This may explain why these strains are not prevalent in the hospital environment where the antibiotic selective pressure is high [17].

To evaluate the prevalence and distribution of SCC mec types, a longitudinal surveillance study was done in the San Francisco County jail system from 1997 to 2002 [18]. The investigators reported an increase in prevalence of MRSA from 29% in 1997 to 74% in 2002 (Fig. 1). They found that 85% of the 154 MRSA isolates were obtained from skin or soft tissue infections and that 91% of the isolates typed were SSCmec type IV, the type found most often in CA-MRSA isolates. SCCmec type IV was seen consistently over the study period and was found in all but one major clonal group. SCCmec type II was found in 5% and type III in two isolates of one clonal group and in one unrelated isolate. Only twelve (9%) isolates with SCCmec type IV were multidrug-resistant MRSA, in contrast with health care–associated strains, which frequently are resistant to other classes of antibiotics.

Clinical significance

The distribution of clinical infections differs between community-acquired and health care–associated MRSA cases. Skin and soft tissue infections are the most common manifestations of CA-MRSA, although serious invasive infections and death may occur. Dermatologic conditions are the most common underlying conditions among pediatric cases, and tobacco use and diabetes among adult cases [19].

Four pediatric soft-tissue infections caused by CA-MRSA resulted in deaths in Minnesota and North Dakota in 1997–99 [20]. The first was a 7-year-old girl with an infected hip joint. Surgical drainage was performed, and she was treated with cefazolin, which was changed to vancomycin when blood and joint fluid cultures grew MRSA. She suffered respiratory failure and was placed on mechanical ventilation; she later suffered acute respiratory distress syndrome, pneumonia, and empyema, requiring chest tube drainage. Her death was due to pulmonary hemorrhage after 5 weeks of hospitalization. Neither she nor any family members had any risks for hospital acquisition of the MRSA infection.

The second was a 16-month-old girl admitted to the hospital in shock and with a temperature of 105.2° F, seizures, a diffuse petechial rash, and irritability. She was treated with ceftriaxone but developed respiratory failure and cardiac arrest, dying within 2 hours of arrival at the hospital. Postmortem blood and CSF cultures grew MRSA susceptible to several

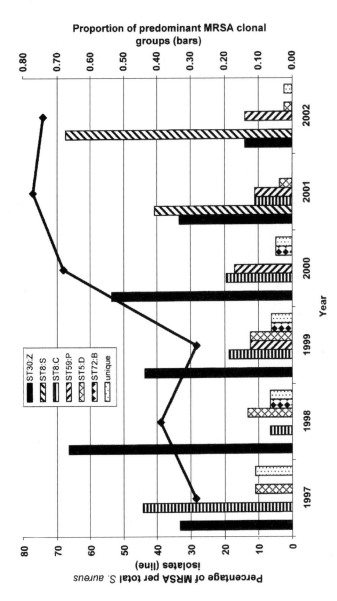

Fig. 1. Annual distribution of methicillin-resistant *Staphylococcus aureus* (MRSA) in isolates obtained from the population of the San Francisco County jail system. The line graph indicates the percentage of MRSA among all *S aureus* isolates. The bar graph indicates the proportions of MRSA isolates associated with different clonal groups. Each clonal group in this study is designated by the combination of multilocus sequence type and pulsed field gel electrophoresis (PFGE) group (eg, "ST30:Z"). An isolate is classified as "unique" if it has a PFGE profile unrelated to that of any other isolate. SCCmec type IV was seen consistently over the study period and was found in all major clonal groups except ST5:D. (*Reproduced from* Pan ES, Diep BA, Carleton HA, et al. Increasing prevalence of methicillin-resistant *Staphylococcus aureus* infection in California jails. Clin Infect Dis 2003;37:1384–8; with permission.)

other antibiotic classes. She had been treated 1 month earlier with amoxicillin for otitis media. She was otherwise healthy, and neither she nor any family members had any known risk factors.

The third was a 13-year-old girl who was admitted to hospital with fever, hemoptysis, and respiratory distress. One day before admission she had a productive cough and a 2-cm papule on her lower lip. Chest radiograph revealed pleural effusion and lower lobe infiltrate. She was treated with ceftriaxone and nafcillin but became hypotensive within 5 hours of arriving at the hospital. She was intubated and treated with vancomycin and cefotaxime but continued to deteriorate and died on the 7th hospital day from progressive cerebral edema and multiorgan failure. Her blood, sputum, and pleural fluid grew MRSA. Neither she nor any family members had any known risk factors.

The fourth patient was a 12-month-old boy admitted to hospital with bronchiolitis, vomiting, dehydration, a temperature of 105.2° F, and a petechial rash. Chest radiograph revealed an infiltrate consistent with pneumonitis. On the second hospital day the patient developed pleural effusion. The next day he developed severe respiratory distress and hypotension and died. The admission blood culture was negative, but pleural fluid and postmortem blood cultures grew MRSA. He had no prior hospitalizations, and no family members had any known risks for hospital acquisition of the infection. His 2-year-old sister had been treated 3 weeks earlier for a culture-confirmed MRSA buttock infection. The isolates had identical antibiotic susceptibility profiles.

The laboratory analysis of the four strains showed an indistinguishable pulsed field gel electrophoresis (PFGE) pattern between the first and fourth case, despite originating in, respectively, Minnesota in 1997 and North Dakota in 1999. The other two strains (North Dakota, 1998 and Minnesota, 1999) differed from these by only two and three bands, suggesting clonal relatedness. In comparison, the PFGE patterns of these strains differed by an average of 10 or more bands when compared with PFGE patterns from nosocomial MRSA isolates from several Minnesota hospitals. None of the isolates produced toxic shock syndrome toxin 1.

Recent outbreaks of community-acquired methicillin-resistant *S aureus*

Several recent outbreaks of CA-MRSA have occurred. In Mississippi, in the 1-year period between November 1999 and November 2000, an outbreak of MRSA skin and soft tissue infections occurred in a state prison, affecting 59 inmates [21]. No MRSA skin infections had been reported in the previous year. To assess carriage in the prison, swab specimens of both anterior nares were collected from 1757 inmates, of whom 86 (4.9%) were MRSA carriers. Representative isolates were genotyped and found to include three predominant strains. Interviews with the affected inmates confirmed direct transmission of the skin infection through poor hygiene practices, close living quarters, and shared personal items.

Another large prison outbreak was reported in Los Angeles County, where 928 inmates were diagnosed with MRSA wound infections in 2002 [19]. Among the 66 inmates hospitalized, 10 later developed invasive disease, including bacteremia, endocarditis, or osteomyelitis. The clone found to predominate in this outbreak was identical to one of those found in the San Francisco County jail surveillance described earlier [18].

Outbreaks also have been reported among athletes in several states during 2000–2003 [22]. During September–October 2000 in Pennsylvania, an outbreak of MRSA skin and soft tissue infections were reported among 10 members of a college football team, seven of whom were hospitalized. The 10 strains were clonally related. Several risk factors were identified, including shared towels and skin trauma from turf burns and shaving.

In September 2002, two cases of MRSA skin infection in college football team members were reported in Los Angeles County. Both patients were hospitalized, one requiring surgical debridement and skin grafts. Again, isolates were clonal, and investigators found several reported transmission risk factors, including minor skin injuries and shared items.

In January 2003, two high school wrestlers in Indiana were diagnosed with MRSA. No direct contact could be demonstrated, as the wrestlers were in different weight classes and had never wrestled each other; however, transmission was postulated to have occurred through shared items.

In Colorado, in February 2003, a cluster of five MRSA infections was reported among members of a fencing club and their household contacts. Two of the isolates were tested for clonality and found to be identical. Shared equipment and sensor wires (used to detect the touch of an opponent's weapon) were probable sources of transmission.

There have been several other reports of MRSA outbreaks among wrestlers and football and rugby players in the United Kingdom [23,24], as well as earlier reports of staphylococcal skin infections transmitted among athletes [25,26]. In all cases, like those discussed previously, transmission was associated with minor skin trauma and sharing of sports or personal care equipment.

Increased virulence associated with community-acquired methicillin-resistant S aureus

The common secreted virulence factors of S aureus include toxic shock syndrome toxin 1 and several staphylococcal enterotoxins, serotypes A through Q (SEA–SEQ). These toxins cause toxic shock and related illnesses though induction of massive cytokine release, both from macrophages and T cells [27]. Another significant virulence factor in S aureus is the Panton-Valentine leukocidin (PVL) [28].

Recent CA-MRSA have shown evidence of increased virulence resulting in some increased prevalence of toxic shock cases and more severe soft tissue infections and in many cases increased mortality. Overall, though, toxic shock syndrome toxin 1 production is not a hallmark of CA-MRSA, being much more common to hospital-acquired MRSA strains [14]. The community-acquired strains also most often produce SEB and SEC.

An outbreak of community-acquired staphylococcal skin infection in Alaska found 86% of isolates to be MRSA [29]. This result led the investigators to study whether the virulence factor PVL (discussed at length later) might be associated with the CA-MRSA skin infections. They conducted a nasal carriage survey including case patients, age-matched controls without infections, and household members of both groups. Overall, 13% of the survey participants carried MRSA and 27% carried methicillin-susceptible S aureus (MSSA), with case patients more likely to carry the MRSA. When tested for PVL, the striking results were that no PVL was found in any MSSA strain, whereas PVL was present in 40 of 41 MRSA strains. Thirty-nine of the 40 MRSA strains were closely related, whereas the MSSA strains were diverse. In addition, clinical surveillance isolates were collected. Among the 111 isolates collected, 71% were MRSA and 89% of these were from skin infections. When tested for PVL, 92% of the MRSA isolates were positive, whereas all of the MSSA isolates were negative. Among the PVL-positive MRSA strains, 79% were closely related to the carriage strains found in the CA-MRSA skin infection outbreak [30].

Genetic markers

Investigators have found that most health care–associated strains belong to six major pandemic clones and that minor clones and sporadic clones are usually restricted to one hospital or geographic area [17]. In contrast, CA-MRSA strains seem to be unrelated to health care–associated strains and are both genetically diverse and carry additional virulence genes. Some of these virulence genes have been used as genetic markers to assess the evolution and genetic background of CA-MRSA strains.

One of the significant virulence factors in S aureus is the PVL. PVL is a member of the recently described family of synergohymenotropic toxins, which damage the membranes of host defense cells through the synergistic activity of two separately secreted, but nonassociated, proteins, LukS and LukF [28,31]. As might be expected of an agent that causes tissue necrosis and leukocyte destruction, PVL is associated with necrotizing cutaneous infections. A study undertaken to determine its effect found PVL in 93% of strains associated with furunculosis and 85% of necrotic hemorrhagic pneumonia among community-acquired strains and in 55% of cellulitis strains, 50% of cutaneous abscess strains, 23% of osteomyelitis strains, and 13% of finger-pulp-infection strains, though the toxin is produced by fewer than 5% of S aureus strains overall [31].

A recent study in Minnesota highlighted both the emerging problem of CA-MRSA infections and their association with severe disease and PVL production [32]. In this study a prospective cohort of patients with MRSA infection were identified at 12 Minnesota laboratory facilities from January through December 2000, comparing community-associated (median age, 23 years) with health care–associated (median age, 68 years) MRSA cases. Of 1100 MRSA infections, 131 (12%) were community associated and 937 (85%) were health care associated. Skin and soft tissue infections were more common among community-associated cases (75%) than among health care–associated cases (37%). Although community-associated MRSA isolates were more likely to be susceptible to other antimicrobial classes, most community-associated infections were initially treated with antimicrobials to which the isolate was nonsusceptible. Community-associated isolates typically possessed exotoxin genes such as PVL, whereas health care–associated isolates did not. This study concluded that clinicians should be aware that therapy with β-lactam antimicrobials can no longer be relied on as the sole empiric treatment for severely ill outpatients whose infections may be staphylococcal in origin.

A study in France seeking to determine the clinical and bacteriologic characteristics of their CA-MRSA detected their first case in 1999 and a total of 14 cases by the end of 2001. PVL was present in all 14 of their community-acquired isolates, as well as in approximately 12% of their *S aureus* isolates overall [33]. All of the CA-MRSA infections were found in previously healthy patients who developed particularly aggressive infections; 11 had skin or soft-tissue infections, one child had pleurisy (caused by CA-MRSA acquired from his mother who had a breast abscess), and two patients had fatal necrotizing pneumonia. Before this, only eight cases of community-acquired pneumonia due to *S aureus* strains carrying the PVL gene had been recorded in France, six of which were fatal [34]. PVL-producing *S aureus* strains caused rapidly progressive, hemorrhagic, necrotizing pneumonia, mainly in otherwise healthy children and young adults, often preceded by influenza-like symptoms and with a high mortality rate. The association between CA-MRSA and PVL toxin production has been noted worldwide [35]. CA-MRSA isolates from the United States, France, Switzerland, Australia, New Zealand, and Western Samoa shared a type IV SCC*mec* cassette and the PVL locus, whereas the distribution of the other toxin genes was quite specific to the strains from each continent. Within each continent, the genetic background of CA-MRSA strains does not correspond to that of the hospital-acquired MRSA.

Susceptibility testing

As mentioned previously, detecting oxacillin (methicillin) resistance in staphylococci that possess the *mec* gene may be difficult because these strains exhibit heteroresistance. Consequently, in the susceptibility test some cells appear resistant and some appear susceptible. Several standardized methods are recommended by the National Committee for Clinical Laboratory Standards (NCCLS) for oxacillin suceptibility testing of S aureus [36,37]. These methods include disk diffusion, broth microdilution, agar dilution, and the oxacillin screen plate test. In vitro testing has been modified to enhance the expression of oxacillin resistance for detection of resistant strains, including incubation of tests at temperatures no greater than 35° C, obtaining final readings after a full 24 hours of incubation, and supplementation of Mueller-Hinton broth or agar with 2% NaCl for dilution tests [36].

Most of the health care–associated MRSA strains are resistant to multiple classes of antimicrobial agents, including aminoglycosides, clindamycin, macrolides, quinolones, sulfanamides, and tetracycline. The observation of multiple resistance is a clue for the microbiologist to the possibility of methicillin resistance. However, most CA-MRSA isolates harboring SCCmec type IV appear to be resistant to β-lactam antibiotics only, making it difficult to suspect methicillin resistance. If the test result is in doubt regarding a possibly methicillin-resistant S aureus strain, it is recommended that additional confirmatory tests, such as the oxacillin-salt-screening test, be performed, especially if CA-MRSA infections have been reported in the area.

Among the reference methods recommended by the NCCLS, the agar screen test, containing 4% NaCl and 6μg/mL oxacillin, has been evaluated in numerous studies and found to be very good for detection of resistant strains, and it has been the recommended method to use in addition to the dilution methods to confirm methicillin resistance [36]. However, when very heteroresistant strains were tested by oxacillin screen plate, the sensitivity decreased [38]. The disk diffusion method has also been evaluated against very heteroresistant strains, and the sensitivity was found to be as low as 61% [39]. More recently, investigators have found that using cefoxitin and monobactam disk diffusion tests detected 100% of all MRSA, including those with very low-level methicillin resistance [40].

Currently, the NCCLS recommends performing standard disk diffusion test with cefoxitin (30 μg) disks for detection of oxacillin (methicillin) resistance [41]. Incubation for 24 hours is recommended, but results may be reported after 18 hours if resistant at that time. The results should be reported for oxacillin and not for cefoxitin.

Automated systems have also been evaluated for detection of oxacillin (methicillin) resistance, but because the software is changed frequently in these systems, it is difficult to make comparisons. Three recent studies showed sensitivities of 95%, 98%, and 99% and specificities of 97%, 100%, and 99.5% for Vitek 1 GPS-106 card [42–44]. For Vitek2 AST GPS 5 card, one study reported sensitivity of 100% and specificity of 97.2% [44]. Several studies have showed that most CA-MRSA strains are susceptible to clindamycin, and therefore, clindamycin has been advocated for treatment of CA-MRSA infections [7,45,46]. However, clinical failures associated with the development of clindamycin resistance have been reported [47]. In the initial reports, strains that were susceptible to clindamycin were usually susceptible to erythromycin, although the reported prevalence of erythromycin resistance among CA-MRSA varies from 38% [47] to 86% [48].

Macrolide-resistance mechanisms in staphylococci are ribosomal methylase, encoded by *erm* genes (MLS$_B$ phenotype) and efflux pump encoded by *msr* genes. Strains presenting the latter mechanism are resistant to erythromycin and susceptible to clindamycin. However, expression of MLS$_B$ phenotype is either constitutive or inducible. When resistance is constitutive, staphylococci are resistant to erythromycin and clindamycin. When the resistance is inducible, the strains are resistant to erythromycin and clindamycin resistance must be induced, usually through exposure to erythromycin. Standard susceptibility broth methods cannot separate inducible resistance from susceptibility to clindamycin. Induction can be demonstrated using a double-disk susceptibility assay. Erythromycin and clindamycin antimicrobial disks are placed in close proximity on an inoculated agar surface, incubated, and examined for interaction as shown by a change in the zone of inhibition for clindamycin on the side next to the erythromycin disk (Fig. 2), usually described as "D-shaped" [49].

Although the prevalence of macrolide phenotypes in CA-MRSA has not been fully studied, laboratories should test for inducible clindamycin resistance in all MRSA that are erythromycin resistant and clindamycin susceptible when tested by standard broth methods.

Fig. 2. The presence of inducible clindamycin resistance in this erythromycin-resistant strain is shown by the "D-zone" of inhibition around the 2 μg clindamycin disk (CC2) on the side nearest the 15 μg erythromycin disk (E15). The disks were placed approximately 15 mm apart (measured from the center of each disk).

Rapid methods for detection of methicillin resistance

As discussed earlier, traditional antimicrobial susceptibility test methods such as disk diffusion, broth microdilution, and oxacillin screen plate require at least 24 hours to perform. Rapid and accurate identification of MRSA is beneficial not only for patient care but also for effective infection control programs to limit the spread of MRSA.

The detection of the *mecA* gene by polymerase chain reaction has been considered the "gold standard" for the detection of MRSA strains [50]; however, this method is not routinely used by most clinical diagnostic laboratories. In recent years, several other methods have been evaluated for the rapid detection of methicillin resistance in *S aureus*, including the Velogene Rapid MRSA Identification Assay (Alexon-Trend, Inc., Ramsey, Minnesota), the MRSA-Screen (Denka Seiken Co., Tokyo, Japan), and the BBL Crystal MRSA ID System (Becton Dickinson, Sparks, Maryland). The Velogene assay is a colorimetric enzyme immunoassay that uses a fluorescein-labeled *mecA* gene probe and a microtiter plate format. The MRSA-Screen is a slide latex agglutination test using latex particles sensitized with a monoclonal antibody against PBP2a. The BBL Crystal MRSA ID System uses a fluorescent indicator of dissolved oxygen in broth as a marker for bacterial growth in wells containing oxacillin.

There have been many recent evaluations of these methods, most reporting a sensitivity of detection of resistant strains of 97% or greater and a specificity of 100% for Velogene and MRSA-Screen and 98% or greater for BBL Crystal MRSA [40,42,43,51,52]. For the MRSA-Screen latex agglutination test, the manufacturer recommends reading the reaction at 3 minutes; however some investigators reported that reading the reaction at 15 minutes increased the detection rate from 90% to 100% among 19 *mec*A-positive strains [43]. Another report showed increased sensitivity by increasing the agglutination time but decreased specificity if agglutination time was increased to 15 minutes or more [42]. In general, turnaround times ranged from 15 minutes for the MRSA-Screen Assay, 2 hours for the Velogene Rapid MRSA, and 4 hours for the BBL Crystal.

The advantages of the rapid tests include rapid turnaround times, ease of use, and the ability to perform phenotypic or genotypic high-volume testing without the equipment requirements and technical complexity involved with polymerase chain reaction. The use of these methods could potentially allow clinicians and infection control practitioners to more effectively control the spread of MRSA in hospitals as well as in the community.

Summary

With the initial appearance of MRSA in the community, the question arose as to whether they represented hospital strains that had spread into the community or whether they were community generated. Many of the factors seen in these CA-MRSA cases suggested that they were in fact different from those arising in health care facilities. First, neither the patients nor their close contacts usually had any recognized risk factors for nosocomial infection such as prior hospitalization, residence in a long-term care facility, health care employment, chronic diseases, kidney dialysis, or intravenous drug use. Secondly, the CA-MRSA isolates were often susceptible to all or most other drug classes, unlike hospital strains of MRSA, which are frequently resistant to many other antimicrobial agents. The distribution of clinical infections differs between community acquired and health care–associated MRSA cases. Compared with health care–associated cases, CA-MRSA infections are more likely to involve skin and soft tissue and less likely to be respiratory or urinary tract infections, although serious invasive infections and death may occur.

Genetic analysis showed that the methicillin-resistance mechanism was predominantly associated with the SSC*mec* type IV variant of the *mec* gene. So, too, was the Panton-Valentine leukocidin, a potent virulence factor of *S aureus*. These findings demonstrated that CA-MRSA are not hospital "escapees." The small size of the SSC*mec* type IV results in it apparently being transported easily between strains, suggesting that the prevalence of methicillin resistance in the community will only increase, potentially even more quickly than it has in the hospital setting. Clonally related CA-MRSA isolates have been detected in many countries and have resulted in severe and often fatal infections in many patients. The possibility of these infections now needs to be considered in patients presenting with severe community-acquired infections, particularly pneumonia and skin infections, and empiric therapy should include agents active against MRSA strains.

References

[1] Robertson L, Caley JP, Moore J. Importance of *Staphylococcus aureus* in pneumonia in the 1957 epidemic of influenza A. Lancet 1958;2:233–6.
[2] Schwarzmann SW, Adler JL, Sullivan RJ Jr, Marine WM. Bacterial pneumonia during the Hong Kong influenza epidemic of 1968–1969. Arch Intern Med 1971;127:1037–41.
[3] Ruben FL, Cate TR. Influenza pneumonia. Semin Respir Infect 1987;2:122–9.
[4] Enright MC, Robinson DA, Randle G, Feil EJ, Grundmann H, Spratt BG. The evolutionary history of methicillin-resistant *Staphylococcus aureus* (MRSA). Proc Natl Acad Sci USA 2002;99:7687–92.
[5] Barrett FF, McGehee RF Jr, Finland M. Methicillin-resistant *Staphylococcus aureus* at Boston City Hospital. Bacteriologic and epidemiologic observations. N Engl J Med 1968; 279:441–8.
[6] Everett ED, McNitt TR, Rahm AE Jr, Stevens DL, Peterson HE. Epidemiologic investigation of methicillin resistant *Staphylococcus aureus* in a burn unit. Mil Med 1978; 143:165–7.
[7] Herold BC, Immergluck LC, Maranan MC, et al. Community-acquired methicillin-resistant *Staphylococcus aureus* in children with no identified predisposing risk. JAMA 1998;279:593–8.

[8] Suntharam N, Hacek D, Peterson LR. Low prevalence of community-acquired methicillin-resistant *Staphylococcus aureus* in adults at a university hospital in the central United States. J Clin Microbiol 2001;39:1669–71.

[9] Suggs AH, Maranan MC, Boyle-Vavra S, Daum RS. Methicillin-resistant and borderline methicillin-resistant asymptomatic *Staphylococcus aureus* colonization in children without identifiable risk factors. Pediatr Infect Dis J 1999;18:410–4.

[10] Shopsin B, Mathema B, Martinez J, et al. Prevalence of methicillin-resistant and methicillin-susceptible *Staphylococcus aureus* in the community. J Infect Dis 2000;182:359–62.

[11] Charlebois ED, Bangsberg DR, Moss NJ, et al. Population-based community prevalence of methicillin-resistant *Staphylococcus aureus* in the urban poor of San Francisco. Clin Infect Dis 2002;34:425–33.

[12] Georgopapadakou NH, Smith SA, Bonner DP. Penicillin-binding proteins in a *Staphylococcus aureus* strain resistant to specific beta-lactam antibiotics. Antimicrob Agents Chemother 1982;22:172–5.

[13] Ubukata K, Nonoguchi R, Matsuhashi M, Song MD, Konno M. Restriction maps of the regions coding for methicillin and tobramycin resistances on chromosomal DNA in methicillin-resistant staphylococci. Antimicrob Agents Chemother 1989;33:1624–6.

[14] Fey PD, Said-Salim B, Rupp ME, et al. Comparative molecular analysis of community- or hospital-acquired methicillin-resistant *Staphylococcus aureus*. Antimicrob Agents Chemother 2003;47:196–203.

[15] Daum RS, Ito T, Hiramatsu K, et al. A novel methicillin-resistance cassette in community-acquired methicillin-resistant *Staphylococcus aureus* isolates of diverse genetic backgrounds. J Infect Dis 2002;186:1344–7.

[16] Ma XX, Ito T, Tiensasitorn C, et al. Novel type of staphylococcal cassette chromosome mec identified in community-acquired methicillin-resistant *Staphylococcus aureus* strains. Antimicrob Agents Chemother 2002;46:1147–52.

[17] Aires de Sousa M, de Lencastre H. Evolution of sporadic isolates of methicillin-resistant *Staphylococcus aureus* (MRSA) in hospitals and their similarities to isolates of community-acquired MRSA. J Clin Microbiol 2003;41:3806–15.

[18] Pan ES, Diep BA, Carleton HA, et al. Increasing prevalence of methicillin-resistant *Staphylococcus aureus* infection in California jails. Clin Infect Dis 2003;37:1384–8.

[19] Outbreaks of community-associated methicillin-resistant *Staphylococcus aureus* skin infections–Los Angeles County, California, 2002–2003. MMWR Morb Mortal Wkly Rep 2003;52:88.

[20] Four pediatric deaths from community-acquired methicillin-resistant *Staphylococcus aureus*–Minnesota and North Dakota, 1997–1999. MMWR Morb Mortal Wkly Rep 1999;48:707–10.

[21] Methicillin-resistant *Staphylococcus aureus* skin or soft tissue infections in a state prison–Mississippi, 2000. MMWR Morb Mortal Wkly Rep 2001;50:919–22.

[22] Methicillin-resistant *Staphylococcus aureus* infections among competitive sports participants–Colorado, Indiana, Pennsylvania, and Los Angeles County, 2000–2003. MMWR Morb Mortal Wkly Rep 2003;52:793–5.

[23] Lindenmayer JM, Schoenfeld S, O'Grady R, Carney JK. Methicillin-resistant *Staphylococcus aureus* in a high school wrestling team and the surrounding community. Arch Intern Med 1998;158:895–9.

[24] Stacey AR, Endersby KE, Chan PC, Marples RR. An outbreak of methicillin resistant *Staphylococcus aureus* infection in a rugby football team. Br J Sports Med 1998;32:153–4.

[25] Bartlett PC, Martin RJ, Cahill BR. Furunculosis in a high school football team. Am J Sports Med 1982;10:371–4.

[26] Sosin DM, Gunn RA, Ford WL, Skaggs JW. An outbreak of furunculosis among high school athletes. Am J Sports Med 1989;17:828–32.

[27] McCormick JK, Yarwood JM, Schlievert PM. Toxic shock syndrome and bacterial superantigens: an update. Annu Rev Microbiol 2001;55:77–104.

[28] Prevost G, Cribier B, Couppie P, et al. Panton-Valentine leucocidin and gamma-hemolysin from *Staphylococcus aureus* ATCC 49775 are encoded by distinct genetic loci and have different biological activities. Infect Immun 1995;63:4121–9.

[29] Baggett HC, Hennessy TW, Leman R, et al. An outbreak of community-onset methicillin-resistant *Staphylococcus aureus* skin infections in southwestern Alaska. Infect Control Hosp Epidemiol 2003;24:397–402.

[30] Baggett HC, Rudolph K, Hennessy TW, et al. Panton-Valentine leukocidin (PVL) is associated with methicillin resistance in an outbreak of community-onset *Staphylococcus aureus* skin infections–Alaska [abstract 126]. 40th Annual Infectious Disease Society of America Meeting. Chicago, IL, October 24–27, 2002.

[31] Lina G, Piemont Y, Godail-Gamot F, et al. Involvement of Panton-Valentine leukocidin-producing *Staphylococcus aureus* in primary skin infections and pneumonia. Clin Infect Dis 1999;29:1128–32.

[32] Naimi TS, LeDell KH, Como-Sabetti K, et al. Comparison of community- and health care-associated methicillin-resistant *Staphylococcus aureus* infection. JAMA 2003;290: 2976–84.

[33] Dufour P, Gillet Y, Bes M, et al. Community-acquired methicillin-resistant *Staphylococcus aureus* infections in France: emergence of a single clone that produces Panton-Valentine leukocidin. Clin Infect Dis 2002;35:819–24.

[34] Gillet Y, Issartel B, Vanhems P, et al. Association between *Staphylococcus aureus* strains carrying gene for Panton-Valentine leukocidin and highly lethal necrotising pneumonia in young immunocompetent patients. Lancet 2002;359:753–9.

[35] Vandenesch F, Naimi T, Enright MC, et al. Community-acquired methicillin-resistant *Staphylococcus aureus* carrying Panton-Valentine leukocidin genes: worldwide emergence. Emerg Infect Dis 2003;9:978–84.

[36] NCCLS. Methods for dilution antimicrobial susceptibility tests for bacteria that grow aerobically; approved standard. 6th edition M7–A6. Wayne (PA): National Committee for Clinical Laboratory Standards; 2003.

[37] NCCLS. Performance standards for antimicrobial disk susceptibility tests; approved standard. 8th edition M2–A8. Wayne, PA: National Committee for Clinical Laboratory Standards; 2003.

[38] Resende CA, Figueiredo AM. Discrimination of methicillin-resistant *Staphylococcus aureus* from borderline-resistant and susceptible isolates by different methods. J Med Microbiol 1997;46:145–9.

[39] Cavassini M, Wenger A, Jaton K, Blanc DS, Bille J. Evaluation of MRSA-Screen, a simple anti-PBP 2a slide latex agglutination kit, for rapid detection of methicillin resistance in *Staphylococcus aureus*. J Clin Microbiol 1999;37:1591–4.

[40] Felten A, Grandry B, Lagrange PH, Casin I. Evaluation of three techniques for detection of low-level methicillin-resistant *Staphylococcus aureus* (MRSA): a disk diffusion method with cefoxitin and moxalactam, the Vitek 2 system, and the MRSA-screen latex agglutination test. J Clin Microbiol 2002;40:2766–71.

[41] NCCLS. Performance standards for antimicrobial susceptibility testing. 14th informational supplement M100–S14. Wayne (PA): National Committee for Clinical Laboratory Standards; 2004.

[42] Yamazumi T, Marshall SA, Wilke WW, Diekema DJ, Pfaller MA, Jones RN. Comparison of the Vitek Gram-Positive Susceptibility 106 card and the MRSA-screen latex agglutination test for determining oxacillin resistance in clinical bloodstream isolates of *Staphylococcus aureus*. J Clin Microbiol 2001;39:53–6.

[43] Swenson JM, Williams PP, Killgore G, O'Hara CM, Tenover FC. Performance of eight methods, including two new rapid methods, for detection of oxacillin resistance in a challenge set of *Staphylococcus aureus* organisms. J Clin Microbiol 2001;39:3785–8.

[44] Sakoulas G, Gold HS, Venkataraman L, DeGirolami PC, Eliopoulos GM, Qian Q. Methicillin-resistant *Staphylococcus aureus*: comparison of susceptibility testing methods and analysis of mecA-positive susceptible strains. J Clin Microbiol 2001;39:3946–51.

[45] Gorak EJ, Yamada SM, Brown JD. Community-acquired methicillin-resistant *Staphylococcus aureus* in hospitalized adults and children without known risk factors. Clin Infect Dis 1999;29:797–800.

[46] Martinez-Aguilar G, Hammerman WA, Mason EO Jr, Kaplan SL. Clindamycin treatment of invasive infections caused by community-acquired, methicillin-resistant and methicillin-susceptible *Staphylococcus aureus* in children. Pediatr Infect Dis J 2003;22:593–8.

[47] Frank AL, Marcinak JF, Mangat PD, et al. Clindamycin treatment of methicillin-resistant *Staphylococcus aureus* infections in children. Pediatr Infect Dis J 2002;21:530–4.

[48] Johnigan RH, Pereira KD, Poole MD. Community-acquired methicillin-resistant *Staphylococcus aureus* in children and adolescents: changing trends. Arch Otolaryngol Head Neck Surg 2003;129:1049–52.

[49] Weisblum B. Insights into erythromycin action from studies of its activity as inducer of resistance. Antimicrob Agents Chemother 1995;39:797–805.

[50] Chambers HF. Methicillin resistance in staphylococci: molecular and biochemical basis and clinical implications. Clin Microbiol Rev 1997;10:781–91.

[51] Louie L, Matsumura SO, Choi E, Louie M, Simor AE. Evaluation of three rapid methods for detection of methicillin resistance in *Staphylococcus aureus*. J Clin Microbiol 2000;38: 2170–3.

[52] Arbique J, Forward K, Haldane D, Davidson R. Comparison of the Velogene Rapid MRSA Identification Assay, Denka MRSA-Screen Assay, and BBL Crystal MRSA ID System for rapid identification of methicillin-resistant *Staphylococcus aureus*. Diagn Microbiol Infect Dis 2001;40:5–10.

ELSEVIER
SAUNDERS

CLINICS IN
LABORATORY
MEDICINE

Clin Lab Med 24 (2004) 419–453

Mechanisms of resistance among respiratory tract pathogens

Michael R. Jacobs, MD, PhD[a],*, Jack Anon, MD[b],
Peter C. Appelbaum, MD, PhD[c]

[a]Department of Pathology, Case Western Reserve University School of Medicine,
University Hospitals of Cleveland, 11100 Euclid Avenue, Cleveland, OH 44106, USA
[b]Department of Otolaryngology, University of Pittsburgh School of Medicine,
Pittsburgh, PA, USA
[c]Department of Pathology, Hershey Medical Center, 500 University Drive,
Hershey, PA 17033 USA

The debate over the clinical significance of antimicrobial resistance among respiratory tract pathogens has been ongoing for years, and clear answers currently are lacking for many important questions. One important question is whether infections caused by resistant organisms are more likely to be associated with adverse outcomes compared with those caused by susceptible ones. Data suggest that adverse outcomes (eg, failure, persistence) may be more likely for certain community-acquired respiratory tract infections (eg, otitis media) caused by resistant pathogens [1–4]. For other infections (eg, pneumonia), the data are less clear [5–12]. Other important clinical questions focus on whether resistant strains are more or less viable or virulent than susceptible strains. Some studies have suggested that penicillin-resistant strains of *Streptococcus pneumoniae* are less viable than susceptible strains, a direct consequence of the very mechanism by which resistance to penicillin is achieved [13–16]. For these strains, resistance may be associated with a significant biologic cost to the organism (ie, decreased viability) [13]. Other studies have suggested that resistant organism are not more virulent than susceptible strains and are not more likely to cause invasive disease. As a result, many experts have postulated that resistant organisms may not be capable of competing with susceptible strains for available resources, and they have "evolved" to a point of self-extinction. However, bacteria have existed on this planet for nearly 3.5 billion years,

* Corresponding author.
E-mail address: mrj6@cwru.edu (M.R. Jacobs).

0272-2712/04/$ - see front matter © 2004 Elsevier Inc. All rights reserved.
doi:10.1016/j.cll.2004.03.011

and an attribute of organisms that have survived this long is the ability to adapt. Thus, there are those who believe that bacteria are capable of overcoming the biologic cost of resistance, and resistant organisms will likely be an issue with which to contend for years to come [17–21].

While these questions are being debated, one thing is evident: resistance is prevalent, and it represents a significant health care—and public health— threat. The concern stems from the continued excessive use of antibiotics for patients with nonbacterial conditions, and the implications this has for the progression of resistance. Nearly 160 million antibiotic prescriptions were written in the ambulatory care setting in 1997—almost a 50% increase from 1992 [22,23]. Antibiotics were the third most commonly prescribed class of drugs, behind medications for cardiovascular/renal disorders and those for pain. Over the past 5 years, several educational efforts directed at health care providers, caregivers, and consumers have been set forth to minimize the excessive use of antibiotics for patients with nonbacterial respiratory tract disease [24,25]. In essence, these educational efforts focus on two basic principles: (1) antibiotics should only be used for patients with bacterial infections, and (2) when antibiotic therapy is appropriate, agents that are most likely to achieve optimal clinical outcomes should be prescribed. There are data to suggest that these efforts are paying off in terms of reducing antibiotic use for patients with nonbacterial conditions. During the 1-year period from 1997 to 1998, the number of antibiotics prescribed for children younger than 15 years with respiratory diseases was 34% lower compared with the 1-year period from 1989 to 1990, before these efforts were implemented [26]. Treatment guidelines also have been developed and published by groups, with input from members of professional organizations and governmental agencies (eg, Centers for Disease Control and Prevention, Food and Drug Administration) and experts in various specialties, to help clinicians improve the diagnosis of bacterial infection and select appropriate therapy [8,27–31].

However, encouraging the use of antimicrobial agents that are most likely to achieve optimal clinical outcomes is more challenging. The considerations involved in determining the "appropriateness" of antibiotic therapy include spectrum of activity, the likely pathogens involved, and the likelihood of those pathogens being resistant. Although the published guidelines have recommended specific agents for the treatment of community-acquired respiratory tract infections, the basis on which these recommendations were developed often is poorly understood. These educational efforts should be reinforced to help clinicians identify which agents are most likely to achieve clinical success. Understanding the rationale behind the antibiotic agents recommended in these treatment guidelines requires a review of the current activity of the various classes of agents against the predominant respiratory tract pathogens. This article reviews the mechanisms of resistance among respiratory tract pathogens to help clinicians understand how the antimicrobial activities of various agents have changed over time, interpret the clinical significance of resistance (ie, whether resistance can be overcome with respect to pharmacokinetics and dosing regimens), and make sound decisions regarding the selection of antibiotic therapy in the clinical setting.

Prevalence of resistance among respiratory tract pathogens

Streptococcus pneumoniae, Haemophilus influenzae, and *Moraxella catarrhalis* are the pathogens responsible for the majority of bacterial infections in acute otitis media, acute rhinosinusitis, acute exacerbations of chronic bronchitis, and community-acquired pneumonia (Table 1) [32]. The susceptibility of these pathogens to the various agents has changed dramatically since the advent of the antibiotic era [33]. Within a time frame that spans little more than 60 years—from the beginning of widespread antibiotic use to today—strains of bacteria that frequently cause community-acquired respiratory tract infection (eg, *S pneumoniae*) have gone from being exquisitely susceptible to highly resistant to many drug classes. During the late 1960s, the overwhelming success of antibiotic therapy and vaccinations in curing and preventing infections led the U.S. Surgeon General at the time, William H. Stewart, to believe that the era of infectious diseases was near an end. The advent of antibiotics resulted in significant advances in medical care at the time; however, as the widespread use of antibiotics continued, resistance began to emerge among respiratory tract pathogens. Today, the outlook on the battle against infectious diseases is much bleaker. The high prevalence of resistance among these pathogens has jeopardized the effectiveness of many antibiotics, because these pathogens are more difficult to eradicate from the site of infection [2].

Streptococcus pneumoniae

Strains of *S pneumoniae* were exquisitely susceptible to penicillin (minimum inhibitory concentration [MIC] ≤ 0.06 μg/mL) when this agent was first used clinically in the 1940s and 1950s. In fact, the vast majority of strains at that time had penicillin MICs ranging from 0.015 μg/mL to

Table 1
Etiology of community-acquired respiratory tract infections

	Prevalence in bacterial infections (%)		
	S pneumoniae	H influenzae	M catarrhalis
Acute exacerbations of chronic bronchitis	15–30	40–60	15–30
Acute otitis media	40–50	30–40	10–15
Acute rhinosinusitis	20–40	20–35	2–10
Community-acquired pneumonia	20–75	3–10	1–2

Data from Refs. [32,118–124].

0.03 μg/mL; thus, this is referred to as the baseline activity of penicillin against S pneumoniae [34,35]. Throughout the years, resistance has become more prevalent, and strains have become increasingly resistant, which represents an alarming trend [33,36–38]. Decreased susceptibility to penicillin among a few isolates of S pneumoniae was noted in the 1960s in Australia and New Guinea and in the 1970s in South Africa [39–41]. These isolates were noted to have penicillin MICs as high as 2 μg/mL to 4 μg/mL, meaning that approximately a 100-fold greater concentration was required to inhibit the growth of these isolates. Isolates with penicillin MICs in this range were rarely found in the United States in the following decade [36]. However, during the late 1980s and throughout the 1990s, the susceptibility of S pneumoniae to penicillin changed dramatically. During this time, the proportion of penicillin nonsusceptible strains increased, and the proportion of resistant isolates increased nearly 60 fold in the past 10 years [42]. To demonstrate the change in MICs over time, the activity of various antibiotic agents was recently compared against archived otitis media isolates (collected before 1985) and isolates collected between 1995 and 1997 [33]. From this study, it was noted that the concentration required to inhibit 90% of the archived strains (MIC_{90}) of S pneumoniae (0.03 μg/mL) was 100-fold lower than that required to inhibit 90% of the strains collected between 1995 and 1997 (2 μg/mL) [33]. Furthermore, the number of infections caused by strains with penicillin MICs $\geq$ 2 μg/mL also has increased, indicating that the problem of increasing resistance is clinically relevant.

Recent surveillance studies have demonstrated that approximately 40% to 50% of U.S. strains of S pneumoniae have penicillin MICs in the susceptible range [33,37,38]. Of the nonsusceptible strains (intermediate and resistant), 25% to 30% have penicillin MICs in the resistant range ($\geq$2 μg/mL), whereas 12% to 16% have penicillin MICs in the intermediate range (0.12 μg/mL to 1 μg/mL) [33,38]. Overall, from the most susceptible strains (ie, baseline activity) to the most resistant strains, the distribution of penicillin MICs ranges over a 1000-fold concentration (0.01 μg/mL to 16 μg/mL), and the MIC distribution for amoxicillin against S pneumoniae is similar to that for penicillin.

In general, the MIC distributions for various cephalosporins against S pneumoniae also range over a 1000fold concentration; however, there are significant differences among these agents with respect to the baseline activity [33]. For example, the baseline activity of cefaclor against S pneumoniae is 0.5 μg/mL to 1 μg/mL, which is an approximate 20- to 30-fold higher concentration than those of penicillin or amoxicillin required to inhibit the most susceptible strains. Other cephalosporins that are more active against S pneumoniae include ceftriaxone and cefuroxime, which have baseline activities similar to penicillin (0.02 μg/mL to 0.03 μg/mL and 0.03 μg/mL to 0.06 μg/mL, respectively) [33]. From the study evaluating the activity of antibiotics against recent and archived isolated, it was noted that the activity of cephalosporins also has changed over the years. The MIC_{90}

for cefaclor against archived isolates was 1 μg/mL, whereas the MIC_{90} against recent isolates was >64 μg/mL [43].

Similar patterns of resistance can be demonstrated for other classes of antibiotics as well. For example, resistance to macrolides among strains of *S pneumoniae* has also increased throughout the past 2 to 3 decades. The baseline activity of macrolides (0.03 μg/mL) and MIC distributions (> 1000-fold concentration range: 0.03 μg/mL to >32 μg/mL) against *S pneumoniae* are somewhat similar to those of penicillin. However, the characteristic of the MIC distribution of macrolides is that there is a trimodal distribution—strains are either exquisitely susceptible (erythromycin MICs ≤ 0.03 μg/mL), "low-level" resistant (erythromycin MICs 1 μg/mL to 16 μg/mL), or highly resistant (erythromycin MICs ≥ 32 μg/mL), with different resistance mechanisms for the two resistant groups [44,45]. Another important characteristic is that resistance among *S pneumoniae* to macrolides and other classes of antibiotics increases with increasing MICs to penicillin [37]. In other words, strains that are nonsusceptible to penicillin are more likely to be resistant to macrolides and other classes of antibiotics (Table 2) [38]. The activity of macrolides against *S pneumoniae* also has changed over the past 2 decades. The MIC_{90} of azithromycin against archived isolates was 0.12 μg/mL compared with >4 μg/mL against recent isolates [43].

Fluoroquinolones with antipneumococcal activity (eg, gatifloxacin, levofloxacin, moxifloxacin, and gemifloxacin) are highly active against the majority of strains of *S pneumoniae*; however, in areas where fluoroquinolones have been prescribed widely, clinically relevant levels of resistance have been described [46].

Haemophilus influenzae

β-Lactamase production among strains of *H influenzae* also has increased throughout the past 2 decades [37]. During the early 1980s, the proportion of strains that produced β-lactamases was approximately 10% to 15%,

Table 2
Prevalence of cross-resistance between penicillin and various antibiotic classes among strains of penicillin-nonsusceptible strains of *S pneumoniae*

Class/Agent	% of Strains resistant			
	Pen-S	Pen-I	Pen-R	All
Macrolides	6	49	76	32
Clindamycin	1	14	28	10
Trimethoprim/sulfamethoxazole	14	57	91	43
Doxycycline	4	25	55	22

Abbreviations: MIC, minimum inhibitory concentration; Pen-I, penicillin intermediate (penicillin MIC 0.12 μg/mL to 1 μg/mL); Pen-R, penicillin resistant (penicillin MIC ≥ 2 μg/mL); Pen-S, penicillin susceptible (penicillin MIC ≤ 0.06 μg/mL).

From Jacobs MR. Worldwide trends in antimicrobial resistance among common respiratory tract pathogens in children. Pediatr Infect Dis J 2003;22(8 Suppl):S109–19; with permission.

whereas more recent surveillance studies have demonstrated a prevalence of approximately 40%. The MIC distribution of amoxicillin against *H influenzae* ranges over a >100-fold concentration, from the baseline activity of 0.12 to 0.25 µg/mL to >16 µg/mL [33]. Non-β-lactamase–producing strains are susceptible to amoxicillin (MICs < 4 µg/mL), whereas β-lactamase–producing strains are usually highly resistant (MICs ≥ 16 µg/mL). The addition of a β-lactamase inhibitor (eg, clavulanate) to amoxicillin restores the activity against β-lactamase–producing strains, with the majority having amoxicillin/clavulanate MICs ≤ 4 µg/mL. From the standpoint of baseline activity, amoxicillin is less active against *H influenzae* compared with activity against *S pneumoniae*. To inhibit the most susceptible strains of *H influenzae* requires a 20- to 50-fold higher concentration of amoxicillin compared with inhibiting the most susceptible strains of *S pneumoniae*. As with *S pneumoniae*, the cephalosporins have varying activities against *H influenzae*. Ceftriaxone, cefpodoxime, and cefixime are highly active against this pathogen; the baseline activity of these agents is approximately 0.01 µg/mL. The activity of β-lactams against non-β-lactamase–producing strains of *H influenzae* has not changed over the past 2 decades; however, the proportion of isolates producing β-lactamases has increased substantially.

In general, the macrolides are much less active against *H influenzae* than they are against *S pneumoniae*. The modal baseline activity of erythromycin and clarithromycin against *H influenzae* is 4 µg/mL and 8 µg/mL, respectively, whereas the baseline activity of azithromycin is 0.5 µg/mL to 1 µg/mL. When these values are compared with the baseline activity against *S pneumoniae*, it is evident that a 100-fold higher concentration of erythromycin or clarithromycin is required to inhibit the most susceptible strains of *H influenzae*. For azithromycin, an approximate 20fold higher concentration is required to inhibit the most susceptible strains. The activity of macrolides against *H influenzae* has remained unchanged throughout the past 20 years. The clarithromycin and azithromycin MIC$_{90}$s against *H influenzae* were 16 µg/mL and 2 µg/mL, respectively, for both archived and recent strains [43].

Resistance to fluoroquinolones among clinical isolates of *H influenzae* is rare; however, surveillance studies have identified a few clinical strains with increased MICs to fluoroquinolones. Fluoroquinolones are considered to be highly active against this pathogen.

Moraxella catarrhalis

β-Lactamase production among strains of *M catarrhalis* also is prevalent. From a recent surveillance study, it was noted that nearly 100% of strains of *M catarrhalis* produce β-lactamases [33]. Amoxicillin is active against *M catarrhalis*, with baseline MICs of 0.12 µg/mL to 0.25 µg/mL when combined with the β-lactamase inhibitor, clavulanate. β-Lactamase–stable cephalosporins, macrolides, and fluoroquinolones all are active against the majority of strains of *M catarrhalis*.

Selection of antibiotic resistance

The changes that have occurred in the susceptibility of pathogens to commonly used antibiotics throughout the past 30 years have been attributed to the relationship between excessive antibiotic use of and the resultant selective pressures that occur during therapy [24,47,48]. Two important factors are necessary for this relationship to explain how resistance has become prevalent and clinically significant. First, an event must take place to allow certain strains of a given organism to become less susceptible to antibiotics, resulting in a survival advantage. Second, the excessive antibiotic use must select for these less susceptible organisms [19].

An infection occurs when bacterial growth overwhelms the defense mechanisms of the host, resulting in clinical signs and symptoms of disease. The primary goal of antibiotic therapy is to eradicate the pathogen from the site of infection by killing or suppressing the growth of bacteria. Host defenses, including inflammatory and immune-mediated responses, are necessary for eradicating any remaining bacteria. Targeting a cellular pathway or process that is specific to the bacteria limits the toxicity to the host, and the antibiotics that have been developed throughout the past 60 years have been successful at targeting a few cellular processes specific to bacteria or sufficiently different from these processes in eukaryotic cells, with

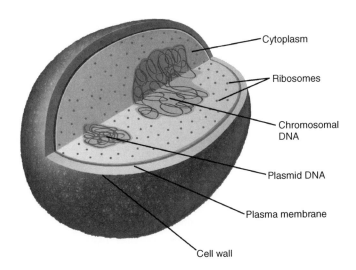

Fig. 1. Major components of the prokaryotic cell. (Copyright Michael R. Jacobs, MD, PhD, Cleveland, OH; used with permission.)

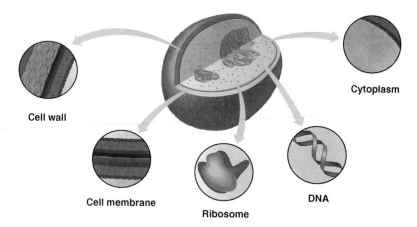

Cytoplasm

Cell wall

Cell membrane

DNA

Ribosome

Fig. 2. Major antibiotic targets of the prokaryotic cell, including cell wall, cell membrane, ribosome, DNA, and cytoplasm. (Copyright Michael R. Jacobs, MD, PhD, Cleveland, OH; used with permission.)

little toxicity to humans (Figs. 1 and 2) [47]. Although the spectrum of activity has changed with new agents throughout the years, a limited number of agents with novel mechanisms of action have been developed. Currently, the various agents commonly used for the treatment of community-acquired respiratory tract infections can be grouped into one of four categories (Table 3). The continued excessive use of agents with similar mechanisms of activity—in human patients and in agriculture—has had a significant impact on the progression of resistance.

Based on recent population estimates, more than one antibiotic was prescribed for every two persons in the United States in 1997 [23], and the use of antibiotics in agriculture each year—to treat and prevent infections, and for growth promotion—is nearly equal to that used in humans [19]. When antibiotics are administered, susceptible strains are killed or suppressed while resistant strains grow and proliferate; this effect occurs throughout the entire body, not only at the site of infection, and is more pronounced when suboptimal doses of antibiotics are used [24]. The

Table 3

Mechanisms of action of commonly used antimicrobials for community-acquired respiratory tract infections

Target	Examples
Cell wall active agents	β-Lactams (penicillins, cephalosporins)
Protein synthesis inhibitors	Microlides, lincosamides (eg, clindamycin), tetracyclines (eg, tetracycline, doxycycline), ketolides
DNA replication inhibitors	Fluoroquinolones
Folic acid metabolism inhibitors	Trimethoprim/sulfamethoxazole

resistant organisms that remain no longer compete with susceptible organisms for the available resources, and they proliferate. Resistant organisms then can be the source of subsequent infection or they can be spread to other members of the community. Of greater concern is that resistant bacteria can transfer their resistance genes not only to their progeny (vertical transfer) but also to other strains and other bacterial species (horizontal transfer) [49]. Thus, the excessive use of antibiotics throughout the past 60 years has provided the means necessary to select resistant strains of bacteria that frequently cause community-acquired respiratory tract infections.

Resistance among bacteria is achieved via alteration in the genetic makeup of the organism, either by mutation (ie, de novo) or acquisition of foreign DNA [50,51]. Regardless of the means, the resultant alterations may limit the effectiveness of the antibiotic by inactivating the antibiotic (eg, β-lactamases), prohibiting it from reaching its target (eg, antibiotic efflux), or by altering the target to which the antibiotic binds to exert its effect [19]. The genes encoding resistance generally are carried on the bacterial chromosome, or on extrachromosomal packets of DNA, called plasmids [51].

Mutations frequently occur in bacterial DNA during replication and can result in new resistance genes or can promote/enhance existing mechanisms (Fig. 3) [51]. Similarly, the acquisition of DNA from other organisms can occur frequently via several different mechanisms. Transduction occurs when the DNA is transferred via a vector (eg, virus) from one bacterium and incorporated into the DNA of another, thereby altering the genetic

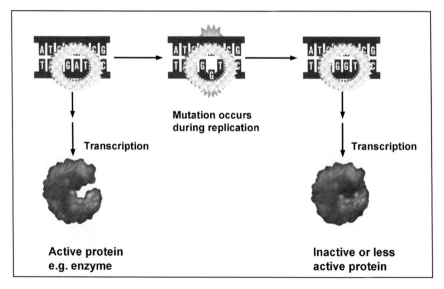

Fig. 3. Bacterial mechanism for acquiring resistance: mutation. (Copyright Michael R. Jacobs, MD, PhD, Cleveland, OH; used with permission.)

composition of the recipient organism. Transformation is the process in which a strand of naked DNA from a lysed bacterium is taken up and incorporated into the chromosome of another (Fig. 4). Bacterial DNA also is frequently shared via conjugation in the form of plasmids and transposons, during which all or some of the DNA from one bacterium is transferred to another during direct cellular contact (Fig. 5). In turn, the recipient may incorporate segments of the donor DNA into its own chromosome via recombination. Translocation also occurs frequently, in which genes encoding resistance are transferred from one section of its own chromosome to another. Translocation is an important process because bacteria tend to concentrate resistance genes in certain packets of DNA (eg, transposons, integrons) [52–54]. Thus, when bacteria "swap" DNA, genes encoding resistance to multiple antibiotics often can be transferred at the same time. However, not all transfers of DNA between bacteria result in resistance. As mentioned previously, the alterations must confer a survival advantage.

Antibiotics with novel mechanisms of action are needed to help combat the problem of antibiotic resistance; however, it may be several years before these agents are available clinically. In the meantime, the best strategy for minimizing the impact and progression of resistance focuses on reducing the use of antibiotics for nonbacterial conditions (eg, viral infection) and selecting appropriate agents capable of overcoming resistance. Understanding the mechanisms of resistance used by the common pathogens is an important factor in determining the "appropriateness" of a particular antibiotic agent.

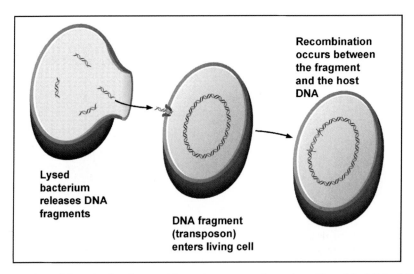

Fig. 4. Bacterial mechanism for acquiring resistance: transformation. (Copyright Michael R. Jacobs, MD, PhD, Cleveland, OH; used with permission.)

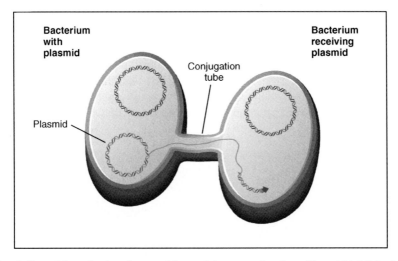

Fig. 5. Bacterial mechanism for acquiring resistance: conjugation. (Copyright Michael R. Jacobs, MD, PhD, Cleveland, OH; used with permission.)

Mechanisms of resistance among respiratory tract pathogens

β-Lactams exert an antimicrobial effect by interfering with the formation and maintenance of the peptidoglycan layer of the bacterial cell wall, which is an important component for bacterial homeostasis and reproduction [55]. For bacteria, the concentration of solutes in the intracellular space is much greater than in the extracellular space. The natural tendency would be for water to move across the cellular membrane to equilibrate this concentration gradient. Without the rigid peptidoglycan layer, the cellular membrane would not hold up to the osmotic pressures, and the cell would lyse. This is exactly what occurs when β-lactam antibiotics interfere with the integrity of the peptidoglycan structure [56].

In *S pneumoniae*, the peptidoglycan layer consists of a polymer of repeating units of a disaccharide of N-acetyl-glucosamine (NAG) and N-acetyl-muramic acid (NAM). Attached to the NAM molecule is a linear peptide consisting of at least three amino acids (L-alanine, D-isoglutamine, L-lysine), known at the stem peptide, and collectively, NAG, NAM, and the stem peptide are referred to as a muropeptide. The formation of the peptidoglycan layer occurs in three stages. First, within the cell membrane, the muropeptides are assembled. Next, each unit is bound to lipid carriers, which assist in the transport of the units across the cell membrane. In the extracellular space, the muropeptides are added to each other or to existing peptidoglycan strands to form linear polymers. The last step in the formation of the peptidoglycan layer is the cross-linking of stem peptides from one polymer to the stem peptides of neighboring polymers, which is an integral process that provides integrity and structure to the bacterial cell wall. The end product is a sack-like molecule that encompasses the entire organism.

The cross-linking of stem peptides is facilitated by enzymes called peptidases, which are located on the extracellular surface of the cell membrane (Fig. 6) [57]. The active site of each peptidase enzyme catalyzes the formation of a covalent bond between amino acids, and the natural substrates for these enzymes are the amino acids that comprise the stem

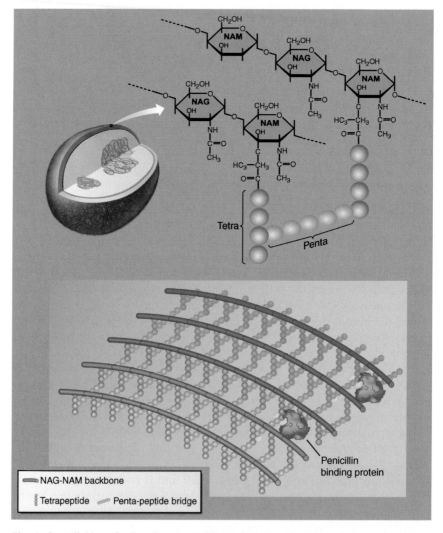

Fig. 6. Cross-linking of cell wall stem peptides to form muropeptide complex, performed by peptidases, which also are know as penicillin-binding proteins. NAG, N-acetyl glucosamine; NAM, N-acetyl muramic acid. (Copyright Michael R. Jacobs, MD, PhD, Cleveland, OH; used with permission.)

peptides. Penicillin, the first β-lactam antibiotic, was shown to exert its antimicrobial effect by binding to these peptidases, thereby interfering with their activity; thus, they frequently are referred to as penicillin binding proteins (PBPs) [58].

Penicillin is a naturally occurring compound that is produced by the mold *Penicillium notatum*, which may have been produced as a defense mechanism against bacteria or as a means for survival. By producing penicillin, the mold was able to kill off other organisms that may have been competing for the same resources. The chemical structure of penicillin, and β-lactams in general, includes a β-lactam ring, a part of which is structurally similar to the D-Ala-D-Ala end of a stem peptide (Fig. 7). Thus, β-lactam antibiotics mimic the natural substrates of the PBPs (ie, stem peptides), and they compete for the same space at the active site of PBPs. The various side chains added to the β-lactam structure determine the spectrum of activity. When β-lactam antibiotics interact with the active site of the PBP, a chemical reaction occurs, during which an irreversible covalent bond forms between the antibiotic and the enzyme. This reaction blocks the active site of PBPs and prevents the stem peptides of the peptidoglycan layers from becoming cross-linked.

Among *S pneumoniae*, there are at least six known PBPs (1a, 1b, 2a, 2b, 2x, 3), each of which is encoded by a respective *pbp* gene (eg, *pbp1a*, *pbp1b*, *pbp2a*) on the bacterial chromosome. The PBPs are differentiated by their molecular weight, and it is the high-molecular weight PBPs, 1a, 2b, and 2x, that are the primary targets of β-lactams because of their involvement with the cross-linking of the peptidoglycan polymers (Fig. 8). Each PBP varies slightly with respect to the amino acid sequence, and the structure of PBP 2x is shown in Fig. 9 [59]. The differences in amino acid composition result in slight differences in the overall structure of the PBP, including the structure of the active site. As a result, the affinity for the natural substrates (and for β-lactams, for that matter) varies among the different PBPs. Similarly, the

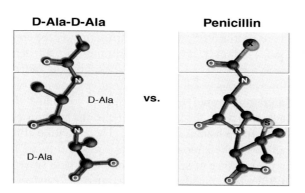

Fig. 7. Similarity between D-Ala-D-Ala of stem peptide and penicillin. (Copyright Michael R. Jacobs, MD, PhD, Cleveland, OH; used with permission.)

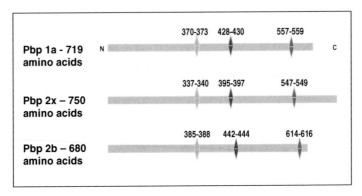

Fig. 8. Primary structures and positions of motifs making up the active transpeptidase sites of Pbp 1a, 2x, and 2b of *S pneumoniae*. (Copyright Michael R. Jacobs, MD, PhD, Cleveland, OH; used with permission.)

β-lactams differ with respect to their molecular structures, which can impact the affinity between the antibiotic and the PBP. In other words, β-lactams may have a greater affinity for certain PBPs, and the affinity between the various PBPs and β-lactam antibiotics is reflected in the baseline activity of each agent.

Agents that have a greater affinity for the various PBPs are more active, and it requires a lesser concentration to inhibit the growth of the organism. For example, the baseline activities of β-lactams such as penicillin, amoxicillin, and ceftriaxone (eg, 0.015 µg/mL to 0.03 µg/mL) are much lower than those of agents such as cefixime and cefaclor (eg, 0.25 µg/mL to 0.5 µg/mL). This is because the PBPs of *S pneumoniae* have a greater affinity for penicillin, amoxicillin, and ceftriaxone compared with cefixime and cefaclor. However, differences in affinity can be overcome if higher concentrations of antibiotic can be achieved at the active site of the enzyme.

Resistance to β-lactams among *S pneumoniae* is achieved via alterations in the *pbp* genes. These alterations result in changes in the amino acid sequence of the respective PBP, which, in turn, can alter the configuration of the enzyme [60]. However, not all alterations in *pbp* genes result in resistance; certain alterations may increase the affinity of PBPs for β-lactam antibiotics. However, this would confer a disadvantage in terms of survival because the antibiotic would be more effective in killing the organism. Resistance is achieved when these genetic alterations result in a PBP that has a reduced affinity for β-lactam antibiotics. Then, continued antibiotic use selects for strains with these resistance genes because they are more capable of surviving in the presence of antibiotics compared with susceptible strains. Alterations in PBPs have also been demonstrated in *H influenzae*, but they are currently rare, with the exception of Japan [38,61].

A unique characteristic of β-lactam resistance via alterations in PBPs is that it occurs in a step-wise fashion. A few alterations in the gene encoding

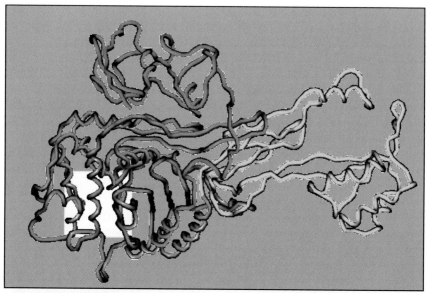

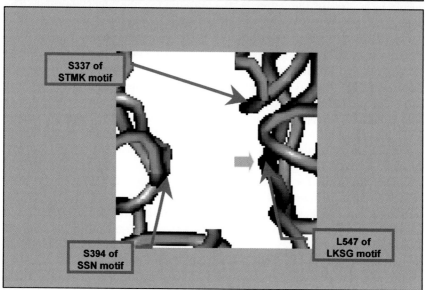

Fig. 9. Tertiary structure of Pbp2x of *S pneumoniae* is shown in the top panel, with the active binding site shown with a white background. The bottom panel shows an enlarged view of the active binding site. Yellow, N-terminal domain; Blue, penicillin-binding/transpeptidase domain; Green, C-terminal domain and connecting loop. (*From* Hakenbeck R, Grebe T, Zahner D, Stock JB. Beta-lactam resistance in *Streptococcus pneumoniae*: penicillin-binding proteins and non-penicillin-binding proteins. Mol Microbiol 1999;33:673–8; with permission.)

for one PBP may shift the penicillin MIC up by a couple of doubling dilutions; however, minor alterations such as this generally do not shift the MICs from susceptible into the intermediate or resistant ranges [62]. This is because penicillin still can bind to other PBPs to exert its antimicrobial effect. For strains of S pneumoniae to become intermediate or resistant, numerous alterations are required in multiple pbp genes [63]. In the laboratory setting, penicillin resistance among strains of S pneumoniae is achieved following numerous point mutations in the pbp genes. Resistance among clinical strains also may be achieved via this mechanism; however, a more likely scenario is that the alterations occur via transformation, in which naked DNA from closely related streptococcal species (eg, S mitis, S oralis) are incorporated into the chromosome of S pneumoniae via transformation [64].

The step-wise approach to resistance is necessary; otherwise, resistance would come at a significant biologic cost to the organism. For example, drastic alterations in pbp genes all at once would be a more efficient means of becoming resistant. However, because of the similarities in structure between the stem peptides and β-lactams, such drastic alterations might also result in a drastic reduction in the affinity for the stem peptides. The structural integrity of the peptidoglycan layer would then be compromised by the effort to become resistant. In fact, even the stepwise approach to resistance may be associated with some consequences. The changes in the configuration of PBPs reduce the affinity for β-lactams and the natural substrates [13]. As a result, the altered PBPs of resistant strains frequently have a greater affinity for stem peptides with a different amino acid sequence than those of susceptible strains [13]. The preferred substrates of altered PBPs (ie, resistant) include branched stem peptides, whereas the preferred substrates of unaltered PBPs (ie, susceptible) are linear stem peptides. The murMN operon among S pneumoniae is composed of two genes (murM and murN) that encode for enzymes involved in the assembly of stem peptides (Fig. 10) [65]. Among resistant strains, the murM gene has a mosaic structure that encodes for enzymes involved in the production of branched stem muropeptides. From a recent study, it was shown that inactivation of the murMN operon in penicillin-resistant strains restores susceptibility [65]. Thus, the ability to produce branched stem peptides is a necessary component for penicillin resistance among strains of S pneumoniae, along with altered PBPs.

The consequence of including branched stem peptides in the peptidoglycan layer is that they often form cross-links with other stem peptides on the same polymer as opposed to stem peptides on neighboring polymers. Thus, the indirect cross-linking of the peptidoglycan layer in intermediate or resistant strains of S pneumoniae is not as structured or highly patterned as that in susceptible strains, which may affect the structural integrity of the peptidoglycan layer [13].

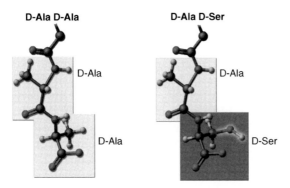

Fig. 10. *mur* genes in strains of *S pneumoniae* with altered penicillin-binding proteins encode for other stem peptide chains, such as D-Ala-D-Ser instead of D-Ala-D-Ala in penicillin-susceptible strains. (Copyright Michael R. Jacobs, MD, PhD, Cleveland, OH; used with permission.)

Fortunately, treatment strategies can be used to overcome this mechanism of resistance. Because alterations in PBPs occur in a step-wise fashion and result in decreased affinity for the β-lactam antibiotic, it would seem that agents with the greatest affinity for unaltered PBPs would be most likely to retain affinity for altered PBPs. In other words, agents with the highest potency (lowest baseline activity) against susceptible strains would be most active against intermediate and resistant strains. In fact, this has been supported by surveillance studies evaluating the in vitro activity against penicillin-susceptible, -intermediate, and -resistant strains of *S pneumoniae* [33,37,66,67]. The results of these studies show that amoxicillin and ceftriaxone are the most active oral β-lactams against some penicillin-intermediate and -resistant strains of *S pneumoniae*.

The reduced affinity resulting from alterations in PBPs also can be overcome by increasing the concentration of β-lactams at the site of infection. A good example is penicillin, which is one of the β-lactams that is in fact most active against penicillin-susceptible and -intermediate strains. However, this agent is not routinely used for the management of community-acquired respiratory tract infections caused by *S pneumoniae* because the oral formulation (penicillin V) has a low bioavailability and is highly bound to serum proteins. Thus, the amount of unbound antibiotic that is available to interact with PBPs at the site of infection is often not adequate to treat infections caused by intermediate (0.12 μg/mL to 1 μg/mL) or resistant (≥2 μg/mL) strains. However, high-dose intravenous penicillin G (8 to 15 million units/day in four to six divided doses, or 20–24 million units/day continuous infusion) has been suggested as an effective option for treating community-acquired pneumonia caused by strains of *S pneumoniae* with penicillin MICs ≤ 4 μg/mL because of the concentrations that can be achieved at the site of infection [68]. Amoxicillin is another example in which higher oral doses have been advocated to provide effective concentrations at the site of infection [69,70]. This treatment strategy has been recommended by different groups for the management of conditions such as acute otitis media and acute bacterial rhinosinusitis [8,28].

The production of β-lactamases is another means by which certain respiratory tract pathogens (*H influenzae, M catarrhalis*) have become resistant to β-lactam antibiotics. β-Lactamases are enzymes that are structurally related to PBPs and have a high affinity for β-lactam antibiotics; the interaction between β-lactams and β-lactamases causes a permanent opening of the β-lactam ring, thereby inactivating the antibiotic (Fig. 11) [56,71]. However, the interaction between β-lactams and β-lactamases does not result in a covalent bond between the antibiotic and the enzyme, unlike the interaction between the antibiotic and PBPs. Thus, after the antibiotic is inactivated, the enzyme is free to interact with other intact β-lactam molecules.

The genes encoding for β-lactamases in *H influenzae* are found primarily on plasmids; however, in some cases, these genes are incorporated into the bacterial chromosome [72]. Two distinct β-lactamases are produced by strains of *H influenzae*: TEM-1 and ROB-1, of which, the TEM-1 β-lactamase is more common [73]. Three β-lactamases are produced by *M catarrhalis*: BRO-1, BRO-2, and BRO-3, which are structurally similar to each other, but distinct from the TEM-1 or ROB-1 β-lactamases [74]. Because of the structural similarities between PBPs and β-lactamases, it is believed that the two enzymes evolved from a common primordial PBP [56].

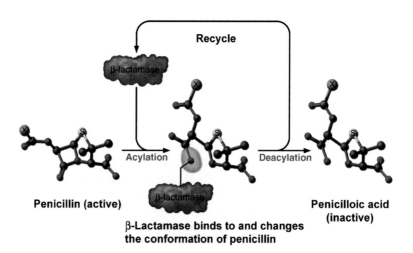

Fig. 11. Antibiotic inactivation by β-lactamases such as those of *H influenzae* and *M catarrhalis*. (Copyright Michael R. Jacobs, MD, PhD, Cleveland, OH; used with permission.)

These enzymes are not bound to the cell membrane, rather they concentrate in the periplasmic space of gram-negative pathogens. β-Lactamases are not known to perform any physiologic function and may have evolved as a defensive mechanism against microorganisms that produce β-lactam compounds [56]. The production of β-lactamases by certain organisms resulted in a survival value over non-β-lactamase producers, which selected for these organisms over time.

Resistance via β-lactamase production cannot be overcome by increasing the dose of the β-lactam antibiotic (ie, the concentration at the site of infection) because the β-lactamase enzyme is regenerated following each interaction with—and subsequent inactivation of—an antibiotic. However, this mechanism of resistance can be overcome by using a combination of a β-lactam antibiotic with a β-lactamase inhibitor (eg, amoxicillin/clavulanate) or by using β-lactam antibiotics that are stable to the actions of β-lactamases (eg, ceftriaxone, cefuroxime, cefpodoxime, cefixime). β-Lactamase inhibitors have a β-lactam ring and closely resemble their antibiotic counterparts. However, β-lactamase inhibitors have very low affinity for PBPs; thus, they do not offer any direct therapeutic value in terms of antimicrobial effect [75,76]. Conversely, the affinity of β-lactamases for β-lactamase inhibitors is very high, and more importantly, the β-lactamase inhibitors act as "suicide substrates" (Fig. 12). When β-lactamase inhibitors interact with β-lactamases, a covalent bond is formed rapidly between the enzyme and the β-lactamase inhibitor, inactivating the enzyme and preventing it from destroying more β-lactam molecules [75]. Thus, the interaction between a β-lactamase inhibitor and a β-lactamase is analogous

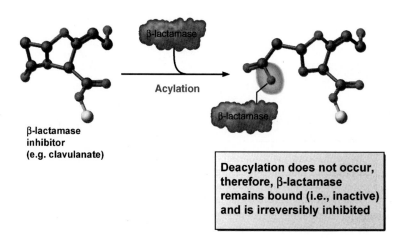

Fig. 12. Irreversible binding of a β-lactamase inhibitor to β-lactamase. (Copyright Michael R. Jacobs, MD, PhD, Cleveland, OH; used with permission.)

to the interaction between a β-lactam antibiotic and a PBP. β-Lactamase stable agents evade the action of β-lactamases due to stereochemical blocking of the attachment site of β-lactamases by the side chains of these agents (Fig. 13).

Protein synthesis inhibitors

Several classes of agents inhibit protein systhesis [77]. Although these agents are chemically and structurally distinct, they all exert an antimicrobial effect by binding to the 50S subunit of bacterial ribosomes and disrupting protein synthesis [78]. The number of 70S ribosomes in a typical bacterium ranges from 20,000 to 70,000, each of which consists of two subunits: 50S and 30S. The 50S subunit is comprised of 34 ribosomal proteins and two strands of ribosomal RNA (rRNA; 23S RNA and 5S RNA). The rRNA provides structure to the 50S subunit and determines the position of the ribosomal proteins (Fig. 14).

An overview of protein synthesis and the sites of action of several classes of agents inhibiting protein synthesis are illustrated in Fig. 15. These examples include the following: (1) puromycin, an aminoacyl-tRNA analog that is incorporated into the nascent peptide chain, thereby causing premature termination and release; (2) tetracyclines, which prevent the binding of charged tRNA to the A site of the ribosome; (3) chloramphenicol, which inhibits the peptidyl transferase reaction of the large subunit of the ribosome; (4) The MLS antibiotics, which include macrolides (erythro-

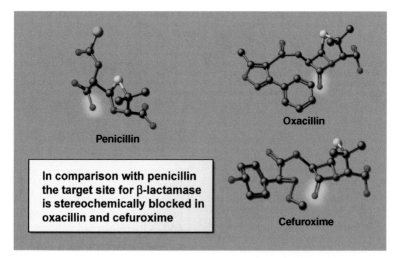

Fig. 13. β-Lactamase stable agents evade the action of β-lactamases due to stereochemical blocking of the attachment site of β-lactamases by side chains of these agents. (Copyright Michael R. Jacobs, MD, PhD, Cleveland, OH; used with permission.)

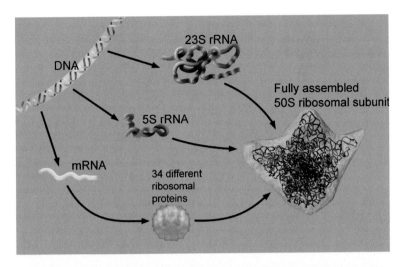

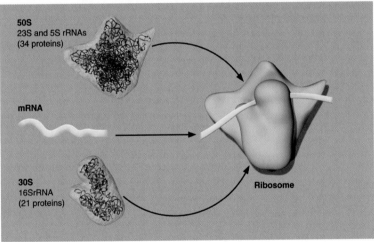

Fig. 14. Bacterial ribosome structure and assembly. Top panel shows components and assembly of 50S ribosomal subunit. Lower panel shows 50S and 30S ribosomal subunits combining to form the complete 70S ribosome. (Copyright Michael R. Jacobs, MD, PhD, Cleveland, OH; used with permission.)

mycin, azithromycin, clarithromycin), lincosamides (eg, clindamycin), ketolides (eg, telithromycin) and streptogramins, which block the ribosome exit tunnel, thereby preventing movement and release of the nascent peptide. During protein synthesis, DNA is transcribed via RNA polymerase, and a strand of messenger RNA (mRNA) is created, which acts as a template for the genes encoding the proteins. Translation is the process during which the mRNA template is "read" by the ribosomes and the protein is assembled. As the strand of mRNA passes between the 50S and 30S RNA subunits, the

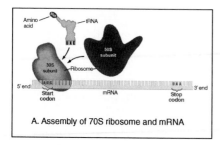

A. Assembly of 70S ribosome and mRNA

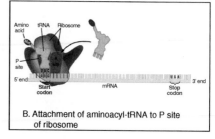

B. Attachment of aminoacyl-tRNA to P site of ribosome

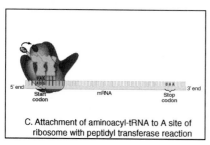

C. Attachment of aminoacyl-tRNA to A site of ribosome with peptidyl transferase reaction

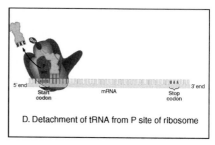

D. Detachment of tRNA from P site of ribosome

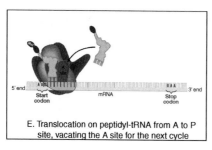

E. Translocation on peptidyl-tRNA from A to P site, vacating the A site for the next cycle

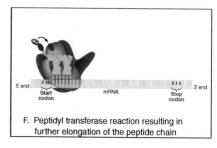

F. Peptidyl transferase reaction resulting in further elongation of the peptide chain

Fig. 15. (A–J) Overview of protein synthesis and sites of action of agents that block protein synthesis. Puromycin is an aminoacyl-tRNA analog that is incorporated into the peptide chain, resulting in premature termination of polypeptide synthesis (A). Tetracyclines prevent binding of aminoacyl-tRNA to the A site (B and D). Chloramphenicol inhibits peptidyl transferase reaction (C and F). MLS agents block the peptide exit tunnel (D and G). (Copyright Michael R. Jacobs, MD, PhD, Cleveland, OH; used with permission.)

codons (groups of three bases) are read. Each codon corresponds with a transfer RNA (tRNA) molecule (ie, anticodon) that carries a specific amino acid. Once the codon is read, the corresponding tRNA molecule carrying the amino acid binds to the aminoacyl site (A site) of the 50S subunit of the ribosome. As the ribosome moves along the mRNA template, the tRNA molecule is translocated from the A site to the peptidyl site (P site) of the ribosome, and a new tRNA molecule corresponding with the next codon binds to the vacant A site. During this process, the amino acid from the tRNA molecule occupying the P site is transferred to the amino acid on the tRNA molecule occupying the A site, thereby forming a peptide.

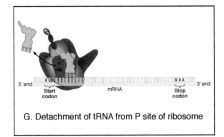

G. Detachment of tRNA from P site of ribosome

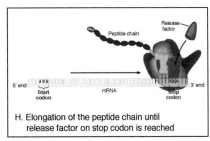

H. Elongation of the peptide chain until release factor on stop codon is reached

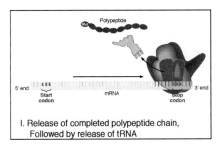

I. Release of completed polypeptide chain, Followed by release of tRNA

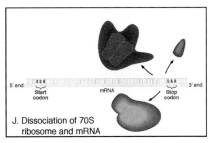

J. Dissociation of 70S ribosome and mRNA

Fig. 15 (*continued*)

This process continues until the ribosome reads a section of the mRNA telling it that the protein is complete [79].

The macrolides exert an antimicrobial effect by binding to a site on the ribosome that is near the peptidyl transferase center, which includes the A and P sites [80,81]. By binding to this location, macrolides block the binding of tRNA to the A site and translocation from the A site to the P site, thereby inhibiting protein synthesis. One mechanism by which *S pneumoniae* demonstrates resistance to macrolides is via an alteration in the macrolide binding site. The enzyme responsible for these alterations is known as adenine methylase (encoded by the *erm* gene), which results in a conformational change in the 23S rRNA of the 50S ribosomal subunit, thereby reducing the affinity for all macrolide agents, and preventing them from blocking protein synthesis [82]. Alterations in ribosomal proteins also have been demonstrated to cause macrolide resistance; although, resistance via this mechanism among clinical isolates is rare [83,84]. Resistance via alterations in ribosomes affects the activity of macrolides, lincosamides, and streptogramin; thus, it is often referred to as MLS resistance [82]. Because of the sheer number of ribosomes in each bacterium, it would seem that macrolides might still be effective in the presence of adenine methylase. However, a unique characteristic of this mechanism of resistance is that it occurs as an "all or none" phenomenon, and overcoming this mechanism of resistance requires treatment with an antibiotic agent from another class [33].

Another mechanism of resistance to macrolides that has been demonstrated among clinical strains of *S pneumoniae* involves an antibiotic efflux pump [45,85,86] This efflux pump, which is encoded by the *mef* gene, is energy dependent and actively transports antibiotic from the intracellular space to the extracellular space [86]. Without the pump, antibiotics freely pass through the cellular membrane; however, with the expression of the *mef* gene the antibiotic gets pumped back out of the cell, thereby preventing the antibiotic from reaching its target (ie, ribosomes). The antibiotic efflux mechanism only confers resistance to 14- and 15-membered macrolides (eg, erythromycin, clarithromycin, azithromycin), but not to clindamycin and 16-membered macrolides [85]. Therefore, this mechanism of resistance is often referred to as M resistance. An increasing number of treatment failures have been reported as a result of this mechanism of resistance [3,87].

Macrolide resistance among strains of *S pneumoniae* in the United States is more commonly mediated via the efflux pump mechanism compared with the ribosomal methylase mechanism [45,85]. However, strains can use both mechanisms of resistance (ie, they express both the *erm* and *mef* genes), which results in high-level resistance to macrolides (erythromycin MIC $\geq$ 32 µg/mL) [88]. Occasional strains of macrolide-resistant *S pneumoniae* are associated with 23S rRNA and ribosomal protein L4 and L22 mutations [83,84]. These mutations block the ribosome exit tunnel of polypeptide chains being synthesized.

The ketolides are a new member of the MLS antibiotic family. The mechanism of action of ketolides is similar to that of macrolides (ie, binding to the 23S rRNA component of the 50S subunit on bacterial ribosomes) [89]. Although similar to macrolides, the ketolides were designed to overcome the M and MLS mechanisms of resistance. The activity of ketolides is not significantly affected by the efflux pump mechanism, and the activity of these agents against macrolide-resistant strains of *S pneumoniae* has shown promise [90]; however, some of these agents have been shown to induce the methylation of rRNA in some strains [91]. *H influenzae* is intrinsically resistant to macrolides, which is associated with the presence of an *acr*AB efflux pump homologous to this mechanism in *E coli*, and which explains the limited activity of these agents against these pathogens [92,93].

Tetracyclines (including tetracycline and doxycycline) exert an antimicrobial effect by binding to the 30S subunit of bacterial ribosomes and preventing tRNA from binding to the A- or P-sites [94]. These agents also interact with human ribosomes; however, there is an active transport mechanism among bacteria that allows for the accumulation of antibiotic within the intracellular space [94]. This enhances the activity against bacteria while minimizing toxicity to humans. The gene that encodes for resistance to tetracycline is the *tet* gene, which protects ribosomes from the actions of this antibiotic [95,96]. Although the exact mechanism by which ribosomes are protected is unclear, it most likely involves an energy-dependent process using guanidine triphosphate that promotes the release of tetracycline from the bacterial ribosome [82]. This mechanism of resistance can only be overcome by using an antimicrobial agent from a different class.

Inhibitors of DNA replication

The quinolones are the most recent addition to the armamentarium against community-acquired respiratory tract infections. These agents have a broad spectrum of activity and exert an antimicrobial effect by interfering with DNA replication, and subsequently, reproduction.

The bacterial chromosome is a circular molecule of DNA, which is large relative to the size of the bacterium. Supercoiling is an integral process conducive to bacterial homeostasis, in which circular DNA is tightly twisted into a compact size and shape; however, replication cannot occur when DNA is supercoiled. Two enzymes important in the replication process are DNA gyrase and topoisomerase IV, which are somewhat similar with respect to the DNA binding sites. DNA gyrase is responsible for relieving the supercoil in DNA to allow for the replication process to take place; the two subunits for this enzyme are encoded by the *gyrA* and *gyrB* genes on the bacterial chromosome [97]. During replication, two DNA gyrase enzymes bind with double-stranded DNA; subsequently, the DNA is spliced, allowing the supercoils to be passed through the splice for unwinding (Fig. 16) [79]. The process facilitated by DNA gyrase is reversible in that this enzyme both relieves supercoiling before replication and introduces super-coiling once the replication process is complete. Topoisomerase IV is the enzyme responsible for separating the two daughter strands of DNA once

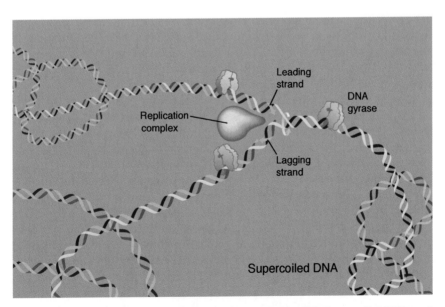

Fig. 16. DNA gyrase function, showing DNA gryase relieving coils of supercoiled DNA, and recoiling DNA after replication. Quinolones block the attachment site of DNA gyrase to DNA. (Copyright Michael R. Jacobs, MD, PhD, Cleveland, OH; used with permission.)

the replication process is complete; this enzyme is encoded by the *parC* and *parE* genes on the bacterial chromosome [98,99].

Because of the structural similarities between DNA gyrase and topoisomerase IV, both enzymes are targets to which quinolones bind to exert an antimicrobial effect [100–102]. Many of the older quinolones bind preferentially with DNA gyrase over topoisomerase IV; however, the newer quinolones tend to bind equally to both enzymes [100]. These agents form a complex between the antibiotic, enzyme (DNA gyrase or topoisomerase IV), and double-stranded DNA, which blocks the activity of the respective enzyme and also prohibits the release of the enzyme from the DNA strand, thereby preventing subsequent DNA replication. In other words, the action of quinolones is two-fold: they inhibit enzyme function and they lock the enzyme onto the DNA and prevent it from moving through the replication fork. The inhibition of DNA gyrase leads to DNA double-strand breakage, which ultimately has a bacteriocidal effect due to accumulation of toxic products. In the case of topoisomerase IV, the effect of quinolones (ie, prohibiting the separation of the two daughter DNA strands) occurs late in the bacterial life cycle, resulting in a slow stop in replication [102].

Resistance to quinolones among strains of *S pneumoniae* and *H influenzae* occurs via alterations in the genes encoding for DNA gyrase or topoisomerase IV. Alterations in certain sections of the genes encoding for DNA gyrase and topoisomerase IV, called the quinolone resistance determining region (QRDR), result in altered affinity between quinolones and the target to which these agents bind to exert an antimicrobial effect [100]. These alterations can occur via spontaneous mutations (ie, de novo) or via the acquisition of DNA from other bacteria, and the sequence in which the alterations occur affects the level of resistance. Depending on the specific quinolone antibiotic, alterations in either *parC* or *gyrA* result in low-level resistance; however, alterations in both genes results in high-level resistance to quinolones [101,103]. Resistance via alterations in *parC* or *gyrA* cannot be overcome by using higher dosages of quinolones; however, the newer quinolones are potent antibiotics, and the prevalence of resistance among clinical strains of *S pneumoniae* and *H influenzae* is low [38]. However, spontaneous quinolone-resistant mutants are readily selected in vitro by exposure to quinolones, and this has resulted in development of considerable resistance to this drug class in other species [104,105].

Certain strains of *S pneumoniae* also use an antibiotic efflux pump as a means of resistance to quinolones [106]. An efflux pump (NorA) encoded by the *norA* gene in *Staphylococcus aureus* has been demonstrated to result in high-level resistance to quinolones, such as norfloxacin [107]. Although the NorA pump has not yet been documented among clinical strains of pneumococci, a similar efflux protein, PmrA (pneumococcal multidrug resistance protein), has recently been reported [108]. This study, evaluating efflux pumps among *S pneumoniae*, has suggested that PmrA is an intrinsic protein that is upregulated among resistant strains [108]. Thus, resistance via this mechanism is most likely attributable to a de novo process (ie, spontaneous mutation), rather than acquisition. Among strains of pneumococci, the PmrA efflux pump affects ciprofloxacin more than other quinolones, such as levofloxacin or moxifloxacin, and it currently is not known whether higher quinolone dosages are effective in overcoming this mechanism of resistance.

Folic acid metabolism inhibitors

Trimethoprim and sulfamethoxazole (used alone or in combination) exert an antimicrobial effect by interfering with cellular metabolism and replication; more specifically, these agents block the production of tetrahydrofolate. Tetrahydrofolate is an important cofactor in many cellular reactions, supplying single carbon moieties for the production of thymidylate, purine nucleotides, methionine, serine, glycine, and other compounds [109]. During normal cellular metabolism, dihydrofolate is reduced to tetrahydrofolate by an enzyme called dihydrofolate reductase (DHFR) [110]. By inhibiting the production of tetrahydrofolate, the bacterial cells die because the lack of thymine prevents DNA replication [111]. Trimethoprim is a substrate analog of dihydrofolate and blocks the reduction of dihydrofolate to tetrahydrofolate by DHFR, whereas sulfamethoxazole is a substrate analog of para-aminobenzoic acid, which is involved in the production of dihydropteroate, a precursor compound of dihydrofolate [110]. Thus, the use of these compounds in combination limits the production of dihydrofolate and prevents the conversion from dihydrofolate to tetrahydrofolate (Fig. 17). Both compounds, trimethoprim and sulfamethoxazole, selectively inhibit bacterial metabolism with little toxicity to humans because humans do not synthesize folic acid, rather, the necessary levels of folic acid are obtained from dietary sources.

Resistance to trimethoprim among strains of S pneumoniae occurs via alteration in the affinity between trimethoprim and DHFR. The decreased affinity is the result of altered genes that encode for DHFR, which often are carried on plasmids or transposons and probably originated from closely related bacteria. Studies have shown that substitutions in the amino acid sequence of DHFR result in resistance to trimethoprim without affecting the affinity of the natural substrates [112–114]. Resistance to sulfamethoxazole among strains of S pneumoniae is the result of a genetic mutation that causes alterations in dihydropteroate synthase [115]. Resistance to trimethoprim/sulfamethoxazole among strains of H influenzae is caused by an increase in the production of DHFR with altered affinity for trimethoprim [116]. Resistance to trimethoprim/sulfamethoxazole also has been noted among strains of M catarrhalis., which is intrinsically resistant to trimethoprim [117].

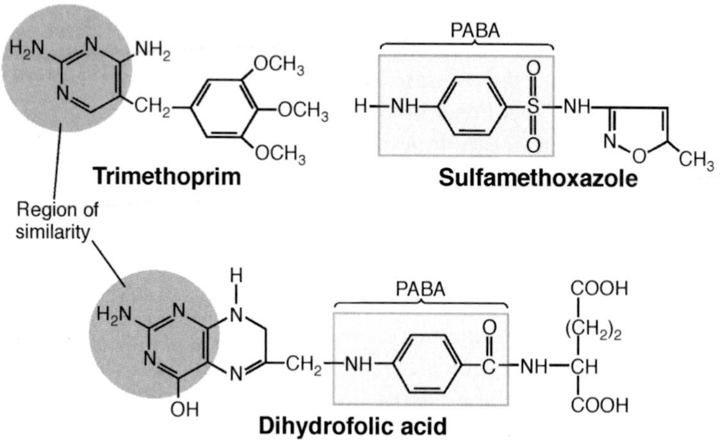

Fig. 17. Mechanism of action of trimethoprim and sulfonamides is by mimicry of dihydrofolic acid components, blocking the enzymes involved in conversion of PABA to dihydrofolic acid, and dihydrofolic acid to tetrahydropholic acid, the active form of the enzyme. (Copyright Michael R. Jacobs, MD, PhD, Cleveland, OH; used with permission.)

Summary

The advent of resistance occurred shortly after antibiotics were first used in the clinical setting, and since that time, resistance among the predominant pathogens has been demonstrated to every antibiotic agent used for the treatment of community-acquired respiratory tract infections. However, it has only been within the past decade that antibiotic resistance has represented a significant threat to health care and public health in general. Community-acquired respiratory tract infections represent one of the most common reasons for which patients seek medical attention, and although many of these cases are nonbacterial, antibiotics are frequently prescribed. The excessive use of antibiotics for patients and for other uses (eg, agriculture) has applied a tremendous selective pressure on bacteria, fostering the growth and progression of resistant organisms. As a result, the effectiveness of many of the antibiotics has been jeopardized.

To effectively combat the problem of antibiotic resistance, several efforts have been put forth to educate health care providers on the means for overcoming resistance and preventing its progression. Selecting appropriate antibiotic therapy for patients with a bacterial community-acquired respiratory tract infection requires a thorough understanding of the mechanisms of action of the various antibiotics and the mechanisms of resistance used by these pathogens. Currently, the available antibiotic agents can be classified into one of four categories, inhibitors of: cell wall synthesis and maintenance, protein synthesis, DNA replication, and folic acid metabolism. Similarly, there are three general mechanisms of resistance used among bacteria: enzymatic inactivation of the antibiotic (eg, β-lactamases), efflux pumps, and alteration in the target to which the antibiotic binds.

An understanding of the mechanisms of resistance used by respiratory tract pathogens is important because it can influence treatment decisions. For example, resistance to β-lactams and macrolides occurs via alteration in the respective target binding site (PBPs and ribosomes). Resistance to β-lactams via PBP alterations can be overcome by using β-lactams with greater activity against *S pneumoniae* or by increasing the antibiotic dose, whereas resistance to macrolides via alterations in ribosomes or an efflux pump cannot be overcome by using higher doses of macrolides. Similarly, resistance to β-lactams among strains of *H influenzae* cannot be overcome by using higher β-lactam doses, but it can be overcome by using a combination β-lactam with a β-lactamase inhibitor, or by using β-lactams that are stable in the presence of β-lactamases. In many cases, overcoming resistance requires the use of agents from another antibiotic class. However, because few agents with novel mechanisms of action are being developed, it requires careful consideration of agents from the existing antibiotic armamentarium.

References

[1] Dagan R, Abramson O, Leibovitz E, et al. Impaired bacteriologic response to oral cephalosporins in acute otitis media caused by pneumococci with intermediate resistance to penicillin. Pediatr Infect Dis J 1996;15(11):980–5.

[2] Dagan R, Leibovitz E, Greenberg D, Yagupsky P, Fliss DM, Leiberman A. Early eradication of pathogens from middle ear fluid during antibiotic treatment of acute otitis media is associated with improved clinical outcome. Pediatr Infect Dis J 1998;17(9): 776–82.

[3] Dagan R, Johnson CE, McLinn S, et al. Bacteriologic and clinical efficacy of amoxicillin/clavulanate vs. azithromycin in acute otitis media. Pediatr Infect Dis J 2000;19(2):95–104.

[4] Brook I, Gober AE. Microbiologic characteristics of persistent otitis media. Arch Otolaryngol Head Neck Surg 1998;124(12):1350–2.

[5] Pallares R, Linares J, Vadillo M, et al. Resistance to penicillin and cephalosporin and mortality from severe pneumococcal pneumonia in Barcelona, Spain. N Engl J Med 1995; 333(8):474–80.

[6] Friedland IR. Comparison of the response to antimicrobial therapy of penicillin-resistant and penicillin-susceptible pneumococcal disease. Pediatr Infect Dis J 1995;14(10):885–90.

[7] Buckingham SC, Brown SP, Joaquin VH. Breakthrough bacteremia and meningitis during treatment with cephalosporins parenterally for pneumococcal pneumonia. J Pediatr 1998; 132(1):174–6.

[8] Dowell SF, Butler JC, Giebink GS, et al. Acute otitis media: management and surveillance in an era of pneumococcal resistance–a report from the drug-resistant *Streptococcus pneumoniae* Therapeutic Working Group. Pediatr Infect Dis J 1999;18(1):1–9.

[9] Turett GS, Blum S, Fazal BA, Justman JE, Telzak EE. Penicillin resistance and other predictors of mortality in pneumococcal bacteremia in a population with high human immunodeficiency virus seroprevalence. Clin Infect Dis 1999;29(2):321–7.

[10] Feikin DR, Schuchat A, Kolczak M, et al. Mortality from invasive pneumococcal pneumonia in the era of antibiotic resistance, 1995–1997. Am J Public Health 2000;90(2): 223–9.

[11] Scott JA, Hall AJ, Muyodi C, et al. Aetiology, outcome, and risk factors for mortality among adults with acute pneumonia in Kenya. Lancet 2000;355(9211):1225–30.

[12] Metlay JP, Hofmann J, Cetron MS, et al. Impact of penicillin susceptibility on medical outcomes for adult patients with bacteremic pneumococcal pneumonia. Clin Infect Dis 2000;30(3):520–8.

[13] Garcia-Bustos J, Tomasz A. A biological price of antibiotic resistance: major changes in the peptidoglycan structure of penicillin-resistant pneumococci. Proc Natl Acad Sci USA 1990;87(14):5415–9.

[14] Magnusdottir AB, Hermansson A, Melhus A. Experimental study of the virulence of Streptococcus pneumoniae with reduced susceptibility to penicillin. Int J Pediatr Otorhinolaryngol 2000;55(1):1–9.

[15] Rocha P, Baleeiro C, Tunkel AR. Impact of antimicrobial resistance on the treatment of invasive pneumococcal infections. Curr Infect Dis Rep 2000;2(5):399–408.

[16] Winston LG, Perlman JL, Rose DA, Gerberding JL. Penicillin-nonsusceptible Streptococcus pneumoniae at San Francisco General Hospital. Clin Infect Dis 1999;29(3):580–5.

[17] Low DE, Kellner JD, Wright GD. Superbugs: how they evolve and minimize the cost of resistance. Curr Infect Dis Rep 1999;1(5):464–9.

[18] Andersson DI, Levin BR. The biological cost of antibiotic resistance. Curr Opin Microbiol 1999;2(5):489–93.

[19] Levy SB. The challenge of antibiotic resistance. Sci Am 1998;278(3):46–53.

[20] Salyers AA, Amabile-Cuevas CF. Why are antibiotic resistance genes so resistant to elimination? Antimicrob Agents Chemother 1997;41(11):2321–5.

[21] Lenski RE. Bacterial evolution and the cost of antibiotic resistance. Int Microbiol 1998; 1(4):265–70.

[22] McCaig LF, Hughes JM. Trends in antimicrobial drug prescribing among office-based physicians in the United States. JAMA 1995;273(3):214–9.

[23] Schappert SM. Ambulatory care visits to physician offices, hospital outpatient departments, and emergency departments: United States, 1997. Vital Health Stat 13 1999;143: i–iv, 1–39.

[24] Dowell SF, Schwartz B. Resistant pneumococci: protecting patients through judicious use of antibiotics. Am Fam Physician 1997;55(5):1647–54, 1657–8.

[25] Dowell SF, Marcy SM, Phillips WR, Gerber MA, Schwartz B. Principles of judicious use of antimicrobial agents for pediatric upper respiratory tract infections. Pediatrics 1998;101: 163–5.

[26] McCaig LF, Besser RE, Hughes JM. Decline in pediatric antimicrobial drug prescribing among office-based physicians in the United states, 1989–1998. Presented at 38th Infectious Disease Society of America Annual Meeting. New Orleans, Louisiana, September 2000.

[27] Heffelfinger JD, Dowell SF, Jorgensen JH, et al. Management of community-acquired pneumonia in the era of pneumococcal resistance: a report from the Drug-Resistant Streptococcus pneumoniae Therapeutic Working Group. Arch Intern Med 2000;160(10): 1399–408.

[28] Antimicrobial treatment guidelines for acute bacterial rhinosinusitis. Sinus and Allergy Health Partnership. Otolaryngol Head Neck Surg 2000;123(1 Pt 2):5–31.

[29] Bartlett JG, Dowell SF, Mandell LA, File TM Jr, Musher DM, Fine MJ. Practice guidelines for the management of community-acquired pneumonia in adults. Infectious Diseases Society of America. Clin Infect Dis 2000;31(2):347–82.

[30] Mandell LA, Bartlett JG, Dowell SF, File TM Jr, Musher DM, Whitney C. Update of practice guidelines for the management of community-acquired pneumonia in immuno-competent adults. Clin Infect Dis 2003;37(11):1405–33.

[31] Anon JB, Jacobs MR, Poole MD, et al. Antimicrobial treatment guidelines for acute bacterial rhinosinusitis. Otolaryngol Head Neck Surg 2004;130(1 Suppl):1–45.

[32] Barnett ED, Klein JO. The problem of resistant bacteria for the management of acute otitis media. Pediatr Clin North Am 1995;42(3):509–17.

[33] Jacobs MR. Increasing antibiotic resistance among otitis media pathogens and their susceptibility to oral agents based on pharmacodynamic parameters. Pediatr Infect Dis J 2000;19(5 Suppl):S47–55 [discussion: S55–6].

[34] Appelbaum PC. Antimicrobial resistance in *Streptococcus pneumoniae*: an overview. Clin Infect Dis 1992;15(1):77–83.

[35] Jacobs MR, Appelbaum PC. Antibiotic-resistant pneumococci. Rev Med Microbiol 1995; 6:77–93.

[36] Doern GV. Trends in antimicrobial susceptibility of bacterial pathogens of the respiratory tract. Am J Med 1995;99(6B):3S–7S.

[37] Jacobs MR, Bajaksouzian S, Zilles A, Lin G, Pankuch GA, Appelbaum PC. Susceptibilities of *Streptococcus pneumoniae* and *Haemophilus influenzae* to 10 oral antimicrobial agents based on pharmacodynamic parameters: 1997 US Surveillance study. Antimicrob Agents Chemother 1999;43(8):1901–8.

[38] Jacobs MR. Worldwide trends in antimicrobial resistance among common respiratory tract pathogens in children. Pediatr Infect Dis J 2003;22(8 Suppl):S109–19.

[39] Appelbaum PC, Bhamjee A, Scragg JN, Hallett AF, Bowen AJ, Cooper RC. *Streptococcus pneumoniae* resistant to penicillin and chloramphenicol. Lancet 1977;2(8046):995–7.

[40] Jacobs MR, Koornhof HJ, Robins-Browne RM, et al. Emergence of multiply resistant pneumococci. N Engl J Med 1978;299(14):735–40.

[41] Caputo GM, Appelbaum PC, Liu HH. Infections due to penicillin-resistant pneumococci. Clinical, epidemiologic, and microbiologic features. Arch Intern Med 1993;153(11):1301–10.

[42] Butler JC, Hofmann J, Cetron MS, Elliott JA, Facklam RR, Breiman RF. The continued emergence of drug-resistant *Streptococcus pneumoniae* in the United States: an update from the Centers for Disease Control and Prevention's Pneumococcal Sentinel Surveillance System. J Infect Dis 1996;174(5):986–93.

[43] Ronchetti MP, Zilles A, Appelbaum PC, Jacobs MR. Susceptibility of current and archived otitis media isolates of *Streptococcus pneumoniae*, *Haemophilus influenzae*, and *Moraxella catarrhalis* to contemporary oral agents. Presented at: 38th Interscience Conference on ANtimicrobial Agents and Chemotherapy. San Diego, September 1998.

[44] Fasola EL, Bajaksouzian S, Appelbaum PC, Jacobs MR. Variation in erythromycin and clindamycin susceptibilities of *Streptococcus pneumoniae* by four test methods. Antimicrob Agents Chemother 1997;41(1):129–34.

[45] Sutcliffe J, Tait-Kamradt A, Wondrack L. *Streptococcus pneumoniae* and *Streptococcus pyogenes* resistant to macrolides but sensitive to clindamycin: a common resistance pattern mediated by an efflux system. Antimicrob Agents Chemother 1996;40(8):1817–24.

[46] Chen DK, McGeer A, de Azavedo JC, Low DE. Decreased susceptibility of *Streptococcus pneumoniae* to fluoroquinolones in Canada. Canadian Bacterial Surveillance Network. N Engl J Med 1999;341(4):233–9.

[47] Neu HC. The crisis in antibiotic resistance. Science 1992;257(5073):1064–73.

[48] Cohen ML. Epidemiology of drug resistance: implications for a post-antimicrobial era. Science 1992;257(5073):1050–5.

[49] Ochman H, Lawrence JG, Groisman EA. Lateral gene transfer and the nature of bacterial innovation. Nature 2000;405(6784):299–304.

[50] Mazel D, Davies J. Antibiotic resistance in microbes. Cell Mol Life Sci 1999;56(9–10): 742–54.

[51] Ziebuhr W, Ohlsen K, Karch H, Korhonen T, Hacker J. Evolution of bacterial pathogenesis. Cell Mol Life Sci 1999;56(9–10):719–28.

[52] Bennett PM. Integrons and gene cassettes: a genetic construction kit for bacteria. J Antimicrob Chemother 1999;43(1):1–4.

[53] Courvalin P, Carlier C. Transposable multiple antibiotic resistance in *Streptococcus pneumoniae*. Mol Gen Genet 1986;205(2):291–7.

[54] Vijayakumar MN, Priebe SD, Guild WR. Structure of a conjugative element in *Streptococcus pneumoniae*. J Bacteriol 1986;166(3):978–84.

[55] Chambers HF. Penicillin-binding protein-mediated resistance in pneumococci and staphylococci. J Infect Dis 1999;179(Suppl 2):S353–9.
[56] Massova I, Mobashery S. Structural and mechanistic aspects of evolution of beta-lactamases and penicillin-binding proteins. Curr Pharm Des 1999;5(11):929–37.
[57] Ghuysen JM. Molecular structures of penicillin-binding proteins and beta-lactamases. Trends Microbiol 1994;2(10):372–80.
[58] Blumberg PM, Strominger JL. Interaction of penicillin with the bacterial cell: penicillin-binding proteins and penicillin-sensitive enzymes. Bacteriol Rev 1974;38(3):291–335.
[59] Hakenbeck R, Grebe T, Zahner D, Stock JB. beta-lactam resistance in *Streptococcus pneumoniae:* penicillin-binding proteins and non-penicillin-binding proteins. Mol Microbiol 1999;33(4):673–8.
[60] Hakenbeck R, Kaminski K, Konig A, et al. Penicillin-binding proteins in beta-lactam-resistant *streptococcus pneumoniae*. Microb Drug Resist 1999;5(2):91–9.
[61] Hasegawa K, Yamamoto K, Chiba N, et al. Diversity of ampicillin-resistance genes in *Haemophilus influenzae* in Japan and the United States. Microb Drug Resist 2003;9(1): 39–46.
[62] Laible G, Hakenbeck R. Five independent combinations of mutations can result in low-affinity penicillin-binding protein 2x of *Streptococcus pneumoniae*. J Bacteriol 1991;173(21): 6986–90.
[63] Nagai K, Shibasaki Y, Hasegawa K, et al. Evaluation of PCR primers to screen for *Streptococcus pneumoniae* isolates and beta-lactam resistance, and to detect common macrolide resistance determinants. J Antimicrob Chemother 2001;48(6):915–8.
[64] Sibold C, Henrichsen J, Konig A, Martin C, Chalkley L, Hakenbeck R. Mosaic pbpX genes of major clones of penicillin-resistant *Streptococcus pneumoniae* have evolved from pbpX genes of a penicillin-sensitive Streptococcus oralis. Mol Microbiol 1994;12(6): 1013–23.
[65] Filipe SR, Tomasz A. Inhibition of the expression of penicillin resistance in *Streptococcus pneumoniae* by inactivation of cell wall muropeptide branching genes. Proc Natl Acad Sci USA 2000;97(9):4891–6.
[66] Mason EO, Lamberth L, Lichenstein R, Kaplan SL. Distribution of *Streptococcus pneumoniae* resistant to penicillin in the USA and in-vitro susceptibility to selected oral antibiotics. J Antimicrob Chemother 1995;36(6):1043–8.
[67] Thornsberry C, Ogilvie PT, Holley HP Jr, Sahm DF. Survey of susceptibilities of *Streptococcus pneumoniae, Haemophilus influenzae*, and *Moraxella catarrhalis* isolates to 26 antimicrobial agents: a prospective US study. Antimicrob Agents Chemother 1999;43(11): 2612–23.
[68] Bryan CS, Talwani R, Stinson MS. Penicillin dosing for pneumococcal pneumonia. Chest 1997;112(6):1657–64.
[69] Harrison CJ, Welch DF. Middle ear effusion amoxicillin concentrations in acute otitis media. Pediatr Infect Dis J 1998;17(7):657–8.
[70] Seikel K, Shelton S, McCracken GH Jr. Middle ear fluid concentrations of amoxicillin after large dosages in children with acute otitis media. Pediatr Infect Dis J 1998;17(10):969–70.
[71] Massova I, Mobashery S. Kinship and diversification of bacterial penicillin-binding proteins and beta-lactamases. Antimicrob Agents Chemother 1998;42(1):1–17.
[72] Jordens JZ, Slack MP. *Haemophilus influenzae:* then and now. Eur J Clin Microbiol Infect Dis 1995;14(11):935–48.
[73] Rubin LG, Medeiros AA, Yolken RH, Moxon ER. Ampicillin treatment failure of apparently beta-lactamase-negative *Haemophilus influenzae* type b meningitis due to novel beta-lactamase. Lancet 1981;2(8254):1008–10.
[74] Wallace RJ Jr, Steingrube VA, Nash DR, et al. BRO beta-lactamases of *Branhamella catarrhalis* and *Moraxella subgenus Moraxella*, including evidence for chromosomal beta-lactamase transfer by conjugation in *B. catarrhalis, M. nonliquefaciens*, and *M. lacunata*. Antimicrob Agents Chemother 1989;33(11):1845–54.

[75] Bush K. Beta-lactamase inhibitors from laboratory to clinic. Clin Microbiol Rev 1988;1(1): 109–23.

[76] Rolinson GN. Evolution of beta-lactamase inhibitors. Rev Infect Dis 1991;13(Suppl 9): S727–32.

[77] Ng WL, Kazmierczak KM, Robertson GT, Gilmour R, Winkler ME. Transcriptional regulation and signature patterns revealed by microarray analyses of *Streptococcus pneumoniae* R6 challenged with sublethal concentrations of translation inhibitors. J Bacteriol 2003;185(1):359–70.

[78] Vazquez D, Monro RE. Effects of some inhibitors of protein synthesis on the binding of aminoacyl tRNA to ribosomal subunits. Biochim Biophys Acta 1967;142(1):155–73.

[79] Voet D, Voet JG, Pratt CW. Fundamentals of biochemistry. New York: John Wiley & Sons, Inc.; 1999. p. 723–931.

[80] Cocito C, Di Giambattista M, Nyssen E, Vannuffel P. Inhibition of protein synthesis by streptogramins and related antibiotics. J Antimicrob Chemother 1997;39(Suppl A):7–13.

[81] Mazzei T, Mini E, Novelli A, Periti P. Chemistry and mode of action of macrolides. J Antimicrob Chemother 1993;31(Suppl C):1–9.

[82] Widdowson CA, Klugman KP. Molecular mechanisms of resistance to commonly used non-betalactam drugs in *Streptococcus pneumoniae*. Semin Respir Infect 1999;14(3): 255–68.

[83] Tait-Kamradt A, Davies T, Cronan M, Jacobs MR, Appelbaum PC, Sutcliffe J. Mutations in 23S rRNA and ribosomal protein L4 account for resistance in pneumococcal strains selected in vitro by macrolide passage. Antimicrob Agents Chemother 2000;44(8):2118–25.

[84] Tait-Kamradt A, Davies T, Appelbaum PC, et al. Two new mechanisms of macrolide resistance in clinical strains of *Streptococcus pneumoniae* from Eastern Europe and North America. Antimicrob Agents Chemother 2000;44(12):3395–401.

[85] Shortridge VD, Flamm RK, Ramer N, Beyer J, Tanaka SK. Novel mechanism of macrolide resistance in *Streptococcus pneumoniae*. Diagn Microbiol Infect Dis 1996;26(2): 73–8.

[86] Tait-Kamradt A, Clancy J, Cronan M, et al. mefE is necessary for the erythromycin-resistant M phenotype in *Streptococcus pneumoniae*. Antimicrob Agents Chemother 1997; 41(10):2251–5.

[87] Lonks JR, Garau J, Gomez L, et al. Failure of macrolide antibiotic treatment in patients with bacteremia due to erythromycin-resistant *Streptococcus pneumoniae*. Clin Infect Dis 2002;35(5):556–64.

[88] Nagai K, Shibasaki Y, Hasegawa K. Rapid identification and penicillin and macrolide resistance screening of *Streptococcus pneumoniae* isolated from US and Europe by PCR. Presented at 40th Interscience Conference on Antimicrobial Agents and Chemotherapy. Toronto, Ontario, Canada, September 2000.

[89] Bryskier A. Ketolides-telithromycin, an example of a new class of antibacterial agents. Clin Microbiol Infect 2000;6(12):661–9.

[90] Davies TA, Ednie LM, Hoellman DM, Pankuch GA, Jacobs MR, Appelbaum PC. Antipneumococcal activity of ABT-773 compared to those of 10 other agents. Antimicrob Agents Chemother 2000;44(7):1894–9.

[91] Zhong P, Cao Z, Hammond R, et al. Induction of ribosome methylation in MLS-resistant *Streptococcus pneumoniae* by macrolides and ketolides. Microb Drug Resist 1999;5(3): 183–8.

[92] Sanchez L, Leranoz S, Puig M, Loren JG, Nikaido H, Vinas M. Molecular basis of antimicrobial resistance in non-typable *Haemophilus influenzae*. Microbiologia 1997;13(3): 309–14.

[93] Sanchez L, Pan W, Vinas M, Nikaido H. The acrAB homolog of *Haemophilus influenzae* codes for a functional multidrug efflux pump. J Bacteriol 1997;179(21):6855–7.

[94] Chopra I, Hawkey PM, Hinton M. Tetracyclines, molecular and clinical aspects. J Antimicrob Chemother 1992;29(3):245–77.

[95] Burdett V, Inamine J, Rajagopalan S. Heterogeneity of tetracycline resistance determinants in Streptococcus. J Bacteriol 1982;149(3):995–1004.

[96] Widdowson CA, Klugman KP, Hanslo D. Identification of the tetracycline resistance gene, tet(O), in Streptococcus pneumoniae. Antimicrob Agents Chemother 1996;40(12):2891–3.

[97] Wang JC. DNA topoisomerases. Annu Rev Biochem 1985;54:665–97.

[98] Kato J, Nishimura Y, Imamura R, Niki H, Hiraga S, Suzuki H. New topoisomerase essential for chromosome segregation in E. coli. Cell 1990;63(2):393–404.

[99] Kato J, Suzuki H, Ikeda H. Purification and characterization of DNA topoisomerase IV in Escherichia coli. J Biol Chem 1992;267(36):25676–84.

[100] Pan XS, Fisher LM. DNA gyrase and topoisomerase IV are dual targets of clinafloxacin action in Streptococcus pneumoniae. Antimicrob Agents Chemother 1998;42(11):2810–6.

[101] Tankovic J, Perichon B, Duval J, Courvalin P. Contribution of mutations in gyrA and parC genes to fluoroquinolone resistance of mutants of Streptococcus pneumoniae obtained in vivo and in vitro. Antimicrob Agents Chemother 1996;40(11):2505–10.

[102] Khodursky AB, Zechiedrich EL, Cozzarelli NR. Topoisomerase IV is a target of quinolones in Escherichia coli. Proc Natl Acad Sci USA 1995;92(25):11801–5.

[103] Munoz R, De La Campa AG. ParC subunit of DNA topoisomerase IV of Streptococcus pneumoniae is a primary target of fluoroquinolones and cooperates with DNA gyrase A subunit in forming resistance phenotype. Antimicrob Agents Chemother 1996;40(10): 2252–7.

[104] Davies TA, Kelly LM, Hoellman DB, et al. Activities and postantibiotic effects of gemifloxacin compared to those of 11 other agents against Haemophilus influenzae and Moraxella catarrhalis. Antimicrob Agents Chemother 2000;44(3):633–9.

[105] Davies TA, Kelly LM, Pankuch GA, Credito KL, Jacobs MR, Appelbaum PC. Antipneumococcal activities of gemifloxacin compared to those of nine other agents. Antimicrob Agents Chemother 2000;44(2):304–10.

[106] Baranova NN, Neyfakh AA. Apparent involvement of a multidrug transporter in the fluoroquinolone resistance of Streptococcus pneumoniae. Antimicrob Agents Chemother 1997;41(6):1396–8.

[107] Kaatz GW, Seo SM, Ruble CA. Efflux-mediated fluoroquinolone resistance in Staphylococcus aureus. Antimicrob Agents Chemother 1993;37(5):1086–94.

[108] Gill MJ, Brenwald NP, Wise R. Identification of an efflux pump gene, pmrA, associated with fluoroquinolone resistance in Streptococcus pneumoniae. Antimicrob Agents Chemother 1999;43(1):187–9.

[109] Hartman PG. Molecular aspects and mechanism of action of dihydrofolate reductase inhibitors. J Chemother 1993;5(6):369–76.

[110] Burchall JJ, Hitchings GH. Inhibitor binding analysis of dihydrofolate reductases from various species. Mol Pharmacol 1965;1(2):126–36.

[111] Then R, Angehrn P. Nature of the bacterial action of sulfonamides and trimethoprim, alone and in combination. J Infect Dis 1973;128(Suppl):498–501.

[112] Adrian PV, Klugman KP. Mutations in the dihydrofolate reductase gene of trimethoprim-resistant isolates of Streptococcus pneumoniae. Antimicrob Agents Chemother 1997;41(11):2406–13.

[113] Maskell JP, Sefton AM, Hall LM. Multiple mutations modulate the function of dihydrofolate reductase in trimethoprim-resistant Streptococcus pneumoniae. Antimicrob Agents Chemother 2001;45(4):1104–8.

[114] Pikis A, Donkersloot JA, Rodriguez WJ, Keith JM. A conservative amino acid mutation in the chromosome-encoded dihydrofolate reductase confers trimethoprim resistance in Streptococcus pneumoniae. J Infect Dis 1998;178(3):700–6.

[115] Maskell JP, Sefton AM, Hall LM. Mechanism of sulfonamide resistance in clinical isolates of Streptococcus pneumoniae. Antimicrob Agents Chemother 1997;41(10):2121–6.

[116] de Groot R, Chaffin DO, Kuehn M, Smith AL. Trimethoprim resistance in Haemophilus influenzae is due to altered dihydrofolate reductase(s). Biochem J 1991;274(Pt 3):657–62.

[117] Burman LG. The antimicrobial activities of trimethoprim and sulfonamides. Scand J Infect Dis 1986;18(1):3–13.

[118] Bluestone CD, Stephenson JS, Martin LM. Ten-year review of otitis media pathogens. Pediatr Infect Dis J 1992;11(8 Suppl):S7–11.

[119] Jacobs MR. Increasing importance of antibiotic-resistant *Streptococcus pneumoniae* in acute otitis media. Pediatr Infect Dis J 1996;15(10):940–3.

[120] Sethi S. Etiology and management of infections in chronic obstructive pulmonary disease. Clin Pulm Med 1999;6:327–32.

[121] Gwaltney JM Jr, Scheld WM, Sande MA, Sydnor A. The microbial etiology and antimicrobial therapy of adults with acute community-acquired sinusitis: a fifteen-year experience at the University of Virginia and review of other selected studies. J Allergy Clin Immunol 1992;90(3 Pt 2):457–61 [discussion 462].

[122] Berg O, Carenfelt C, Kronvall G. Bacteriology of maxillary sinusitis in relation to character of inflammation and prior treatment. Scand J Infect Dis 1988;20(5):511–6.

[123] Bartlett JG, Mundy LM. Community-acquired pneumonia. N Engl J Med 1995;333(24): 1618–24.

[124] Wald ER, Reilly JS, Casselbrant M, et al. Treatment of acute maxillary sinusitis in childhood: a comparative study of amoxicillin and cefaclor. J Pediatr 1984;104(2): 297–302.

CLINICS IN
LABORATORY
MEDICINE

Clin Lab Med 24 (2004) 455–475

Macrolide resistance in Streptococci and *Haemophilus influenzae*

Bülent Bozdogan, MD, PhD*,
Peter C. Appelbaum, MD, PhD

*Department of Pathology, Hershey Medical Center, 500 University Drive,
Pennsylvania State University, Hershey, PA 17033, USA*

Antimicrobial resistance is a growing problem among pathogens from respiratory tract infections. β-Lactam resistance rates are escalating among *Streptococcus pneumoniae* and *Haemophilus influenzae* [1]. Macrolides are increasingly used for the treatment of respiratory tract infections, but their utility is compromised by intrinsic and acquired resistance. This review analyses macrolide-resistance mechanisms and their worldwide distributions in *S pneumoniae, S pyogenes,* and *H influenzae.*

Mode of action of macrolides

Erythromycin is a natural antibiotic produced by *Streptomyces erytreus* isolated in the Philippines as a mixture of three antibiotics, erythromycin A, B, and C [2]. Among these structurally similar antibiotics, erythromycin A is used therapeutically. Researchers at Lilly Research Laboratories purified and commercialized erythromycin as "Ilotycin" in 1952. In the same year Haight and Finland [3] reported development of resistance to erythromycin in vivo during treatment of *Staphylococcus aureus* infection and in vitro by multistep selection in pneumococci, enterococci, and staphylococci. Erythromycin-resistant strains also were resistant to other antibiotics including carbomycin [4], spiramycin, oleandomycin, and streptogramin [5].

The macrolides are classified by the number of carbon atoms that the lactone ring contains. Erythromycin A contains a 14-membered lactone ring with two sugars attached, D-desosamine to the hydroxyl group at position 5 and L-cladinose at position 3 [6]. The absence of L-cladinose does not decrease the biologic activity of erythromycin but decreases the ability of the antibiotic

---

* Corresponding author.
E-mail address: bxb44@psu.edu (B. Bozdogan).

to induce ribosomal methylase-mediated resistance [7,8]. Clarithromycin is a semi-synthetic derivative of erythromycin by methylation at position 6 (6-O-methy-erythromycin) [9]. Azithromycin is a 15-membered synthetic derivative of erythromycin A and has a methyl group at position 9a [10]. There are also several 16-membered macrolides, which are natural products produced by S ambofaciens (spiramycin), S narbonensis var. josamyceticus (josamycin), S fradiae (tylosin), and S mycarofaciens (midecamycin) [7].

Macrolides bind to the peptidyl transferase center in the 23S RNA component of the 50S ribosomal subunit of bacteria, inhibiting protein synthesis. Mutations that generate resistance to erythromycin lie in close proximity within the peptidyl transferase loop. Indirect evidence has indicated that erythromycin binds to A2058 and A2059 [11]. The main action of erythromycin is the stimulation of the dissociation of peptidyl-tRNA during translocation [12]. This causes early release of polypeptide before the completion of whole protein synthesis. It was shown also that erythromycin inhibits ribosome assembly. Chittum and Champney [13] proposed that the hydroxyl group at position 6 of erythromycin interacts with lysine at position 63 of ribosomal protein L4 and inhibits fixation of this protein on 23S rRNA.

Spectrum of activity of macrolides

Macrolides have a narrow spectrum, mainly being active against Gram-positive bacteria and Gram-negative cocci. Most Gram-negative bacilli are naturally resistant to macrolides. Some Gram-negative bacteria such as Bordetella, Legionella, Campylobacter, Chlamydia, and Treponema spp. are more susceptible. The natural resistance in Gram-negative bacteria was thought to be the result of the impermeability of the external cell membrane to these hydrophobic antibiotics [14]. Recently efflux pumps have been identified in E coli as well as other Gram-negative bacteria and have been shown to have a role in the natural resistance of Gram-negative bacteria to macrolide antibiotics [15–17].

Macrolide resistance mechanisms

A variety of macrolide resistance mechanisms has been described, including ribosomal target site modification, either enzymatically or by mutation, key ribosomal protein mutations, and cell membrane–based efflux pumps.

Target modification

Methylation of 23S rRNA

The most common mechanism of macrolide resistance is the modification of 23S rRNA by mono or di-methylation of the adenine at position 2058 of the domain V of 23S rRNA (Fig. 1). Domain V of 23S rRNA contains the peptidyl transferase center. These methylases are encoded by *erm* (erythromycin resistance methylase) genes. The genes *erm*(B) and *erm*(TR) are most common *erm* genes in streptococci and enterococci, whereas *erm*(A) and *erm*(C) are common in staphylococci.

Ribosomal methylation confers resistance to macrolides, lincosamides, and streptogramin B and is called the mLS$_B$ phenotype. The proximity of the binding sites of these antibiotics on the ribosome may explain this cross-resistance [11]. The methylation of A2058 is thought to change the conformation of the ribosome, preventing these antibiotics from binding to the ribosome.

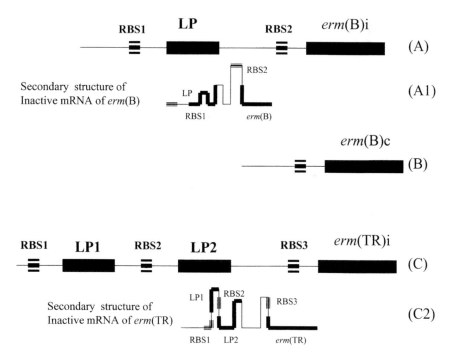

Fig. 1. Regulatory regions of inducible and constitutive *erm*(B) and inducible *erm*(TR) genes. Inducible *erm*(B) has one leader peptide (LP), and inverted repeat sequence which lets the mRNA to fold in its secondary structure. Without induction the mRNA in its inactive structure makes the RBS (ribosome binding site) and start codon of the *erm*(B) gene inaccessible to ribosome. In panel (*B*) the constitutively expressed *erm*(B) gene which doesn't have the regulatory region and leader peptide is represented. The *erm*(TR) gene has two leader peptides and 6 inverted repeats which may fold in three stem-loops and hide the RBS and start codon of *erm*(TR) from ribosome and translation (C1 and C2). (*Adapted from* Rosato A, Vicarini H and Leclercq R. Inducible or constitutive expression of resistance in clinical isolates of streptococci and enterococci cross-resistant to erythromycin and lincomycin. J Antimicrob Chemother 1999;43:559–62; with permission and Fines M, Gueudin M, Ramon A, Leclercq R. In vitro selection of resistance to clindamycin related to alterations in the attenuator of the *erm*(TR) gene of *Streptococcus pyogenes* UCN1 inducibly resistant to erythromycin. J Antimicrob Chemother 2001;48(3):411–6; with permission.)

The expression of *erm* genes may be constitutive or inducible [18]. If the resistance is constitutive, the strain is resistant to macrolides, lincosamides, and streptogramin B. When the resistance is inducible, the strain is susceptible to lincosamides and 16-membered macrolides, but resistant to 14- and 15-membered macrolides, including erythromycin, clarithromycin, and azithromycin. However, 14- and 15-membered macrolides are potent inducers of resistance in staphylococci and streptococci, whereas lincosamides are generally weaker inducers [19]. The induction properties of an antibiotic may depend on multiples factors, including the bacterial species, the structure of the antibiotic, and the regulatory region of the *erm* gene (Fig. 2) [20]. The inducible *erm*(C) gene is transcribed with a leader sequence with paired segments that may have a secondary hairpin structure. In this region there is an open reading frame, which encodes for a peptide of 19 amino acids, called leader peptide (LP). Without induction, the ribosome-binding site (RBS) of the *erm* gene is hidden in the hairpin so no translation occurs. The presence of an inducer changes the conformation of the messenger RNA by straightening out the hairpin bend, allowing methylase synthesis. In strains with *erm*(TR), the level of macrolide resistance is much lower than that with *erm*(B) (Table 1). Even after induction with

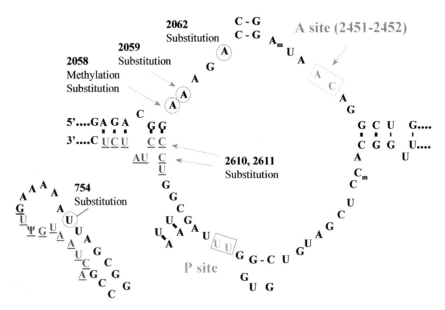

Fig. 2. Peptidyl transferase center in domain V and hairpin 35 of domain II in 23S rRNA. Bases that result in resistance when substituted are circled. Bases that may pair between domain II and domain V are underlined. The A (aminoacyl) and P (peptidyl) sites where aminoacyl- and peptidyl-tRNAs bind are marked. Methylation of adenine at position 2058 or substitution of bases at positions 2058, 2059, 2610, 2611 causes resistance to macrolides. Substitution at position 2062 causes resistance to 16-membered macrolides. Mutation at position 754 of domain II causes macrolide and ketolide resistance.

Table 1

Resistance mechanisms and susceptibilities of macrolide-resistant *S pneumoniae*, *S pyogenes*, and *H influenzae*

| | MICs (µg/mL) | | | | |
	Clindamycin	Erythromycin	Azithromycin	Telithromycin	References
S pneumoniae					
Susceptible	≤0.06	≤0.06	≤0.12	≤0.06	[54]
Methylase					
erm(B)	0.06–>64	2–>64	4–>64	0.004–2	[54,64]
erm(TR)	0.06–0.125	1–4	2–8	0.03	[81]
Efflux					
mef(A)	0.06–0.125	1–16	1–16	0.016–0.5	[54,64]
Mutation					
23S rRNA	0.78–12.5	≥64	>64	<0.016–0.5	[46–49,51,52]
L4	0.03–0.125	≥64	≥64	0.06–0.25	[47,48,54,64]
L22	≤0.06	1–4	2–4	0.25–0.5	[56,57]
S pyogenes					
Susceptible	≤0.06	≤0.06	≤0.12	≤0.06	[98]
Methylase					
erm(B)	0.125–>64	>64	>64	2–32	[111,112]
erm(TR)	0.06–>64	0.5–>64	2–>64	<0.008–8	[111,112]
Efflux					
mef(A)	0.03–0.125	4–16	8	0.125–0.5	[111,112]
Mutation					
23S rRNA	2	0.12	2	0.06	[35]
L4	0.06–0.125	0.5–2	1–8	0.06–0.125	[35,38,53]
L22	—	—	—	—	
H influenzae					
Efflux (intrinsic)	—	—	0.25–4	0.25–2	[42]
Mutation					
23S rRNA	—	—	>64	—	[42]
L4	—	—	8–64	—	[42]
L22	—	—	8–>64	—	[42]

Abbreviation: MIC, minimal inhibitory concentration.

erythromycin, the level of macrolide resistance does not increase as it does in strains with *erm*(A), *erm*(B), or *erm*(C). Erythromycin induction works but only increases the minimal inhibitory concentration level for clindamycin [21].

erm(B) gene. The inducible form of this gene has a regulatory region of approximately 318 base pairs, with a leader peptide of 36 amino acids and 14 inverted complementary segments that may fold into hairpins [22]. Deletion of leader peptide results in the *erm*(B) gene being constitutively expressed [23]. Rosato et al [19] analyzed the regulatory regions of *erm*(B) genes isolated from enterococci and streptococci with inducible or constitutive phenotypes. In constitutive strains they observed a shorter regulatory region without a control peptide or a mutation that generated a stop codon resulting in a shorter leader peptide (see Fig. 1). Smaller deletions in the leader peptide were detected in both inducible and constitutive strains. Among the regulatory region of three inducible *erm*(B) genes, two had complete leader peptide, whereas the third had a shorter leader peptide [19]. Deletion, insertion, or multiple point mutations in the regulatory regions of *erm*(A), *erm*(B), or *erm*(C) have been shown to cause constitutive expression of macrolide resistance [23–25].

erm(TR). This gene was described first in *S pyogenes* [26]. The sequence homology of the *erm*(TR) gene to *erm*(A) (82.5%) led the investigators to suggest that this gene encodes for a methylase and confers resistance to macrolides [26]. The *erm*(TR) gene, similar to *erm*(A), has two open reading frames upstream of the structural gene, which are predicted to encode 15- and 19-amino acid leader peptides (see Fig. 1). The *erm*(TR) gene has also been detected in *S pneumoniae* [27].

Mutations in 23S-RNA and ribosomal proteins

The mutations are responsible for conformational changes at the binding site of the macrolides, which decrease or inhibit their activity. Mutations in domains II or V of 23S rRNA or in ribosomal proteins L4 and L22, which confer high-level resistance to macrolides, have been detected in clinical strains of multiple species.

23S rRNA ribosomal alterations

Domain V of 23S rRNA is involved in transfer of the peptide during translocation. Most mutations that affect macrolide susceptibility are found in the peptidyl transferase center of 23S rRNA (see Fig. 2). The number of *rrnB* operons, which encode 23S rRNA, are different in various bacterial species. In *Halobacterium halobium* there is only one operon, whereas in *S pneumoniae* there are four, and in *E coli* there are eight operons. The expression of macrolide resistance depends on the number of copies of the operon that have mutated. The bacteria that have few copy numbers, such as *Helicobacter pylori* and Mycobacteria, easily develop resistance by mutation. A2058G or A2059G mutations were reported among clinical *H pylori* strains, which are resistant to macrolides [28]. A2058G, C, or U mutations in *Mycobacterium intracellulare* were found to be responsible for macrolide resistance [29]. Similarly, macrolide- and clindamycin-resistant *Brachyspira hydrosenteriae* had adenine at the same position replaced by uracil [30]. The activities of macrolides as well as ketolides are affected by U754A changes in domain II of 23S rRNA [31]. A deletion of 12 nucleotides in the same domain causes expression of a pentapeptide, called E-peptide, which confers resistance to erythromycin without altering its binding to a ribosome [32].

Ribosomal protein mutations

Ribosomal proteins L4 and L22 bind to domain I of 23S rRNA. Alterations in L4 and L22 cause conformation changes in domains II, III, and V of 23S rRNA [33]. The extended loops of ribosomal protein L4 and L22 are involved in the structure of the exit tunnel of the nascent peptide

[34]. Mutations that affect macrolide susceptibility occur in these loops [35,36]. The mutations in ribosomal protein L4 prevent the macrolide binding to the ribosome, and mutations in L22 neutralize the effects of macrolide binding [36]. Ribosomal protein alterations were detected in high-level macrolide-resistant *E coli* strains, with K63E mutations in L4 or $_{82}$MKR$_{84}$ deletion in L22 [37].

Macrolide efflux

Multidrug efflux mechanisms are widely disseminated among Gram-negative bacteria, and these efflux mechanisms have a role in the macrolide resistance of these strains [38]. Acquired efflux pumps, which are responsible for macrolide resistance, have been reported in Gram-positive bacteria. An ATP-dependent efflux pump encoded by *msrA* gene confers resistance in staphylococci to macrolides and streptogramins B [39]. This resistance phenotype is named MS$_B$ phenotype. Acquired macrolide efflux pumps, encoded by *mefA* and *mefE*, were identified in *S pyogenes* and *S pneumoniae*, respectively [40,41]. These genes have 90% of homology. Mef efflux pump confers resistance to 14- and 15-membered macrolides, but lincosamides and streptogramins remain active (see Table 1). This phenotype of resistance is named the M phenotype.

H influenzae isolates usually have an intrinsic macrolide efflux pump, and truly macrolide susceptible strains are rare. Less than 2% of clinical isolates of *H influenzae* are reported to have no macrolide resistance mechanisms [42]. Although most *H influenzae* isolates have an efflux mechanism, which accounts for the high MICs of macrolides, lincosamides, and streptogramins, they are still regarded as susceptible to azithromycin and clarithromycin according to current National Committee for Laboratory Standards (NCCLS) breakpoints [42].

Unusual macrolide resistance mechanisms in clinical isolates of streptococci and *H influenzae*

S pneumoniae

Most macrolide-resistant clinical isolates have either *erm*- or *mef*-mediated resistance. However, other resistance mechanisms are occasionally found. Macrolide-resistant *S pneumoniae*, produced by multistep selection in the laboratory, had 23S rRNA mutations, with the following substitutions: A2058G or U; A2059G; C2610U; or C2611A, G, or U; these changes were associated with streptogramin B or clindamycin resistance [43]. Laboratory-selected macrolide and ketolide-resistant strains have also been reported: one strain derived from a macrolide-susceptible parent had deletion of adenine at position 752 of 23S rRNA [44], and another mutant selected from parent with inducible *erm*(B) had a deletion in the regulatory region of *erm*(B) and a L94G mutation in L22 [45].

23S rRNA mutations have been reported in macrolide-resistant *S pneumoniae* isolates from patients (Fig. 3). The A2059G change is the most common mutation reported [46–49]. Other mutations, including A2058G [49] and C2611G [48,49], also have been reported. These mutations confer high-level macrolide resistance; however, clindamycin MICs are lower than in strains with *erm*-mediated ribosomal methylation of position 2058 (see Table 1). A clinical strain with A2062C mutation was susceptible to 14- and 15-membered macrolides but resistant to spiramycin and josamycin, which are 16-membered macrolides [50].

Occurrence of mutations in 23S rRNA during macrolide treatment has also been reported. The failure of azithromycin therapy in a case of community-acquired pneumococcal pneumonia was due to development of A2059G mutation [51]. Development of A2058T mutation during erythromycin treatment also resulted in clinical failure of erythromycin treatment in a patient with disseminated pneumococcal infection [52].

The most common mutation in 23S rRNA L4 protein among clinical *S pneumoniae* isolates is $_{69}GTI_{71}$ to TPS [46,53,54]. Substitution of these three amino acids is usually associated with high-level macrolide resistance, but clindamycin and telithromycin MICs remain low (see Table 1). Other

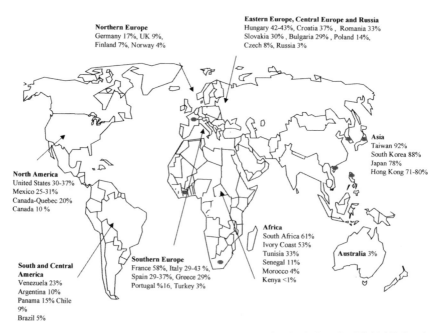

Fig. 3. Distribution of pneumococcal macrolide resistance in North America [79,92,93], South America [100,101], North Europe [67,102–104], South Europe [106,107], Eastern and Central Europe [54,64,105] and Russia [47], Asia [69,109], Africa [73,108], and Australia [110]. Countries with >50% macrolide resistance are marked with dots.

rare mutations have also been reported in L4, but their effect on macrolide resistance is not clear [55]. Insertion of six amino acids after position 71 in ribosomal protein L4 caused moderate increases in MICs of macrolides and telithromycin [46].

Macrolide resistance due to 23S rRNA L22 protein alteration is rare among clinical *S pneumoniae* strains. Two strains with tandem duplication of amino acids 103–107 in L22, with low-level macrolide MIC increases, have been reported [56]. Treatment failure during treatment of pneumococcal pneumonia with azithromycin was due to development of macrolide resistance by tandem duplication of six amino acids after position 102 in L22. This insertion was associated with higher MICs of erythromycin, azithromycin, and quinupristin/dalfopristin [57].

S pyogenes

Mutations in 23S rRNA or ribosomal protein L4 conferring resistance to macrolides have been reported in *S pyogenes*. Deletion of two amino acids, WR, at positions 65 and 66 occurred during treatment with azithromycin and midecamycin [53]. Other deletions or insertions in highly conserved regions of L4 protein have also been found in strains isolated from patients treated with azithromycin [58]. A two–amino acid insertion, KG, after position 69 in L4, and a C2611U substitution in domain V of 23S rRNA have been associated with macrolide resistance. These mutations alter the extended loop of the L4 protein. The $_{69}GTI_{71}$ to TPS mutation, which is common and confers high-level macrolide resistance in *S pneumoniae*, has not been observed in clinical *S pyogenes* strains. L4 mutations found in *S pyogenes* confer low-level macrolide resistance (see Table 1).

H influenzae

Ribosomal alterations confer high-level macrolide resistance in *H influenzae*. In vitro multistep selection with azithromycin and clarithromycin causes development of high-level macrolide resistance associated with ribosomal alterations [59]. These mutations occurred in 23R rRNA (A2059C or A2058G) and in L4 by deletion ($_{65}GR_{66}$, $_{66}RA_{67}$) or by substitution (G53A, G65D). Mutations were found in L22 ribosomal proteins of in vitro selected macrolide-resistant *H influenzae* by insertion (72KIFVEVA), by deletion (82M, $_{82}MKR_{85}$), or by substitution (R88P, A94E) [59]. Mutations in 23S rRNA confer high-level macrolide and clindamycin resistance. The level of resistance is relatively low with ribosomal protein mutations, and clindamycin MICs are not affected [59]. Clinical *H influenzae* strains with high-level macrolide resistance have similar alterations in 23S rRNA and ribosomal protein L4 and L22 by substitution, deletion, or insertion [42].

Epidemiology of resistance

Global survey studies have shown an increase in the resistance rates among streptococci [60]. Antibiotic consumption is correlated with antibiotic resistance among pathogenic bacteria, and some antibiotics such as macrolides are more powerful selectors of multidrug-resistant strains than others [61]. Macrolide resistance rates are increasing worldwide probably in parallel with the increased use of macrolides.

S pneumoniae

The highest prevalence of macrolide resistance is in Far Eastern countries. However, in the same continent, macrolide resistance rates between neighboring countries differ considerably, which may indicate that other factors, including macrolide consumption, may play a role in development of resistance. For example, macrolide resistance is 36% in the United States and 10% in Canada [62,63], 30% in Slovakia and 8% in the Czech Republic [64], 29% in Greece and 2% in Turkey [65,66], 58% in France and 16% to 17% in Germany [67,68].

In Asia the highest rates of macrolide resistance among clinical *S pneumoniae* strains are detected in Taiwan (92%), South Korea (88%), Japan (78%), and Hong Kong (71% to 80%) (see Fig. 3) [69,70]. In Europe the highest prevalence is found in Southern Europe, in France (48% to 58%), Spain (29% to 37%), Italy (29% to 43%), and Croatia (37%) [64,65,68,71]. However, resistance rates are relatively low in Northern Europe: Finland (7%), Norway (4%), the United Kingdom (9%), and Germany (17%) [48,67,72]. A high prevalence of macrolide resistance has been reported in some countries in Africa, such as South Africa (61%), Ivory Coast (53%), and Tunisia (33%) but it is lower in other countries, such as Senegal (11%), Morocco (4%), and Kenya (1%) [1,73].

The *mef*-encoded efflux mechanism is the most prevalent macrolide resistance mechanism in North America, except in Quebec, Canada, where *erm*(B) type resistance is the most common [74]. The efflux mechanism is also widespread in Asia, except for Hong Kong, where the MLS_B phenotype is dominant.

In France, almost 100% of the erythromycin-resistant isolates have the *erm*(B) gene [75]. Consumption of 16-membered macrolides like josamycin and spiramycin is thought to be the cause of the predominance of this resistance mechanism because the *mef*-encoded efflux pump is not active against 16-membered macrolides. Ribosomal methylation is the most common resistance mechanism in most European countries, except for Bulgaria and Russia, where the prevalence of *mef*-encoded efflux is higher [64].

The *erm*(TR) is a very rare resistance gene in *S. pneumoniae* in most parts of the world, but it is responsible for macrolide resistance in 13% of Australian strains [76]. Macrolide resistance by ribosomal mutation, which was very unusual a couple of years ago, is now a frequent resistance mechanism, especially in Eastern Europe (Table 2).

S pyogenes

Katz et al [77] have shown an association of increased macrolide resistance in S pyogenes with the increase in the number of prescriptions of newer macrolides, azithromycin and clarithromycin, in Canada. The macrolide-resistance rate, which was 2.1% in 1997, climbed to 14.4% in 2001 in Ontario [77,78]. In the United States, a recent study showed 5.5% of clinical strains were resistant to macrolides [79]. The level of macrolide resistance is often similar to that of S pneumoniae in many countries, such as Greece (31% to 38%), Spain (24%), and Italy (25% to 36%), where erythromycin resistance rates are high [80–84]. However, in France the macrolide-resistance rate of S pyogenes was 10%, which is low compared with that of S pneumoniae [85]. In Asia, macrolide resistance rates are high: 41% in South Korea and 26% in Hong Kong [70,86]. Resistance is lower in Northern Europe: 14% in Germany [55,67], 11% in Russia [47], 11% in Finland [87], and 7% in Belgium [88]. Turkey has a low level of macrolide resistance (3%) compared with Greece (31% to 38%), its neighbor [89]. In South America, low resistance rates have been reported, such as 8% in Argentina [90] and 2% in Brazil [91].

The most prevalent resistance mechanism was efflux in North America (Table 3) [92,93]. In Asia, such as in Taiwan and Japan, as well as in Australia, mef-encoded efflux is dominant [69,76], but in Hong Kong resistance by erm-encoded methylases was higher [70]. In Europe erm-encoded methylases are most common except for Greece, Spain, Croatia, and Bulgaria, where mef-encoded methylases were more frequent (see Table 3).

Macrolide resistance mechanisms and ketolides

S pneumoniae with erm genes are resistant to erythromycin and clarithromycin (14-membered macrolides) and azithromycin (15-membered macrolide) (Fig. 4). If the resistance mechanism is inducible, these strains are susceptible to clindamycin. However, it may not be safe to use clindamycin for treatment because clindamycin can induce resistance in pneumococci. Ketolides, such as telithromycin and cethromycin, do not appear to induce resistance and may be safe to use for treatment of infections caused by S pneumoniae with erm(B) [94]. However, rare strains with erm(B) have been resistant to telithromycin [64]. Telithromycin resistance of in vitro selected mutants is associated with L22 mutations and a shortened regulatory region [45]. Mutations in the second domain of 23S rRNA cause ketolide resistance [31]. The methylases encoded by erm(B) gene and some erm(TR) genes alter the activity of telithromycin against S pyogenes. The reason why the same gene has a different effect on S pneumoniae versus S pyogenes is unknown.

Table 2
Distribution of macrolide resistance (% of all isolates) and distribution of macrolide- resistance mechanisms in *S pneumoniae*

	Macrolide resistance (%)	erm(B)/MLS_B phenotype (%)	mef(A)/M phenotype (%)	erm(B) + mef(A) MLS_B phenotype (%)	erm(TR) genotype (%)	Mutation/ unknown	Reference
Americas							
United States	37	23	**64**				[76]
Canada-Quebec	20	58	**37**	4		1	[99]
Canada	8	46	**49**	3		2	[93]
Chile	—	43	**57**			—	[113]
Asia							
Korea	88	**43**	18	39			[114]
Hong Kong	80	25	63			2	[109]
Japan		**53**	42	3			[114]
Oceania							
New Zealand	—	33	5	62			[115]
Australia	—	40	40		13	7	[76]
Europe							
France	48	**97**	3				[71]
Greece	43	40	**58**			2	[80]
Croatia	35	**68**	32				[64]
Belgium	33	**91**	9			—	[88]
Italy	33	63	33	4			[116]
Romania	33	**97**	—			3	[64]
Slovakia	30	**81**				12	[64]
Bulgaria	29	41	**56**			3	[64]
Germany	17	50	50				[67]
Poland	14	**86**				14	[64]
Slovenia	11	**83**	17				[64]
Czech	8	**50**	37.5			12.5	[64]
Lithuania	7	50	50				[64]
Finland	7	38	**51**			11	[104]
Latvia	5	**100**					[64]
Russia	3	33	42			25	[47]

The results shown by (*) indicate prevalence of M and MLS_B phenotypes without genetic studies.

Table 3
Distribution of macrolide resistance (% of all isolates) and distribution of macrolide resistance mechanisms in *S pyogenes*

	Macrolide resistance (%)	*erm*(B)/i/cMLS$_B$ phenotype (%)	*erm*(TR)/iMLS$_B$ phenotype (%)	*mef*(A) M phenotype (%)	Mutation/ unknown	Reference
Americas						
Canada	14	5	3	**92**		[93]
Argentina	8	2	2	**96**		[90]
United States	5					[92]
Brazil	2		50	50		[91]
Asia						
Hong Kong	26	**42**	10	32	16	[70]
Taiwan	24	20		**80**		[69]
Japan	—	5	24	**71**		[76]
Oceania						
Australia	—			100		[76]
Europe						
Greece	38	1	45	**54**	—	[84]
Italy	36	**52**	12	35		[117]
Slovakia	25	7	**60**	33		[111]
Spain	24	2	2	**95**	1	[81]
Czech	17	**47**	**47**	6		[111]
Croatia	16	13	31	**56**		[111]
Germany	14	10	38	42	—	[67]
Russia	11	—	**89**	8	3	[47]
France	10	**45**	21	34		[85]
Romania	9	13	**50**	25	12	[111]
Lithuania	8	13	87	—		[111]
Belgium	7	**84**	—	16	—	[88]
Hungary	7	**76**	13		13	[111]
Slovenia	7	—	**86**	14	—	[111]
Bulgaria	5	—	40	**60**		[111]
Turkey	3	14	39	**47**		[89]
Latvia	1	—	100	—		[111]
Poland	1	—	100	—		[111]
Finland	—	4*	38*	61*		[87]

Results shown by (*) indicate prevalence of M and MLS$_B$ phenotypes without genetic studies. Macrolide resistance mechanism that dominates in each country is shown is bold.

H influenzae has an intrinsic resistance mechanism to macrolides by efflux as discussed earlier, and it does not seem to be appropriate to use macrolides for treatment of infections due to *H influenzae* [95,96]. Similarly, ketolide MICs against *H influenzae* are in the same range as those of azithromycin, so that ketolides also are likely to have little utility clinically for treatment of infections due to *H influenzae* [97].

Summary

Streptococcus pyogenes, *Streptococcus pneumoniae*, and *Haemophilus influenzae* are major bacterial pathogens of respiratory tract infections.

A. Azithromycin

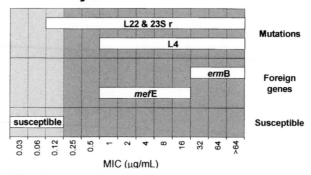

B. Clindamycin

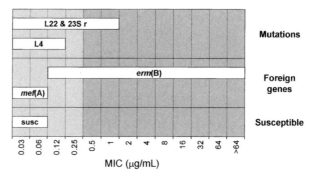

C. Telithromycin

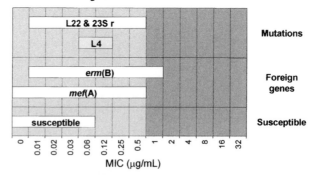

Fig. 4. The activities of azithromycin (*A*), clindamycin (*B*), and telithromycin (*C*) by resistance mechanism. (*A*) All mechanisms result in azithromycin resistance, as well as resistance to other macrolides (clarithromycin and erythromycin). (*B*) Clindamycin remains active if the resistance mechanism is due to *mef*-encoded resistance or most ribosomal protein alterations. (*C*) Except for rare cases of *erm*(B)-mediated resistance, telithromycin MICs against *S. pneumoniae* are low. (*Adapted from* Nagai K, Appelbaum PC, Davies TA, et al. Susceptibilities to telithromycin and six other agents and prevalence of macrolide resistance due to L4 ribosomal protein mutation among 992 pneumococci from 10 Central and Eastern European countries. Antimicrob Agents Chemother 2002;46:371–7; with permission.)

Macrolide resistance rates among streptococci are very high in Asia, Southern Europe, some of the countries in Eastern Europe, and in the United States but are relatively low in Northern Europe, Russia, South America, and Australia. The main macrolide-resistance mechanisms in streptococci are a *mef*-encoded efflux mechanism or macrolide ribosomal target modification by *erm*-encoded ribosomal methylases; occasionally resistance is associated with key mutations in 23S rRNA or in ribosomal proteins, L4 and L22. Virtually all isolates of *H influenzae* are intrinsically macrolide resistant, associated with an *acr*AB efflux mechanism similar to the efflux mechanism intrinsic to *Enterobacteriaceae*. Higher level macrolide resistance is occasionally found in *H influenzae* and is due to ribosomal mutations similar to those found in streptococci with this macrolide-resistance mechanism. Macrolide-resistance rates have been increasing worldwide in *S pyogenes* and *S pneumoniae*, and these increases have been associated with increased use of the newer macrolides.

References

[1] Jacobs MR, Felmingham D, Appelbaum PC, Gruneberg RN. The Alexander Project 1998–2000: susceptibility of pathogens isolated from community-acquired respiratory tract infection to commonly used antimicrobial agents. J Antimicrob Chemother 2003;52: 229–46.

[2] Haight TH, Finland M. Observations on mode of action of erythromycin. Proc Soc Exp Biol Med 1952;81:188–93.

[3] Haight TH, Finland M. Resistance of bacteria to erythromycin. Proc Soc Exp Biol Med 1952;81:183–8.

[4] Finland M, Wilcox C, Wright SS, Purcell EM. Cross resistance to antibiotics: effect of exposures of bacteria to carbomycin or erythromycin in vitro. Proc Soc Exp Biol Med 1952;81:725–9.

[5] Finland M, Jones WF Jr, Nichols RL. Development of resistance and cross-resistance in vitro to erythromycin, carbomycin, spiramycin, oleandomycin and streptogramin. Proc Soc Exp Biol Med 1956;93:388–93.

[6] Tadanier J, Martin JR, Egan RS, et al. Some chemical and stereochemical modifications of the erythromycin lactone rings. J Org Chem 1974;39:2495–501.

[7] Asselineau J, Zalta JP. Les antibiotiques; structure et exemples de mode d'action. Paris: Hermann; 1973.

[8] Rosato A, Vicarini H, Bonnefoy A, Chantot JF, Leclercq R. A new ketolide, HMR 3004, active against streptococci inducibly resistant to erythromycin. Antimicrob Agents Chemother 1998;42:1392–6.

[9] Neu HC. The development of macrolides: clarithromycin in perspective. J Antimicrob Chemother 1991;27(Suppl A):1–9.

[10] Fiese EF, Steffen SH. Comparison of the acid stability of azithromycin and erythromycin A. J Antimicrob Chemother 1990;25(Suppl A):39–47.

[11] Moazed D, Noller HF. Chloramphenicol, erythromycin, carbomycin and vernamycin B protect overlapping sites in the peptidyl transferase region of 23S ribosomal RNA. Biochimie 1987;69:879–84.

[12] Menninger JR, Otto DP. Erythromycin, carbomycin, and spiramycin inhibit protein synthesis by stimulating the dissociation of peptidyl-tRNA from ribosomes. Antimicrob Agents Chemother 1982;21:811–8.

[13] Chittum HS, Champney WS. Erythromycin inhibits the assembly of the large ribosomal subunit in growing Escherichia coli cells. Curr Microbiol 1995;30:273–9.

[14] Leclercq R, Courvalin P. Intrinsic and unusual resistance to macrolide, lincosamide, and streptogramin antibiotics in bacteria. Antimicrob Agents Chemother 1991;35: 1273–6.

[15] Elkins CA, Nikaido H. 3D structure of AcrB: the archetypal multidrug efflux transporter of Escherichia coli likely captures substrates from periplasm. Drug Resist Updat 2003;6: 9–13.

[16] Sanchez L, Leranoz S, Puig M, Loren JG, Nikaido H, Vinas M. Molecular basis of antimicrobial resistance in non-typable Haemophilus influenzae. Microbiologia 1997;13: 309–14.

[17] Sanchez L, Pan W, Vinas M, Nikaido H. The acrAB homolog of Haemophilus influenzae codes for a functional multidrug efflux pump. J Bacteriol 1997;179:6855–7.

[18] Weisblum B, Siddhikol C, Lai CJ, Demohn V. Erythromycin-inducible resistance in Staphylococcus aureus: requirements for induction. J Bacteriol 1971;106:835–47.

[19] Rosato A, Vicarini H, Leclercq R. Inducible or constitutive expression of resistance in clinical isolates of streptococci and enterococci cross-resistant to erythromycin and lincomycin. J Antimicrob Chemother 1999;43:559–62.

[20] Weisblum B. Insights into erythromycin action from studies of its activity as inducer of resistance. Antimicrob Agents Chemother 1995;39:797–805.

[21] Syrogiannopoulos GA, Grivea IN, Ednie LM, et al. Antimicrobial susceptibility and macrolide resistance inducibility of Streptococcus pneumoniae carrying erm(A), erm(B), or mef(A). Antimicrob Agents Chemother 2003;47:2699–702.

[22] Horinouchi S, Byeon WH, Weisblum B. A complex attenuator regulates inducible resistance to macrolides, lincosamides, and streptogramin type B antibiotics in Streptococcus sanguis. J Bacteriol 1983;154:1252–62.

[23] Martin B, Alloing G, Mejean V, Claverys JP. Constitutive expression of erythromycin resistance mediated by the ermAM determinant of plasmid pAM beta 1 results from deletion of 5' leader peptide sequences. Plasmid 1987;18:250–3.

[24] Murphy E. Nucleotide sequence of ermA, a macrolide-lincosamide-streptogramin B determinant in Staphylococcus aureus. J Bacteriol 1985;162:633–40.

[25] Lampson BC, Parisi JT. Naturally occurring Staphylococcus epidermidis plasmid expressing constitutive macrolide-lincosamide-streptogramin B resistance contains a deleted attenuator. J Bacteriol 1986;166:479–83.

[26] Seppala H, Skurnik M, Soini H, Roberts MC, Huovinen P. A novel erythromycin resistance methylase gene (ermTR) in Streptococcus pyogenes. Antimicrob Agents Chemother 1998;42:257–62.

[27] Syrogiannopoulos GA, Grivea IN, Tait-Kamradt A, et al. Identification of an erm(A) erythromycin resistance methylase gene in Streptococcus pneumoniae isolated in Greece. Antimicrob Agents Chemother 2001;45:342–4.

[28] Versalovic J, Shortridge D, Kibler K, et al. Mutations in 23S rRNA are associated with clarithromycin resistance in Helicobacter pylori. Antimicrob Agents Chemother 1996;40: 477–80.

[29] Meier A, Kirschner P, Springer B, et al. Identification of mutations in 23S rRNA gene of clarithromycin-resistant Mycobacterium intracellulare. Antimicrob Agents Chemother 1994;38:381–4.

[30] Karlsson M, Fellstrom C, Heldtander MU, Johansson KE, Franklin A. Genetic basis of macrolide and lincosamide resistance in Brachyspira (Serpulina) hyodysenteriae. FEMS Microbiol Lett 1999;172:255–60.

[31] Xiong L, Shah S, Mauvais P, Mankin AS. A ketolide resistance mutation in domain II of 23S rRNA reveals the proximity of hairpin 35 to the peptidyl transferase centre. Mol Microbiol 1999;31:633–9.

[32] Dam M, Douthwaite S, Tenson T, Mankin AS. Mutations in domain II of 23 S rRNA facilitate translation of a 23 S rRNA-encoded pentapeptide conferring erythromycin resistance. J Mol Biol 1996;259:1–6.

[33] Gregory ST, Dahlberg AE. Erythromycin resistance mutations in ribosomal proteins L22 and L4 perturb the higher order structure of 23 S ribosomal RNA. J Mol Biol 1999;289: 827–34.

[34] Zengel JM, Jerauld A, Walker A, Wahl MC, Lindahl L. The extended loops of ribosomal proteins L4 and L22 are not required for ribosome assembly or L4-mediated autogenous control. RNA 2003;9:1188–97.

[35] Malbruny B, Nagai K, Coquemont M, et al. Resistance to macrolides in clinical isolates of Streptococcus pyogenes due to ribosomal mutations. J Antimicrob Chemother 2002; 49:935–9.

[36] Gabashvili IS, Gregory ST, Valle M, et al. The polypeptide tunnel system in the ribosome and its gating in erythromycin resistance mutants of L4 and L22. Mol Cell 2001;8:181–8.

[37] Chittum HS, Champney WS. Ribosomal protein gene sequence changes in erythromycin-resistant mutants of Escherichia coli. J Bacteriol 1994;176:6192–8.

[38] Zgurskaya HI, Nikaido H. Multidrug resistance mechanisms: drug efflux across two membranes. Mol Microbiol 2000;37:219–25.

[39] Ross JI, Eady EA, Cove JH, Cunliffe WJ, Baumberg S, Wootton JC. Inducible erythromycin resistance in staphylococci is encoded by a member of the ATP-binding transport super-gene family. Mol Microbiol 1990;4:1207–14.

[40] Clancy J, Petitpas J, Dib-Hajj F, et al. Molecular cloning and functional analysis of a novel macrolide-resistance determinant, mefA, from Streptococcus pyogenes. Mol Microbiol 1996;22:867–79.

[41] Tait-Kamradt A, Clancy J, Cronan M, et al. mefE is necessary for the erythromycin-resistant M phenotype in Streptococcus pneumoniae. Antimicrob Agents Chemother 1997;41:2251–5.

[42] Peric M, Bozdogan B, Jacobs MR, Appelbaum PC. Effects of an efflux mechanism and ribosomal mutations on macrolide susceptibility of Haemophilus influenzae clinical isolates. Antimicrob Agents Chemother 2003;47:1017–22.

[43] Tait-Kamradt A, Davies T, Cronan M, Jacobs MR, Appelbaum PC, Sutcliffe J. Mutations in 23S rRNA and ribosomal protein L4 account for resistance in pneumococcal strains selected in vitro by macrolide passage. Antimicrob Agents Chemother 2000;44:2118–25.

[44] Canu A, Malbruny B, Coquemont M, Davies TA, Appelbaum PC, Leclercq R. Diversity of ribosomal mutations conferring resistance to macrolides, clindamycin, streptogramin, and telithromycin in Streptococcus pneumoniae. Antimicrob Agents Chemother 2002;46: 125–31.

[45] Walsh F, Willcock J, Amyes S. High-level telithromycin resistance in laboratory-generated mutants of Streptococcus pneumoniae. J Antimicrob Chemother 2003;52: 345–53.

[46] Tait-Kamradt A, Davies T, Appelbaum PC, et al. Two new mechanisms of macrolide resistance in clinical strains of Streptococcus pneumoniae from Eastern Europe and North America. Antimicrob Agents Chemother 2000;44:3395–401.

[47] Kozlov RS, Bogdanovitch TM, Appelbaum PC, et al. Antistreptococcal activity of telithromycin compared with seven other drugs in relation to macrolide resistance mechanisms in Russia. Antimicrob Agents Chemother 2002;46:2963–8.

[48] Pihlajamaki M, Kataja J, Seppala H, et al. Ribosomal mutations in Streptococcus pneumoniae clinical isolates. Antimicrob Agents Chemother 2002;46:654–8.

[49] Farrell DJ, Douthwaite S, Morrissey I, et al. Macrolide resistance by ribosomal mutation in clinical isolates of Streptococcus pneumoniae from the PROTEKT 1999–2000 study. Antimicrob Agents Chemother 2003;47:1777–83.

[50] Depardieu F, Courvalin P. Mutation in 23S rRNA responsible for resistance to 16-membered macrolides and streptogramins in Streptococcus pneumoniae. Antimicrob Agents Chemother 2001;45:319–23.

[51] Kays MB, Wack MF, Smith DW, Denys GA. Azithromycin treatment failure in community-acquired pneumonia caused by Streptococcus pneumoniae resistant to macrolides by a 23S rRNA mutation. Diagn Microbiol Infect Dis 2002;43:163–5.

[52] Butler JC, Lennox JL, McDougal LK, Sutcliffe JA, Tait-Kamradt A, Tenover FC. Macrolide-resistant pneumococcal endocarditis and epidural abscess that develop during erythromycin therapy. Clin Infect Dis 2003;36:e19–25.

[53] Bozdogan B, Appelbaum PC, Ednie L, Grivea IN, Syrogiannopoulos GA. Development of macrolide resistance by ribosomal protein L4 mutation in Streptococcus pyogenes during miocamycin treatment of an eight-year-old Greek child with tonsillopharyngitis. Clin Microbiol Infect 2003;9:966–9.

[54] Nagai K, Appelbaum PC, Davies TA, et al. Susceptibilities to telithromycin and six other agents and prevalence of macrolide resistance due to L4 ribosomal protein mutation among 992 Pneumococci from 10 Central and Eastern European countries. Antimicrob Agents Chemother 2002;46:371–7.

[55] Reinert RR, Wild A, Appelbaum P, Lutticken R, Cil MY, Al-Lahham A. Ribosomal mutations conferring resistance to macrolides in Streptococcus pneumoniae clinical strains isolated in Germany. Antimicrob Agents Chemother 2003;47:2319–22.

[56] Jones RN, Farrell DJ, Morrissey I. Quinupristin-dalfopristin resistance in Streptococcus pneumoniae: novel L22 ribosomal protein mutation in two clinical isolates from the SENTRY antimicrobial surveillance program. Antimicrob Agents Chemother 2003;47:2696–8.

[57] Musher DM, Dowell ME, Shortridge VD, et al. Emergence of macrolide resistance during treatment of pneumococcal pneumonia. N Engl J Med 2002;346:630–1.

[58] Bingen E, Leclercq R, Fitoussi F, et al. Emergence of group A streptococcus strains with different mechanisms of macrolide resistance. Antimicrob Agents Chemother 2002;46:1199–203.

[59] Clark C, Bozdogan B, Peric M, Dewasse B, Jacobs MR, Appelbaum PC. In vitro selection of resistance in Haemophilus influenzae by amoxicillin-clavulanate, cefpodoxime, cefprozil, azithromycin, and clarithromycin. Antimicrob Agents Chemother 2002;46:2956–62.

[60] Schito AM, Schito GC, Debbia E, et al. Antibacterial resistance in Streptococcus pneumoniae and Haemophilus influenzae from Italy and Spain: data from the PROTEKT surveillance study, 1999–2000. J Chemother 2003;15:226–34.

[61] Baquero F, Baquero-Artigao G, Canton R, Garcia-Rey C. Antibiotic consumption and resistance selection in Streptococcus pneumoniae. J Antimicrob Chemother 2002;50(Suppl S2):27–37.

[62] Waites K, Brown S. Antimicrobial resistance among isolates of respiratory tract infection pathogens from the southern United States: data from the PROTEKT US surveillance program 2000/2001. South Med J 2003;96:974–85.

[63] Zhanel GG, Palatnick L, Nichol KA, Bellyou T, Low DE, Hoban DJ. Antimicrobial resistance in respiratory tract Streptococcus pneumoniae isolates: results of the Canadian Respiratory Organism Susceptibility Study, 1997 to 2002. Antimicrob Agents Chemother 2003;47:1867–74.

[64] Bozdogan B, Appelbaum PC, Kelly LM, et al. Activity of telithromycin and seven other agents against 1034 pediatric Streptococcus pneumoniae isolates from ten central and eastern European centers. Clin Microbiol Infect 2003;9:653–61.

[65] Soriano F, Granizo JJ, Fenoll A, et al. Antimicrobial resistance among clinical isolates of Streptococcus pneumoniae isolated in four southern European countries (ARISE project) from adult patients: results from the cefditoren surveillance program. J Chemother 2003;15:107–12.

[66] Gur D, Ozalp M, Sumerkan B, et al. Prevalence of antimicrobial resistance in Haemophilus influenzae, Streptococcus pneumoniae, Moraxella catarrhalis and Streptococcus pyogenes: results of a multicentre study in Turkey. Int J Antimicrob Agents 2002;19:207–11.

[67] Reinert RR, Lutticken R, Bryskier A, Al-Lahham A. Macrolide-resistant Streptococcus pneumoniae and Streptococcus pyogenes in the pediatric population in Germany during 2000–2001. Antimicrob Agents Chemother 2003;47:489–93.

[68] Jones RN, Biedenbach DJ. Comparative activity of garenoxacin (BMS 284756), a novel desfluoroquinolone, tested against 8,331 isolates from community-acquired respiratory tract infections: North American results from the SENTRY Antimicrobial Surveillance Program (1999–2001). Diagn Microbiol Infect Dis 2003;45:273–8.

[69] Hsueh PR, Teng LJ, Lee CM, et al. Telithromycin and quinupristin-dalfopristin resistance in clinical isolates of Streptococcus pyogenes: SMART Program 2001 Data. Antimicrob Agents Chemother 2003;47:2152–7.

[70] Ip M, Lyon DJ, Leung T, Cheng AF. Macrolide resistance and distribution of erm and mef genes among beta-haemolytic streptococci in Hong Kong. Eur J Clin Microbiol Infect Dis 2002;21:238–40.

[71] Decousser JW, Ovetchkine P, Collignon A, et al. Multicentre study of the molecular epidemiology, serotypes and antimicrobial susceptibility patterns of invasive Streptococcus pneumoniae invasive isolated from children in the Ille de France area. Eur J Clin Microbiol Infect Dis 2004;23:27–33.

[72] Felmingham D, Robbins MJ, Tesfaslasie Y, Harding I, Shrimpton S, Gruneberg RN. Antimicrobial susceptibility of community-acquired lower respiratory tract bacterial pathogens isolated in the UK during the 1995–1996 cold season. J Antimicrob Chemother 1998;41:411–5.

[73] Benbachir M, Benredjeb S, Boye CS, et al. Two-year surveillance of antibiotic resistance in Streptococcus pneumoniae in four African cities. Antimicrob Agents Chemother 2001; 45:627–9.

[74] Weiss KGuilbault C, Cortes L, Restieri C, Low DE. Genotypic characterization of macrolide-resistant strains of Streptococcus pneumoniae isolated in Quebec, Canada, and in vitro activity of ABT-773 and telithromycin. J Antimicrob Chemother 2002;50:403–6.

[75] Fitoussi F, Doit C, Geslin P, Brahimi N, Bingen E. Mechanisms of macrolide resistance in clinical pneumococcal isolates in France. Antimicrob Agents Chemother 2001;45: 636–8.

[76] Farrell DJ, Morrissey I, Bakker S, Felmingham D. Molecular characterization of macrolide resistance mechanisms among Streptococcus pneumoniae and Streptococcus pyogenes isolated from the PROTEKT 1999–2000 study. J Antimicrob Chemother 2002; 50(Suppl S1):39–47.

[77] Katz KC, McGeer AJ, Duncan CL, et al. Emergence of macrolide resistance in throat culture isolates of group a streptococci in Ontario, Canada, in 2001. Antimicrob Agents Chemother 2003;47:2370–2.

[78] De Azavedo JC, Yeung RH, Bast DJ, Duncan CL, Borgia SB, Low DE. Prevalence and mechanisms of macrolide resistance in clinical isolates of group A streptococci from Ontario, Canada. Antimicrob Agents Chemother 1999;43:2144–7.

[79] Doern GV, Brown SD. Antimicrobial susceptibility among community-acquired respiratory tract pathogens in the USA: data from PROTEKT US 2000–01. J Infect 2004;48:56–65.

[80] Ioannidou S, Tassios PT, Zachariadou L, et al. In vitro activity of telithromycin (HMR 3647) against Greek Streptococcus pyogenes and Streptococcus pneumoniae clinical isolates with different macrolide susceptibilities. Clin Microbiol Infect 2003;9:704–7.

[81] Alos JI, Aracil B, Oteo J, Torres C, Gomez-Garces JL. High prevalence of erythromycin-resistant, clindamycin/miocamycin-susceptible (M phenotype) Streptococcus pyogenes: results of a Spanish multicentre study in 1998. Spanish Group for the Study of Infection in the Primary Health Care Setting. J Antimicrob Chemother 2000;45:605–9.

[82] Dicuonzo G, Fiscarelli E, Gherardi G, et al. Erythromycin-resistant pharyngeal isolates of Streptococcus pyogenes recovered in Italy. Antimicrob Agents Chemother 2002;46: 3987–90.

[83] Busetti M, Longo B, Campello C. Low rates of antimicrobial resistance in respiratory pathogens from a pediatric population in north-eastern Italy. Pediatr Med Chir 2003;25: 131–4.

[84] Syrogiannopoulos GA, Grivea IN, Fitoussi F, et al. High prevalence of erythromycin resistance of Streptococcus pyogenes in Greek children. Pediatr Infect Dis J 2001;20:863–8.

[85] Weber P, Filipecki J, Bingen E, et al. Genetic and phenotypic characterization of macrolide resistance in group A streptococci isolated from adults with pharyngo-tonsillitis in France. J Antimicrob Chemother 2001;48:291–4.

[86] Cha S, Lee H, Lee K, Hwang K, Bae S, Lee Y. The emergence of erythromycin-resistant Streptococcus pyogenes in Seoul, Korea. J Infect Chemother 2001;7:81–6.

[87] Kataja J, Huovinen P, Skurnik M, Seppala H. Erythromycin resistance genes in group A streptococci in Finland. The Finnish Study Group for Antimicrobial Resistance. Antimicrob Agents Chemother 1999;43:48–52.

[88] Descheemaeker P, Chapelle S, Lammens C, et al. Macrolide resistance and erythromycin resistance determinants among Belgian Streptococcus pyogenes and Streptococcus pneumoniae isolates. J Antimicrob Chemother 2000;45:167–73.

[89] Acikgoz ZC, Gocer S, Tuncer S. Macrolide resistance determinants of group A streptococci in Ankara, Turkey. J Antimicrob Chemother 2003;52:110–2.

[90] Martinez S, Amoroso AM, Famiglietti A, de Mier C, Vay C, Gutkind GO. Genetic and phenotypic characterization of resistance to macrolides in Streptococcus pyogenes from Argentina. Int J Antimicrob Agents 2004;23:95–8.

[91] d'Oliveira RE, Barros RR, Mendonca CR, Teixeira LM, Castro AC. Antimicrobial susceptibility and survey of macrolide resistance mechanisms among Streptococcus pyogenes isolated in Rio de Janeiro, Brazil. Microb Drug Resist 2003;9:87–91.

[92] Mason EO Jr, Wald ER, Bradley JS, Barson WJ, Kaplan SL. Macrolide resistance among middle ear isolates of Streptococcus pneumoniae observed at eight United States pediatric centers: prevalence of M and MLSB phenotypes. Pediatr Infect Dis J 2003;22:623–7.

[93] Hoban DJ, Wierzbowski AK, Nichol K, Zhanel GG. Macrolide-resistant Streptococcus pneumoniae in Canada during 1998–1999: prevalence of mef(A) and erm(B) and susceptibilities to ketolides. Antimicrob Agents Chemother 2001;45:2147–50.

[94] Low DE, Brown S, Felmingham D. Clinical and bacteriological efficacy of the ketolide telithromycin against isolates of key respiratory pathogens: a pooled analysis of phase III studies. Clin Microbiol Infect 2004;10:27–36.

[95] Dagan R, Johnson CE, McLinn S, et al. Bacteriologic and clinical efficacy of amoxicillin/ clavulanate vs. azithromycin in acute otitis media. Pediatr Infect Dis J 2000;19:95–104.

[96] Dagan R, Leibovitz E, Fliss DM, et al. Bacteriologic efficacies of oral azithromycin and oral cefaclor in treatment of acute otitis media in infants and young children. Antimicrob Agents Chemother 2000;44:43–50.

[97] Bozdogan B, Clark C, Bryskier A, Jacobs MR, Appelbaum PC. Activities of HMR 3787 and RU 64399 compared with those of four other agents against Haemophilus influenzae and Haemophilus parainfluenzae. Antimicrob Agents Chemother 2003;47:405–7.

[98] Bozdogan B, Appelbaum PC, Kelly LM, et al. Activity of telithromycin compared with seven other agents against 1039 Streptococcus pyogenes pediatric isolates from ten centers in central and eastern Europe. Clin Microbiol Infect 2003;9:741–5.

[99] Weiss K, Guilbault C, Cortes L, et al. Genotypic characterization of macrolide-resistant strains of Streptococcus pneumoniae isolated in Quebec, Canada, and in vitro activity of ABT-773 and telithromycin. J Antimicrob Chemother 2002;50(3):403–6.

[100] Jacobs MR, Appelbaum PC. Susceptibility of 1100 Streptococcus pneumoniae strains isolated in 1997 from seven Latin American and Caribbean countries. Laser Study Group. Int J Antimicrob Agents 2000;16(1):17–24.

[101] Mendes C, Marin ME, Quinones F, et al. Antibacterial resistance of community-acquired respiratory tract pathogens recovered from patients in Latin America: results from the PROTEKT surveillance study (1999–2000). Braz J Infect Dis 2003;7(1):44–61.

[102] Bergan T, Gaustad P, Hoiby EA, et al. Antibiotic resistance of pneumococci in Norway. Int J Antimicrob Agents 1998;10(1):77–81.

[103] Felmingham D, Robbins MJ, Tesfaslasie Y, et al. Antimicrobial susceptibility of community-acquired lower respiratory tract bacterial pathogens isolated in the UK during the 1995–1996 cold season. J Antimicrob Chemother 1998;41(3):411–5.

[104] Pihlajamaki M, Jalava J, Huovinen P, et al. Antimicrobial resistance of invasive pneumococci in Finland in 1999–2000. Antimicrob Agents Chemother 2003;47(6):1832–5.

[105] Dobay O, Rozgonyi F, Hajdu E, et al. Antibiotic susceptibility and serotypes of Streptococcus pneumoniae isolates from Hungary. J Antimicrob Chemother 2003;51(4):887–93.

[106] Soriano F, Granizo JJ, Fenoll A, et al. Antimicrobial resistance among clinical isolates of Streptococcus pneumoniae isolated in four southern European countries (ARISE project) from adult patients: results from the cefditoren surveillance program. J Chemother 2003; 15(2):107–12.

[107] Jones ME, Blosser-Middleton RS, et al. In vitro susceptibility of Streptococcus pneumoniae, Haemophilus influenzae and Moraxella catarrhalis: a European multicenter study during 2000-2001. Clin Microbiol Infect 2003;9(7):590–9.

[108] Liebowitz LD, Slabbert M, Huisamen A. National surveillance programme on susceptibility patterns of respiratory pathogens in South Africa: moxifloxacin compared with eight other antimicrobial agents. J Clin Pathol 2003;56(5):344–7.

[109] Ip M, Lyon DJ, Cheng AF. Patterns of antibiotic resistance, serotype distribution, and patient demographics of Streptococcus pneumoniae in Hong Kong. Chemotherapy 2001; 47(2):110–6.

[110] Canton R, Morosini M, Enright MC, et al. Worldwide incidence, molecular epidemiology and mutations implicated in fluoroquinolone-resistant Streptococcus pneumoniae: data from the global PROTEKT surveillance programme. J Antimicrob Chemother 2003; 52(6):944–52.

[111] Bozdogan B, Appelbaum PC, Kelly LM, et al. Activity of telithromycin compared with seven other agents against 1039 Streptococcus pyogenes pediatric isolates from ten centers in central and eastern Europe. Clin Microbiol Infect 2003;9(7):741–5.

[112] Nagai K, Appelbaum PC, Davies TA, et al. Susceptibility to telithromycin in 1,011 Streptococcus pyogenes isolates from 10 central and Eastern European countries. Antimicrob Agents Chemother 2002;46(2):546–9.

[113] Palavecino EL, Riedel I, Duran C, et al. Macrolide resistance phenotypes in Streptococcus pneumoniae in Santiago, Chile. Int J Antimicrob Agents 2002;20(2):108–12.

[114] Inoue M, Lee NY, Hong SW, et al. PROTEKT 1999-2000: a multicentre study of the antibiotic susceptibility of respiratory tract pathogens in Hong Kong, Japan and South Korea. Int J Antimicrob Agents 2004;23(1):44–51.

[115] Bean DC, Klena JD. Prevalence of erm(A) and mef(B) erythromycin resistance determinants in isolates of Streptococcus pneumoniae from New Zealand. J Antimicrob Chemother 2002;50(4):597–9.

[116] Montanari MP, Mingoia M, Cochetti I, et al. Phenotypes and genotypes of erythromycin-resistant pneumococci in Italy. J Clin Microbiol. 2003;41(1):428–31.

[117] Dicuonzo G, Fiscarelli E, Gherardi G, et al. Erythromycin-resistant pharyngeal isolates of Streptococcus pyogenes recovered in Italy. Antimicrob Agents Chemother 2002;46(12): 3987–90.

ELSEVIER
SAUNDERS

CLINICS IN
LABORATORY
MEDICINE

Clin Lab Med 24 (2004) 477–502

Application of pharmacokinetics and pharmacodynamics to antimicrobial therapy of respiratory tract infections

David Andes, MD[a],*, Jack Anon, MD[b], Michael
R. Jacobs, MD, PhD[c], William A. Craig, MD[a]

[a]*Department of Medicine, Section of Infectious Diseases, University of Wisconsin, 600 Highland Avenue, Room H4/572, Madison, WI 53792, USA*
[b]*Department of Otolaryngology, University of Pittsburgh School of Medicine, Pittsburgh, PA, USA*
[c]*Department of Pathology and Clinical Microbiology, Case Western Reserve University, University Hospitals of Cleveland, Cleveland, OH, USA*

Antimicrobial dosing regimens historically have been based on the premise that serum concentrations must be higher than the minimum inhibitory concentration (MIC) of the antimicrobial against the pathogen. However, the relationship between serum concentrations and bacterial eradication has only recently been clearly defined, and MICs of some pathogens that are regarded as susceptible to some antimicrobial agents are actually higher than peak serum concentrations of these agents. Although the MIC is an important measure of antimicrobial activity, it does not take into account patient-, drug-, and pathogen-related factors that influence the outcome of antimicrobial therapy. Increasing pathogen resistance and documented treatment failures, particularly in respiratory tract infections, indicate a need to reevaluate dosing strategies with available agents to maximize antimicrobial effectiveness and limit the spread of resistance. It is now understood that to achieve bacteriologic and clinical success, sufficient concentrations of antimicrobial at the site of infection must be maintained for an adequate period of time. These dynamics are determined by combining drug pharmacokinetic and pharmacodynamic (PK/PD) data with MIC data. Different classes of antimicrobials have different patterns of bactericidal action based on pharmacokinetic and pharmacodynamic characteristics, and these patterns influence antimicrobial efficacy. PK/PD characteristics of an antimicrobial

* Corresponding author.
E-mail address: dra@medicine.wisc.edu (D. Andes).

need to be integrated with MIC data to guide dosing strategies and predict bacteriologic and clinical outcomes. This approach not only improves antimicrobial efficacy but also serves to limit development of further pathogen resistance.

Principles of pharmacokinetics and pharmacodynamics

Pharmacokinetics describes the absorption, distribution, metabolism, and elimination characteristics of a drug in the human body (Table 1). Pharmacokinetic parameters that have been shown to correlate with antimicrobial efficacy are area under the serum-concentration-time profile (AUC), peak serum concentration (C_{max}), amount of time that the serum concentration of drug is above the MIC (T > MIC), the serum half-life, and penetration of drug into tissues [1]. For modeling purposes, pharmacokinetic parameters can be calculated either as one- or two-compartment models. In a one-compartment model, it is assumed that the drug is distributed equally and simultaneously to all body tissues. In a two-compartment model, drugs are considered to be distributed in the body in two phases: an initial equilibrating distribution phase into the blood and tissues with high blood flow and a second, slower equilibrating phase.

Pharmacodynamics refers to the actions the drug exerts in the body, including therapeutic effects. Drug pharmacodynamic correlates for antimicrobial therapy are MIC and duration of bactericidal effects, including persistent antibiotic (PAE) effects, rate of killing, and rate of development of

Table 1
Definitions of pharmacokinetic parameters (many of these parameters can be expressed as total serum values or as free [non protein-bound] serum values)

Parameter	Description
Bioavailability	Proportion of drug absorbed into the systemic circulation after administration. Drugs administered intravenously are usually 100% bioavailable (some are given as prodrugs); other dosage forms may be less bioavailable.
C_{max}	Peak serum concentration of drug achieved following administration of a single dose.
T_{max}	Time to peak serum concentration.
V_d	Volume of distribution. A relative measure of the distribution of the drug throughout the body. $V_d > 3$ L indicates drug is distributed outside the plasma.
AUC	Area under the serum concentration-time curve.
$t_{1/2}$	Elimination half-life. Time required for serum concentration of drug to be reduced by 50%. Also referred to as $\beta t_{1/2}$ to differentiate it from $\alpha t_{1/2}$, which designates the distribution $t_{1/2}$ of a drug.
T > MIC	Amount of time that the serum concentration is above the minimum inhibitory concentration required for bactericidal/static effects. Applicable to antimicrobials only.

resistant mutants. Some antimicrobials continue to have bactericidal effects even after the antimicrobial has been cleared from the infection site. These post-antibiotic effects (PAEs) are observed in vivo with inhibitors of protein and nucleic acid synthesis with Gram-negative bacilli and Gram-positive cocci and with β-lactams against *Staphylococcus aureus*, but not with β-lactams against Gram-negative bacilli or streptococci [2,3]. Thus, β-lactams that exhibit time-dependent killing usually have minimal or short PAEs, which are therefore of negligible value in contributing to additional antimicrobial efficacy. Antimicrobials that inhibit protein and nucleic acid synthesis can be thought of as having a substantial PAE. A long PAE prevents regrowth after antimicrobial concentrations fall below the MIC. Antimicrobials exhibiting PAEs may be administered less frequently than would be predicted based on elimination half-life ($t_{1/2}$). Thus, PAEs have a major impact on dosing. An understanding of these concepts has lead to improved dosing regimens for current antibiotics as well as the establishment of appropriate dosing regimens for new antibiotics. This has improved patient care. The interrelationships between these parameters are illustrated in Fig. 1. The PK/PD parameters that best correlate with efficacy for the various classes of antimicrobials are shown in Table 2.

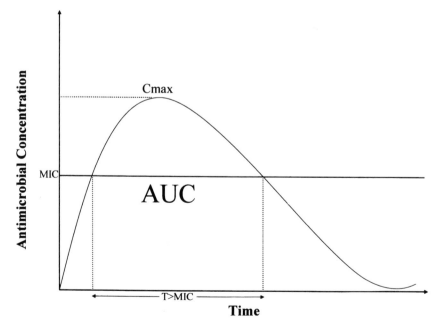

Fig. 1. Correlation between antimicrobial serum pharmacokinetics and pharmacodynamics of antimicrobials. Antimicrobial agents exhibit either time-dependent killing, in which efficacy correlates with duration of time the concentration exceeds the minimum inhibitory concentration (T > MIC), or concentration-dependent killing, in which efficacy correlates with C_{max}/AUC or AUC/MIC. AUC, area under the serum concentration-time curve; C_{max}, maximum plasma concentration.

Table 2
Antimicrobial agents classified by pattern of bactericidal activity

Drug Class	Pharmacodynamic class	Therapeutic goal (for S pneumoniae)
β-lactams penicillins cephalosporins	Time-dependent	Time above MIC greater than 40% to 50% of the dosing interval
Macrolides erythromycin clarithromycin azithromycin	Time-dependent (with moderate to prolonged persistent effect)	AUC to MIC ratio of 25–35 for macrolides; unknown for telithromycin
Ketolides telithromycin	Concentration-dependent (with prolonged persistent effect)	
Fluoroquinolones gatifloxacin gemifloxacin levofloxacin moxifloxacin		AUC to MIC ratio of 25–35

Abbreviations: AUC, area under the serum concentration-time curve; MIC, minimum inhibitory concentration.

Adapted from Anon JB, Jacobs MR, Pode MD, et al. Antimicrobial treatment guidelines for acute bacterial rhinosinusitis. Otolaryngol Head Neck Surg 2004;130(1 Suppl):1–45; with permission.

Time-dependent agents with no significant post-antiobiotic effects

For agents with time-dependent effects, killing occurs once a threshold has been reached, and ceases once the drug concentration falls below this point. However, antimicrobial concentrations need not be above the MIC for the entire dosing interval. The duration of time that the nonprotein-bound drug fraction in serum is above the MIC of the pathogen is the PK/PD parameter that correlates with bactericidal efficacy and is expressed as a percentage of the dosing interval [4]. Time above MIC can be maximized by dosing more frequently, using sustained release delivery systems, using repository dosage forms, or with the concomitant use of a drug that inhibits the elimination of the antimicrobial (eg, probenecid with some β-lactams). Attaining concentrations significantly higher than the MIC does not provide additional meaningful growth reductions.

In animal models such as in the neutropenic mouse thigh infection model, maximal survival 4 days after *S pneumoniae* inoculation was seen when serum concentrations of amoxicillin or amoxicillin-clavulanate exceeded the MIC of the test organism for 40% or more of an 8-hour dosing interval [5]. In four different animal models of *S pneumoniae* infection, bactericidal activity of penicillin occurred when concentrations exceeded the MIC for at least 65% of the dosing interval in murine infections and at least 35% of the dosing interval in rabbit tissue cage infection models [5]. For broad-spectrum cephalosporins, concentrations above the MIC for 35% to 40% of the dosing interval produce bacteriostatic effects against *S pneumoniae* despite variations in MIC, and maximal efficacy is approached when concentrations are above the MIC for 60% to 70% of the dosing interval [3]. With staphylococci, concentrations above the MIC for 40% or more of the dosing interval are sufficient. For immunocompetent individuals, bacteriostatic effects are deemed acceptable for a positive outcome, because host defenses play a significant role in eradicating infection. Thus, it is generally agreed that for β-lactams, significant bacterial reduction is achieved when concentrations are above the MIC for approximately 40% to 50% of the dosing interval, regardless of infecting pathogen and level of resistance. Evidence suggests that for the carbapenems, a shorter time above the MIC is necessary for efficacy (20% to 30%) than for β-lactams [6].

Time-dependent agents with significant post-antibiotic effects

The PK/PD profile seen with macrolides/azalides (such as eythromycin, clarithromycin, and azithromycin), clindamycin, tetracyclines, and oxazoli-dinones is time-dependent killing with prolonged PAEs [7–9]. The goal of the dosing regimen is to optimize the amount of drug exposure, with AUC:MIC ratio the major parameter correlating with efficacy. Compared with erythro-mycin, the newer macrolides, azithromycin and clarithromycin, have im-proved oral bioavailability, longer elimination $t_{1/2}$, long PAEs, and achieve higher intracellular concentrations [10,11]. The differences in pharmacoki-netic profiles among the macrolides influence their varying efficacy profiles against respiratory pathogens. In an early pharmacodynamic study, the antibacterial effects of azithromycin and clarithromycin were compared using strains of *S pneumoniae, S aureus, H influenzae*, and *M catarrhalis*, using a pharmacodynamic model simulating the dynamics of serum concentrations of each drug found in human serum after oral administration of recommended doses [12]. In general, killing was dependent on C_{max}/MIC ratios, as well as the duration of time levels exceeded the MIC. Killing by azithromycin occurred at a slower rate compared with clarithromycin. Regrowth after reduction of the initial inoculum was observed with azithromycin in all cultures, but not with clarithromycin.

A more recent study evaluated the serum bactericidal activity (SBA) of clarithromycin and azithromycin against *S pneumoniae* strains [13]. Healthy volunteers received a 500-mg oral dose of clarithromycin, and after a 1-week washout, a 500-mg dose of azithromycin. Blood samples, obtained before dosing and at 2-hour intervals for 12 hours after drug administration, were used to determine serum bacteriostatic and bactericidal titers against a reference strain and various clinical isolates of *S pneumoniae*. Clarithromycin exhibited SBA for 6 hours (50% of its normal dosing interval) for strains with MICs less than or equal to 2 µg/mL, and, although SBA was not observed at MICs greater than 4 µg/mL, clarithromycin did inhibit clinical isolates with

MICs equal to 4 µg/mL. In contrast, azithromycin exhibited SBA for 6 hours (25% of its dosing interval) for MICs less than or equal to 0.5 µg/mL only, and inhibitory activity was observed only for strains with MICs equal to 1.0 µg/mL. The differences between the two compounds were postulated to be explained by higher peak serum concentrations attained with clarithromcyin.

Peak serum levels of azithromycin and clarithromycin do not reach the MICs of these agents against *H influenzae* [14]. Combined with the fact that the major respiratory pathogens are located extracellularly, while macrolides accumulate intracellularly, it is not surprising that these agents are virtually inactive against this respiratory pathogen in sites where serum concentrations are predictive of local drug concentrations [15,16].

Animal models of infection suggest that the AUC/MIC ratio based on free-drug AUC values that correlate with efficacy against *S pneumoniae* for most macrolides, azalides, and clindamycin is 25 to 50, whereas higher ratios (up to 100) improve survival [9,17].

Concentration-dependent killing

For antimicrobials that exhibit concentration-dependent killing, the ratios of unbound serum C_{max}/MIC and area under the unbound serum concentration-time curve (AUC)/MIC are the parameters that correlate best with bactericidal efficacy. Increasing the dose of a drug with concentration-dependent effects is associated with increased bacterial killing.

Several pharmacokinetic features of the quinolones make them attractive for use in respiratory tract infections. They are extensively distributed into neutrophils, macrophages, and respiratory and lung tissues in concentrations higher than those attained in serum [11,18]. Quinolones exhibit concentration-dependent killing, and their efficacy relates to either the ratio of AUC/MIC or C_{max}/MIC. In general, optimal bactericidal activity of all quinolones against Gram-positive pathogens occurs at an AUC/MIC ratio of at least 25 to 30 [19–21]. In a recent study using an in vitro pharmacokinetic model, total eradication of four different *S pneumoniae* strains with gatifloxacin was achieved when AUC/MIC ratios were at least 27 to 36 [19]. With AUC/MIC values of between 17 and 22, viable bacterial counts were unchanged or increased. Against Gram-negative pathogens, AUC/MIC ratios for the quinolones should be at least 100 or 125 for optimal bactericidal efficacy [21].

Compared with other classes of antimicrobials, the PK/PD of the quinolone family have been more extensively studied, including as predictors of efficacy in clinical trials. The pharmacodynamics of levofloxacin and their relationship to efficacy outcomes were studied prospectively in 134 hospitalized patients with culture-proven infections, the majority of which (75%) were of the respiratory tract [22]. Therapeutic dosages of levofloxacin (500 mg twice daily for 5 to 14 days) were associated with a clinical success rate of 99% when C_{max}/MIC ratio was equal to or greater than 12 and AUC/MIC ratio was equal to or greater than 100, whereas clinical success rate was 88.5% when C_{max}/MIC ratio was between 3 and 12 and AUC/MIC ratio was between 25 and 100 [22,23].

Although the pharmacokinetic properties of many quinolones make them attractive for use in the treatment of respiratory tract infections, safety issues [24–26] and resistance development [27,28] raise concerns about their broad use. For example, several fluoroquinolones have been withdrawn from the market (eg, temafloxacin for hemolysis, grepafloxacin for cardiotoxicity) or have had warnings added to their labeling (eg, hepatotoxicity with trovafloxacin, QTc interval prolongation with gatifloxacin) following discovery of severe adverse events associated with their use [24,29,30]. In addition, all fluoroquinolones have the same mechanisms of action and resistance; by inhibiting bacterial DNA gyrase and topoisomerase IV, they inhibit DNA supercoiling and relaxation, ultimately leading to bacterial cell death [31]. Consequently, when microbial resistance develops against one fluoroquinolone, it is likely to affect all fluoroquinolones, although to varying degrees. If widespread use of fluoroquinolones continues, microbial resistance to these agents also will increase, decreasing the clinical utility of this class of antimicrobials. To prevent this occurrence, fluoroquinolones should be reserved for patients who do not improve after treatment with other classes of antimicrobials or those with severe disease.

Ketolides also have concentration-dependent activity, although the PK/PD relationships of these agents are still under investigation. For one of the ketolides, telithromycin, the AUC/MIC ratio that correlates with efficacy for *S pneumoniae* may be much higher (between 50 and ≥ 200) than for other agents in this class [17,32].

Mutant prevention concentration

Recently, another PK/PD parameter has been proposed as a means by which the selection of resistant mutant strains can be restricted [33–35]. This concept applies to antimicrobials where the primary mechanism of resistance is simple selection of resistant mutants in a population of a pathogen [36]. Therapeutic concentrations of antimicrobials that are active against the majority of susceptible pathogens are often those at which the resistant mutant population of the bacterial colonies can become selectively enriched [34]. The mutation prevention concentration (MPC) is defined as the lowest concentration of antimicrobial that prevents bacterial colony formation from a culture containing more than 10^{10} bacteria. The mutant selection window is defined as the concentration range in which resistant mutants are selectively enriched during antimicrobial therapy. The concept of MPC and mutant selection window for the effects of ciprofloxacin and norfloxacin on *S aureus* in vitro are illustrated in Fig. 2 [35]. The PK/PD parameter that avoids selection of resistant mutants is to achieve an AUC/MIC ratio of >100, whereas AUC/MIC ratios of 25 to 100 are regarded as being in the mutant selection window, and AUC/MIC ratios of < 25 generally fail to suppress the growth of susceptible populations [36].

Application of pharmacokinetics and pharmacodynamics to antimicrobial agents

Comparative clinical trial data of adequate power to discriminate between the efficacies of antimicrobial agents is the cornerstone of determining drug efficacy. In antimicrobial clinical research, however, obtaining and identifying pathogens involved in respiratory tract infections and monitoring bacteriologic response to antimicrobial therapy in sufficient numbers of patients is difficult because of several factors, including: unwillingness of patients to submit to invasive and uncomfortable procedures to obtain samples for

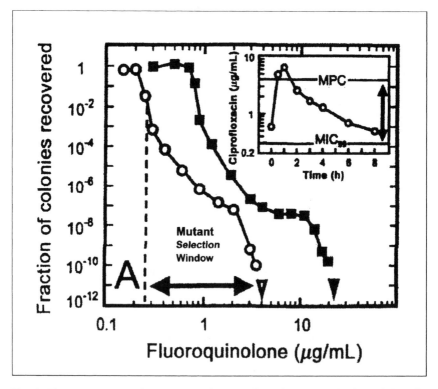

Fig. 2. The mutant prevention concentration (MPC) and mutant selection window for fluoroquinolones (ciprofloxacin and norfloxacin) against *Staphylococcus aureus* in vitro (*Adapted from* Zhao X, Drlica K. Restricting the selection of antibiotic-resistant mutant bacteria: measurement and potential use of the mutant selection window. J Infect Dis 2002;185(4):561–2; with permission.)

culture from the middle ear, lungs, or sinuses; difficulties in separating the contribution of host defense mechanisms from antimicrobial activity to infection eradication; inconclusiveness of culture results when samples of infected tissue/fluids are obtained; and the time and costs necessary to evaluate efficacy over a broad therapeutic dose range. Nevertheless, bacteriologic efficacy studies have frequently been performed in otitis media studies and allowed PK/PD correlations to be made in humans. Given the problems inherent in obtaining dose-response relationships in clinical infection studies, the majority of antimicrobial PK/PD data are obtained from animal models of infection and in vitro models. Such data are compelling even in the absence of clinical data when multiple studies using a variety of experimental methods arrive at the same conclusions, as has been the case in antimicrobial research.

Animal models of infection

Animal models are an integral part of the evaluation of antimicrobials. Studies in rats, mice, and rabbits have been used to define PK/PD parameters for antimicrobials, including the time course of antimicrobial activity, degree of drug penetration to the site of infection, magnitude of the parameters that correlate with antimicrobial efficacy, dose-response relationships, and comparative efficacy between agents. The neutropenic mouse model is one of the most common animal infection models used in this regard. A neutropenic state, achieved by injecting intraperitoneal cyclophosphamide several days before injection of inoculum, eliminates the contribution of host defense mechanisms to the eradication of infection or allows use of pathogens with low virulence in mice such as some serotypes of pneumococci. A thigh injection model is advantageous for study because the thigh muscle can be easily inoculated, removed, and homogenized for assessment of study parameters. A limitation to the application of this model to humans is that thigh infections do not simulate common human sites of infections by these pathogens.

The thigh infection model in neutropenic mice was used to describe the in vivo post-antibiotic effects of various antimicrobials (discussed earlier) [2]. In these experiments, infection was created by injecting the thighs of the mice with clinical isolates of 10^5 to 10^6 colony-forming units (CFU) of *S aureus, Streptococcus pneumoniae, Klebsiella pneumoniae, Streptococcus pyogenes, Pseudomonas aeruginosa*, or *Escherichia coli*. Beginning 2 hours after inoculation, mice received subcutaneous injections of one of the antimicrobial agents being studied, the doses of which were based on producing serum concentrations exceeding the MICs of the study organisms for 1 to 4 hours. Pharmacokinetic parameters were described for single doses; post-antibiotic effects were determined from pharmacokinetic observations, MIC, and log changes in bacterial load in the thighs over time obtained after multiple inoculations and antimicrobial injections.

Neutropenic mice also were used to demonstrate the importance of the dosing interval to β-lactam efficacy and the AUC/MIC ratio to aminoglycoside efficacy in thigh infection and pneumonia models [4]. Neutropenia and *K pneumoniae* thigh infections were induced as described earlier [2]. Pneumonia was induced by exposing mice to aerosolized cultures of 4 to 5×10^{12} CFU/min of *K pneumoniae* in a closed chamber. Various dosing regimens, achieving serum concentrations above and below those achieved in humans, were used for treating infected mice. Changes in bacterial load, serum pharmacokinetics, and tissue concentrations of drug were assessed. E_{max} (maximum drug effect) modeling, effective in determining the slope of the dose-response curve, determined that the dosing interval had significant impact on antimicrobial efficacy. The duration of time that serum levels exceeded the MIC during a 24-hour period was the only pharmacokinetic parameter that had significant correlation to β-lactam efficacy in both infection models. For aminoglycosides, the important pharmacokinetic parameter predicting efficacy was AUC/MIC ratio.

Although antimicrobial agents generally are eliminated much more rapidly in animals than in humans, the magnitude of the pharmacokinetic parameters is similar. To more closely simulate human pharmacokinetics, renal impairment can be produced in mice with peritoneal uranyl nitrate injections at least 3 days before study. This method was used in neutropenic mice to correlate in vivo efficacy of amoxicillin and amoxicillin-clavulanate with time above MIC in thigh infections caused by *S pneumoniae* [37].

Other animal models of infection include pneumococcal murine peritonitis, bacteremia, otitis media, and rabbit tissue cage infection [5,38]. PK/PD data obtained from murine peritonitis and rabbit tissue cage infection models correlated well with data obtained from pneumococcal murine thigh and pneumonia infections.

In vitro pharmacokinetic models of infection

In vitro pharmacokinetic models are becoming increasingly popular in antimicrobial research [19,39–44]. Results from studies using these models complement animal data. Although various models have been described, in general, they use a series of reservoirs, pumps, filters, and tubing to simulate a two-compartment pharmacokinetic model, in which the first (central) compartment mimics distribution of drug through the systemic circulation, and the second (peripheral) compartment represents distribution of drug to the site of infection. Bacteria are introduced into the model at concentrations similar to those that would be expected in infection, with incubation and constant stirring to ensure continued growth and homogenous mixing of the culture. Antimicrobial agents are added to the model at varying concentrations and intervals, exposing bacteria to changing antimicrobial concentrations. Drug pharmacokinetics are simulated by changing concentrations through the addition of broth diluent and elimination of drug-containing broth through an elimination reservoir. Other, more sophisticated systems use computer-controlled flow meters and pumps for more accurate simulation of the human serum-concentration time profile [39].

In vitro pharmacokinetic models are easily reproducible and amenable to manipulation of antimicrobial concentration, antimicrobial elimination half-life, bacterial load, and pH, and thus accommodate a wide variety of pharmacodynamic applications. They are far less costly and time-consuming than clinical trials. In addition, the problem of host defense mechanisms contributing to bacterial reduction is eliminated. These characteristics make in vitro models valuable adjuncts to animal models and clinical data for antimicrobial pharmacodynamic evaluations.

In an in vitro pharmacokinetic model, the effects of different doses of amoxicillin were compared for treatment of simulated pneumococcal otitis media [42]. Nine different clinical isolates of logarithmic phase cultures of S $pneumoniae$ were exposed to amoxicillin peak concentrations of 3, 6, and 9 μg/mL every 12 hours to reflect middle-ear concentrations following oral doses of 15, 35, and 45 mg/kg every 12 hours, respectively. Adjusting pump flow rate simulated a $t_{1/2}$ of 6 hours. Amoxicillin doses and elimination $t_{1/2}$ from the middle-ear fluid were estimated based on the few published data available in chinchillas and humans. All three doses rapidly decreased bacterial counts for penicillin-susceptible strains, with equal rates of killing. For penicillin-intermediate and -resistant strains, results were more variable. The 3-μg/mL peak was unable to maintain reductions in viable bacterial counts for two of three penicillin-intermediate strains and all penicillin-resistant strains tested. For penicillin-resistant strains, this effect was evident during the first 12-hour dosing interval. Viable counts of both penicillin-intermediate and -resistant strains were reduced by the higher dosages. The 6- and 12-μg/mL peaks were active against most of the penicillin nonsusceptible strains; the minimum effect being able to reduce growth by at least 1.5 logs. When inoculum regrowth was observed, it coincided closely to the time when the amoxicillin concentration fell below the MIC, supporting the time-dependent pattern of activity of β-lactams. These data, together with limited human data, were among the first to influence changes in standard amoxicillin dosing in acute otitis media (AOM).

Correlation between plasma and tissue concentrations

Because many common bacterial infections are extracellular, it is the concentration of antimicrobial in the interstitial fluid that is pharmacodynamically active against these infections. Determining antimicrobial pharmacokinetics, including the extent of penetration, in an infected interstitial area has not been achieved easily. The volume of distribution (V_d), calculated from serum pharmacokinetics, gives an idea of the compartment size occupied by the drug in the body but does not reveal the actual sites of distribution. For example, a V_d greater than 3 L merely indicates that drug is distributed outside the plasma, because this compartment comprises a volume of 3 L [45]. The ability of a drug to penetrate tissues also depends on its lipid solubility and plasma protein binding. Drugs that are hydrophilic, such as β-lactams and aminoglycosides, diffuse freely into the interstitial fluid without penetrating cells. Only the free, unbound portion of drug is able to be distributed outside the plasma and be pharmacodynamically active. Thus, free serum concentrations are a more accurate measure of available drug than total serum concentrations. Protein binding can affect drug clearance, thereby increasing serum concentrations. Observations that increased protein binding of antimicrobials eliminated by glomerular filtration increases the $t_{1/2}$ of the drug and prolongs the time above MIC have been important in the development of some cephalosporins [46,47]. Human serum drug concentrations often are considered an acceptable surrogate marker when determining antimicrobial PK/PD in nonmeningeal infections, because they are more accurate than tissue concentrations obtained in animal models of infection using tissue homogenates. Tissue homogenates mix interstitial, intracellular, and vascular compartments within the tissue and thus may underestimate or overestimate the concentration of drug in the interstitial space, depending on the intracellular penetration of the agent being investigated.

The newer macrolide and quinolone antimicrobials are distributed extensively to body tissues, including respiratory tissues, at concentrations higher than those attained in serum [18,48,49]. However, not all agents penetrate to the same degree, and free antibacterial concentrations in serum may not be proportional to those in other body fluids with all macrolides or quinolones. Indeed, serum levels of ciprofloxacin are below the MIC of drug necessary to inhibit 90% of isolates (MIC_{90}) of S pneumoniae, and borderline against S aureus, although there is some evidence that levels attained at the site of infection are bactericidal [18]. A recent experiment used human tonsillar pharmacokinetic data for azithromycin and roxithromycin in the central compartment of an in vitro pharmacokinetic model to compare their antibacterial effects [40]. The areas between the control growth and time-kill curves were 22% and 36% greater with azithromycin than with roxithromycin for S pyogenes and S pneumoniae, respectively. In addition, bacterial regrowth was observed with roxithromycin but not with azithromycin. These differences might not have been apparent had plasma concentrations been used, because the plasma concentration of roxithromycin is higher than that of azithromycin. However, in tonsillar tissues, the concentration of azithromycin is 55 times greater than that of roxithromycin, and in sinus mucosa, the azithromycin concentration is six times higher than that of roxithromycin.

Thus, for some antimicrobials, their efficacy in respiratory tract infections might best be elucidated using tissue instead of plasma concentrations. In a human otitis media study, plotted amoxicillin middle-ear fluid concentrations after a 25-mg/kg dose were generally less than those attained in serum, and time to peak concentration (T_{max}) was delayed slightly [50]. Nonetheless, in 60% of children studied, middle-ear fluid concentrations were above the amoxicillin breakpoint for resistant pneumococci (>2.0 µg/mL).

A blister technique is sometimes used for assessing interstitial antimicrobial concentrations. After multiple doses of the antimicrobial under study are administered to achieve steady state, blister formation is induced on the forearm with an irritant/vesicant preparation. Blister fluid samples and plasma samples can then be compared pharmacokinetically to determine the relative penetration of the antimicrobial. For example, using this method, the C_{max}, T_{max}, $t_{1/2}$, and AUC were determined for linezolid, a member of the oxazolidinones, a new class of antimicrobials, in both plasma and blister fluid [51]. The mean penetration of linezolid into inflammatory fluid relative to plasma was 104%.

Whenever possible, known human tissue pharmacokinetic data at the site of infection should be used in antimicrobial pharmacokinetic analyses. When these are not available, free serum concentrations are a reasonable alternative.

Effects of obesity on pharmacokinetics/pharmacodynamics

Obesity is associated with increased V_d and enhanced total body clearance of antimicrobials [52]. Depending on the patient and drug, the magnitude of these changes can affect antimicrobial efficacy. With hydrophilic antimicrobials such as β-lactams and aminoglycosides, using total body weight for dosing overestimates V_d and may result in overdosage. Conversely, using ideal body weight for hydrophilic antimicrobials underestimates V_d. For this reason, the use of a correction factor is advocated to normalize V_d when dosing hydrophilic antimicrobials in obese patients [52,53]. Increased renal elimination and hepatic metabolism also have been documented in obese patients; thus, drugs eliminated by these mechanisms may not achieve adequate concentrations at the site of infections for sufficient periods of time at standard doses [52,53]. Unfortunately, the net effect of these changes on antimicrobial dosing in respiratory tract infections in obese patients is largely unknown because of the paucity of data on this subject.

Correlation of pharmacokinetic/pharmacodynamics parameters to antimicrobial efficacy for combinations of antimicrobials

Pharmacodynamic relationships have not been adequately defined for combinations of antimicrobials. One study suggests that the same PK/PD parameters determining efficacy of agents used alone apply to agents used in combination [54]. Additive or synergistic effects between agents that exhibit different patterns of killing may alter the magnitude of the PK/PD relationship, and additional work is needed in this area.

Pharmacokinetic/pharmacodynamic relationships and bacterial resistance

The increasing prevalence of antimicrobial resistance, including multiple drug resistance, among the three key respiratory pathogens *S pneumoniae,*

H influenzae, and *M catarrhalis* has been well documented through ongoing surveillance programs [55–59]. It has been suggested that reports of treatment failures now being seen in clinical practice and documented in the literature represent the "tip of the iceberg" with respect to the impact that resistance has on successful clinical treatment of infection [60–62]. Thus, in addition to successfully treating the infection at hand, a primary goal of antimicrobial therapy is to limit the spread of resistance. Recently, several reports of clinical failure after empiric treatment of pneumococcal infections with azithromycin (500 mg orally on day 1, followed by 250 mg orally on days 2 to 4), clarithromycin (500 mg orally twice daily), or levofloxacin (500 mg orally once daily) have been published [63–65]. Of particular note is a case report involving a 28-year-old patient who died of complications relating to treatment failure with intravenous azithromycin (500 mg once daily) [66]. Evaluation of sputum cultures revealed that the initial isolate was susceptible to penicillin, clindamycin, erythromycin, azithromycin, and quinupristin-dalfopristin. However, a mutation near the macrolide-binding site on the 23s RNA occurred during the course of treatment, resulting in development of resistance to erythromycin, azithromycin, and quinupristin-dalfopristin. Consequently, the patient relapsed and died.

Numerous pathways exist by which resistant bacteria are selected. These include acquisition of resistance through genetic mutations, horizontal transfer of genetic material from a resistant genus or species to a susceptible one, emergence of inducible resistance, and selection of a small, resistant subpopulation of organisms [67]. A change in as little as a single amino acid can result in the genetic promulgation of resistance.

The magnitude of PK/PD parameters required to produce clinically meaningful antimicrobial efficacy in susceptible organisms is not different in resistant organisms [1,5,20]. In four different animal *S pneumoniae* infection models, the bactericidal activity of penicillin correlated with time above MIC and was significant when time above MIC was at least 65% of the experimental time for both penicillin-susceptible and -nonsusceptible strains [5]. Similarly, a number of experiments have shown that the AUC/MIC ratios required for various quinolones to produce a 2 $\log_{10}$ kill of ciprofloxacin-resistant *S pneumoniae* strains were similar to those for ciprofloxacin-susceptible strains [20].

Resistant mutants represent the minority of a given susceptible bacterial population. Once resistant mutants are generated, they can be selected for and flourish under certain environmental conditions, such as during prolonged exposure to subinhibitory antimicrobial concentrations or when bacteria are exposed to very high antimicrobial concentrations for a very short period followed by prolonged subtherapeutic levels. These conditions can be created via inadequate dosing and poor compliance with antimicrobial therapy. Susceptible bacteria will be killed but those with mutations that lead to resistance will proliferate. This phenomenon has been demonstrated in clinical settings, where suboptimal antimicrobial PK/PD in lower respiratory tract infections were found to be a risk factor for the emergence of resistant strains [68]. Data from 107 patients (128 organisms) participating in four clinical trials of nosocomial lower respiratory tract infections at one study site demonstrated that the probability of developing resistance increased significantly when the AUC/MIC ratio was less than 100, with the exception of β-lactam monotherapy against Bush type 1 β-lactamase–producing Gram-negative organisms. Thus, by maximizing PK/PD parameters with adequate dosing, the selection of resistance can be minimized. If infection with an antimicrobial-resistant pathogen is suspected or likely because of patient risk factors, higher doses of certain antimicrobials may be used. Guidelines for the management of acute otitis media and acute bacterial sinusitis recommend higher doses of amoxicillin or amoxicillin/clavulanate in patients at risk of infection with resistant pathogens (eg, previous antimicrobial therapy) [69,70].

The concept of the MPC and mutant selection window is based on the idea that an antimicrobial concentration exists at which resistant mutants can be selectively amplified, with the upper boundary being the antimicrobial concentration that blocks growth of resistant mutants, and the lower boundary being the drug concentration at which growth of the susceptible cells begins [34,71]. In vitro studies using various isolates of *Mycobacterium tuberculosis* have estimated the MPCs of fluoroquinolones and other antituberculosis agents by plating more than 10^{10} cells on drug-containing agar and determining the concentration that allowed no growth of colonies [72]. Of the agents tested, only two fluoroquinolones had MPCs that were below their serum C_{max} values; thus, only these agents would be expected to restrict the selection of resistant mutants when used at recommended doses (Table 3). Other in vitro studies have shown that structural changes in the quinolone molecule substantially impact the magnitude of the MPC [33].

The MPC and mutant selection window have been determined with numerous antimicrobials and bacteria (although not with common respiratory pathogens), and findings suggest they are probably applicable to most pathogen-antimicrobial relationships. Confirmation of these observations is necessary in animal and clinical infection models to more completely support the MPC concept. If relevant concentrations of an antimicrobial in the infected tissue can be maintained above the MPC, then selection of mutants should be severely restricted. Additional work with MPC and mutant selection window may prove to have important implications for limiting the spread of resistance by changing dosing patterns.

Use of pharmacokinetics and pharmacodynamics to optimize treatment and minimize resistance

Drug PK/PD can be combined with MIC values to determine the adequacy of antimicrobial dosing regimens. For example, plasma and middle-ear fluid data were used to determine the pharmacodynamics of

Table 3
The activity (expressed as minimum inhibitory concentration for 99% of organisms [MIC$_{99}$] and mutation prevention concentration [MPC]) and maximum serum concentrations (C$_{max}$) of antituberculosis agents against *Mycobacterium tuberculosis*

Agent	Dose (mg)	MIC$_{99}$ (µg/mL)	MPC (µg/mL)	C$_{max}$
Rifampin	600	0.02	>80	9.5
Streptomycin	1000	0.2	>320	34
Isoniazid	250	0.06	20	7.6
Ciprofloxacin	750	0.15	8	4.4
Moxifloxacin	400	0.037	2.5	4.5
Sparfloxacin	200	0.075	2.5	1.4

Adapted from Dong Y, Zhao X, Kreiswirth BN, Drlicak. Mutant prevention as a measure of antibiotic potency: studies with clinical isolates of *Mycobacterium tuberculosis*. Anitmicrob Agents Chemother 2000;44(9):2581–4.

amoxicillin in the treatment of AOM [50]. Thirty-four children with AOM received amoxicillin doses of 40 mg/kg/day divided in three doses for 2 to 3 days, followed by a single 25-mg/kg dose of amoxicillin. Serum and middle-ear fluid amoxicillin concentrations from the infected ear(s) were measured 0.5 to 4 hours after the 25-mg/kg dose. The most frequently occurring bacterial pathogens were *S pneumoniae* and *H influenzae*. Total middle-ear fluid amoxicillin concentrations were maintained above 1 µg/mL for 4 hours (50% of the dosing interval) and above 2.0 µg/mL for 2.5 hours (31% of the dosing interval). This corresponded to plasma concentrations being above 2.0 µg/mL for 62% of the dosing interval, predicting approximately 100% killing even of most penicillin-resistant pneumococci. Plasma concentrations following a 13.3-mg/kg dose, estimated assuming linear absorption kinetics, only exceeded an MIC of 1.0 µg/mL for 30% of the dosing interval. Thus, at standard dosing of 25 mg/kg/day, amoxicillin is ineffective against penicillin-resistant pneumococci. Based on these observations, the investigators recommended an amoxicillin dosing increase from 40 mg/kg/day to 75 to 90 mg/kg/day.

Drug PK/PD also guide new antimicrobial drug development. Two new formulations of amoxicillin/clavulanate have been developed to increase the effectiveness of the combination against pathogens with increasing resistance to amoxicillin. The pediatric formulation, previously mentioned, has a recommended dosing schedule of 90 mg/kg/day divided every 12 hours. The second, adult formulation provides both immediate- and sustained-release amoxicillin in a 16:1 ratio with clavulanate (2 g amoxicillin/125 mg clavulanate per dose; recommended dosing every 12 hours) [73]. In healthy adults, this new formulation was as well tolerated as the current formulation. In addition, the duration of time that serum levels exceeded 4 µg/mL was 49.4% of a 12-hour dosing interval. Compared with conventional amoxicillin-clavulanate formulations, the pharmacokinetically enhanced formulation has a slower decline in plasma concentrations, contributing to a longer time above MIC (Fig. 3).

Once the PK/PD breakpoint has been established, the question remains as to how frequently it is achieved in patients. The closer MIC values of pathogens are to breakpoints, the more variation between individuals. Monte Carlo simulation affords a means by which probability outcomes, such as achieving the PK/PD target, can be attained without the rigor, time, and expense of a clinical trial. It has been recently introduced in the area of pharmacodynamics [74–77]. Pharmacokinetic values for levofloxacin obtained from a sample of patients and published levofloxacin MIC surveillance data for clinical isolates were used to generate thousands of random, single-point AUC/MIC estimates, and their probability of occurrence were plotted. Using this methodology and sample data from patients, the probability of attaining an AUC/MIC ratio greater than or equal to 30 with levofloxacin was 99% [76]. Another Monte Carlo simulation assessed the probability of achieving target AUC/MIC ratios for *S pneumoniae* with intravenous, once-daily gatifloxacin 400 mg or levofloxacin 500 mg with AUC data obtained from acutely ill patients with community-acquired infections [77]. The median AUC/MIC ratios were 144 for gatifloxacin and 50 for levofloxacin. The probability of attaining AUC:MIC ratios of 30 and 100 for gatifloxacin were

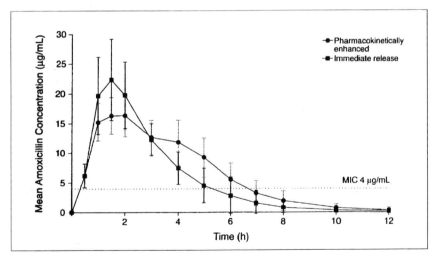

Fig. 3. Concentration-time profile in serum of amoxicillin after oral administration of a new pharmacokinetically enhanced formulation of amoxicillin-clavulanate (immediate-release amoxicillin 1125 mg plus 875 mg sustained-release amoxicillin) and after conventional amoxicillin-clavulanate (2000 mg amoxicillin). Only the new formulation exceeds the duration of time the concentration exceeds the minimum inhibitory concentration (T > MIC) for 4.8 hours (40% of the 12-hour dosing interval) at an MIC of 4 μg/mL. The new formulation present at a concentration of 4 μg/mL for 49% of the dosing interval compared with 38% for the same dose of the immediate-release formulation. (*Reproduced from* Kaye CM, Allen A, Perry S, et al. The clinical pharmacokinetics of a new pharmacokinetically enhanced formulation of amoxicillin/clavulanate. Clin Ther 2001;23(4):578–84; with permission.)

99% and 68%, and for levofloxacin were 82% and 17%, respectively (Fig. 4). Gatifloxacin in this study therefore had a higher probability of achieving these target AUC:MIC ratios than levofloxacin at a 500-mg dose, and use of the new 750-mg dose of levofloxacin is recommended. Monte Carlo simulation, using patient-based AUC and MIC distributions, may have implications for selection of optimal antibiotics for the empiric treatment of infections. Using PK/PD values from sick patients rather than healthy individuals provides a more accurate portrayal of antimicrobial PK/PD. For example, the mean levofloxacin AUC in healthy volunteers is 47.5 mg·L/hour. In the Monte Carlo analysis described previously in which patients received once-daily doses of levofloxacin 500 mg, 92% of patients had AUC values greater than or equal to 51, and 12% had AUC values greater than or equal to 121.75 The differences between these values reflect the effects of age (many patients were older than 70 years of age), renal function (the mean creatinine clearance of patients was half that of younger, healthy volunteers), and possibly other aspects relating to infection that might alter drug pharmacokinetics. Had published AUC values for young, healthy volunteers been used, the accuracy of the derived probabilities would be in question.

Another model, the Poole Therapeutic Outcome Model, can be used to predict bacteriologic and clinical efficacy of various antimicrobials based on frequency distributions of pathogens, spontaneous resolution rates of the pathogens, PK/PD parameters, and antimicrobial resistance patterns [70,78]. This model is a tool to help predict the likelihood of bacteriologic success in diseases such as AOM and acute sinusitis with particular antimicrobial agents by accounting for various factors including: (1) the proportion of patients with a clinical diagnosis of acute bacterial infection and a positive culture from the site of infection; (2) the clinical resolution of disease in the culture-negative patient group; (3) the distribution of pathogens frequently encountered in the disease; (4) the spontaneous resolution rate associated with each pathogen; and (5) the in vitro susceptibility of the predominant pathogens to antimicrobial agents at PK/PD breakpoints. The model can predict overall clinical outcomes for the total patient group (ie, those with either bacterial or nonbacterial disease) and for the bacterial infection group.

A probability model has also been developed to estimate the impact of antimicrobial resistance on clinical outcomes for adult outpatients with community-acquired pneumonia [79]. This model assumed patients would be evaluated at 48 to 72 hours, with those failing to improve being either hospitalized or switched to a different antibiotic. Two strategies were considered: amoxicillin followed by erythromycin (amoxicillin/erythromycin) and erythromycin followed by levofloxacin (erythromycin/levofloxacin). Analyses were conducted based on susceptibility of the major pathogens in France, a country with high rates of resistance in respiratory pathogens, and the United Kingdom, where resistance rates are low. Primary outcome measures were the proportion of patients successfully treated with first-line therapy and the proportion of patients subsequently hospitalized. The model

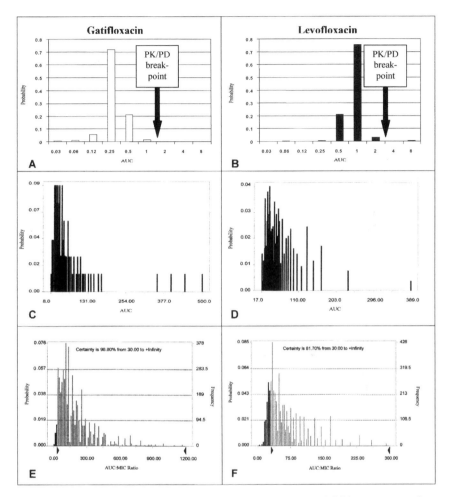

Fig. 4. (*A, B*) Distribution of gatifloxacin and levofloxacin minimum inhibitory concentrations (MICs) against *Streptococcus pneumoniae* from the 1999–2000 Sentry Respiratory Surveillance Program study. (*C*) Distribution of gatifloxacin free-drug area under the concentration-time curve $(AUC)_{0-24}$ (μg·hr/mL) ratio in the patient population. (*D*) Distribution of levofloxacin free-drug area under the concentration-time curve $(AUC)_{0-24}$ (μg·hr/mL) ratio in the patient population. (*E*) Results of a 5000-patient Monte Carlo simulation for gatifloxacin based on MIC and AUC distributions presented in (*A, C*). The dark bars represent the number of simulated patients with AUC:MIC ratios <30, whereas the light bars represent patients with AUC:MIC ratios of ≥30. The probability of gatifloxacin attaining an AUC:MIC ratio of at least 30 is 98.80%. (*F*) Results of a 5000-patient Monte Carlo simulation for levofloxacin based on MIC and AUC distributions presented in (*B, D*). The dark bars represent the number of simulated patients with AUC:MIC ratios <30, whereas the light bars represent patients with AUC:MIC ratios of ≥30. The probability of levofloxacin attaining an AUC:MIC ratio of at least 30 is 81.7%. (*Adapted from* Nicolau DP, Ambrose PG. Pharmacodynamic profiling of levofloxacin and gatifloxacin using Monte Carlo simulation for community-acquired isolates of *Streptococcus pneumoniae*. Am J Med 2001;111(Suppl 9A):13S–18S [discussion 36S–38S]; with permission.)

estimated that in France, the amoxicillin/erythromycin strategy would lead to 67.8% improving within 48 to 72 hours and 12.7% subsequently being hospitalized, compared with 48.6% and 13.7% for erythromycin/levofloxacin. For the United Kingdom, first-line success and hospitalization rates were, respectively, 71.7% and 8.1% for amoxicillin/erythromycin, and 65.3% and 9.3% for erythromycin/levofloxacin. The model estimated that antimicrobial resistance was responsible for > 40% of hospitalizations in France and 15% in the United Kingdom. These data suggest that antimicrobial resistance may be a significant contributor to subsequent hospitalization in adults initially treated as outpatients for community-acquired pneumonia and that choice of outpatient treatment strategy should consider local resistance rates to minimize treatment failures and hospitalizations.

Nasopharyngeal carriage of pathogens represents an important component in the development and spread of respiratory tract infections, including those caused by resistant strains. In certain types of infection in which nasopharyngeal carriage rates are high, such as pediatric otitis media, a goal of antimicrobial therapy should be to prevent nasopharyngeal colonization by resistant organisms to reduce the development of infection, outbreaks, and resistance. Higher dosages of antimicrobials may be needed in these cases. It has been suggested that a concentration above the MIC for 80% to 100% of the dosing interval is necessary to achieve high rates of eradication in the nasopharynx [14]. This may not be possible with many standard antimicrobial regimens used for respiratory tract infections, and additional work in this area is needed.

Finally, drug pharmacokinetics and pharmacodynamics are now being used in surveillance testing to determine susceptibility breakpoints in a more clinically meaningful way [56,59,80,81]. Susceptibility breakpoints are defined in this manner as either: (1) for time-dependent antimicrobials with minimal PAE, the unbound concentration in serum that is maintained for at least 40% to 50% of a dosing interval, based on published serum pharmacokinetics and standard dosing regimens or (2) for time-dependent antimicrobials with prolonged PAE and for concentration-dependent agents, unbound serum AUC divided by 25. The differences in susceptibility of *S pneumoniae* and *H influenzae* isolates to various antimicrobials using PK/PD breakpoints versus MIC breakpoints have been demonstrated [23,56]. Significant differences exist in both the breakpoint and the percentage of isolates susceptible based on how the breakpoint is determined (Table 4). Using the PK/PD breakpoints of the antimicrobials tested, only amoxicillin-clavulanate and newer quinolones would be effective against more than 90% of *S pneumoniae* and *H influenzae* strains. This type of information has important implications in the empiric treatment of respiratory infections, as well as consideration of the need to cover "atypical" pathogens, such as *Mycoplasma pneumoniae, Chlamydia pneumoniae,* and *Legionella pneumophila* in community-acquired pneumonia. Antimicrobial breakpoints based on PK/PD breakpoints have been adopted by the National Committee for Clinical Laboratory Standards

Table 4
Percent of world-wide isolates of *S pneumoniae* and *H influenzae* susceptible to various antimicrobials based on NCCLS and pharmacokinetic/pharmacodynamic (PK/PD) breakpoints

Antimicrobial	*Streptococcus pneumoniae*				*Haemophilus influenzae*			
	NCCLS		PK/PD		NCCLS		PK/PD	
	Breakpoint (μg/mL)	Susceptible (%)	Breakpoint (μg/mL)	Susceptible (%)	Breakpoint (μg/mL)	Susceptible (%)	Breakpoint (μg/mL)	Susceptible (%)
Amoxicillin	≤2	95.1	≤2	95.1	≤4	83.2	≤2	81.6
Amoxicillin-clavulanate	≤2	95.5	≤2	95.5	≤4	99.6	≤2	98.1
Amoxicillin-clavulanate, new formulations	NA	NA	≤4	97.9	NA	NA	≤4	99.6
Cefaclor	≤1	60.2	≤0.5	21.8	≤8	89.7	≤0.5	1.4
Cefuroxime axetil	≤1	78.6	≤1	78.6	≤4	98.1	≤1	83.6
Cefixime	NA	NA	≤1	69.2	≤1	99.8	≤1	99.8
Cefprozil	≤2	79.7	≤1	78.1	≤8	92.5	≤1	22.3
Cefdinir	≤0.5	76.5	≤0.5	76.5	≤1	97.6	≤0.5	92.0
Clarithromycin	≤0.25	75.5	≤0.25	75.5	≤8	79.6	≤0.25	<0.3
Azithromycin	≤0.5	75.4	≤0.12	74.3	≤4	99.5	≤0.12	<1.2
Ckindamycin	≤0.25	86.0	NA	NA	NA	NA	NA	NA
Doxyxycline	NA	NA	≤0.25	71.3	NA	NA	≤0.25	28.9
Trimethoprim-sulfamethoxazole	≤0.5	63.3	≤0.5	63.3	≤0.5	78.3	≤0.5	78.3
Gemifloxacin	NA	NA	≤0.25	99.9	≤NA	NA	≤0.25	99.9
Levofloxacin	≤2	98.9	≤2	98.9	≤2	99.9	≤2	99.9
Gatifloxacin	≤1	98.5	≤1	98.5	≤1	99.9	≤1	99.9
Moxifloxacin	≤1	98.9	≤1	98.9	≤1	99.8	≤1	99.8

Abbreviations: NCCLS, National Committee for Clinical Laboratory Standards; NA, not reported.

Adapted from Jacobs MR, Felmingham P, Appelbaum PC, Gruneberg RN. The Alexander Project 1998–2000: susceptibility of pathogens isolated from community-acquired respiratory tract infection to commonly used antimicrobial agents. J Antimicrob Chemother 2003;52(2):229–46.

(NCCLS) for *S pneumoniae*, but many breakpoints are still in need of revision, particularly for *H influenzae* [82].

Summary

Our knowledge of the impact of drug pharmacokinetics and pharmacodynamics on antimicrobial efficacy has been elucidated during the past 20 years using animal, in vitro, and limited clinical observations. We now know that classes of antimicrobials fall into one of three patterns of killing: time-dependent, concentration-dependent, or time-dependent plus PAEs, with each class exhibiting a similar magnitude of activity against a pathogen, including resistant strains. The efficacy of an antimicrobial agent can be predicted based on its pattern of activity relative to the MIC against a pathogen. These observations have led to a change in the paradigm of treating respiratory infections, developing new antimicrobials and dosing regimens, and establishing clinically relevant susceptibility breakpoints.

Currently, unbound serum concentrations are used to define antimicrobial pharmacodynamics because they are easy to obtain and reflect, to some measure, the extracellular concentration of drug at many sites of infection. However, the penetration of antimicrobials into sites of infection is variable, and not all penetrate to the same degree relative to serum concentrations. A more accurate prediction of antimicrobial efficacy would be to use pharmacokinetic data for drugs at the site of infection obtained during an active infection. Unfortunately, such information is rarely available and is confounded by the need to distinguish between intracellular and extracellular compartments.

For some newer antimicrobials, respiratory tissue concentrations in healthy volunteers have been determined, and it may be more appropriate to use these data rather than serum concentrations. However, evidence for currently available agents supports use of serum, and not tissue, pharmacokinetic parameters for extracellular pathogens [62]. For the seriously ill patient, individual pharmacokinetic data and organism MIC data should be obtained to optimize dosing.

The prevalence of resistance and patterns of infection are varied depending on patterns in a given geographic area. The clinician should consult local antimicrobial surveillance data when selecting treatment for respiratory tract infections. Applying PK/PD parameters to dosing not only increases the likelihood of successful treatment of that infection but also serves to limit resistance. Agents should have adequate potency to minimize the selection and spread of resistant strains, while the most potent antimicrobials should be kept in reserve when treating respiratory tract infections in outpatients. In the future, the MPC and mutant selection window may, like susceptibility breakpoints, guide researchers and clinicians in selecting optimal antimicrobial therapy.

References

[1] Craig WA. Pharmacokinetic/pharmacodynamic parameters: rationale for antibacterial dosing of mice and men. Clin Infect Dis 1998;26(1):1–10[quiz 11–2].

[2] Vogelman B, Gudmundsson S, Leggett J, Turnidge J, Ebert S, Craig WA. Correlation of antimicrobial pharmacokinetic parameters with therapeutic efficacy in an animal model. J Infect Dis 1988;158(4):831–47.

[3] Craig WA. Interrelationship between pharmacokinetics and pharmacodynamics in determining dosage regimens for broad-spectrum cephalosporins. Diagn Microbiol Infect Dis 1995;22(1–2):89–96.

[4] Leggett JE, Fantin B, Ebert S, et al. Comparative antibiotic dose-effect relations at several dosing intervals in murine pneumonitis and thigh-infection models. J Infect Dis 1989; 159(2):281–92.

[5] Erlendsdottir H, Knudsen JD, Odenholt I, et al. Penicillin pharmacodynamics in four experimental pneumococcal infection models. Antimicrob Agents Chemother 2001;45(4): 1078–85.

[6] Mouton JW, Touzw DJ, Horrevorts AM, Vinks AA. Comparative pharmacokinetics of the carbapenems: clinical implications. Clin Pharmacokinet 2000;39(3):185–201.

[7] den Hollander JG, Knudsen JD, Mouton JW, et al. Comparison of pharmacodynamics of azithromycin and erythromycin in vitro and in vivo. Antimicrob Agents Chemother 1998; 42(2):377–82.

[8] Novelli A, Fallani S, Cassetta MI, Arrigucci S, Mazzei T. In vivo pharmacodynamic evaluation of clarithromycin in comparison to erythromycin. J Chemother 2002;14(6): 584–90.

[9] Craig W, Kiem S, Andes D. Free drug 24-hr AUC/MIC is the PK/PD target that correlates with in vivo efficacy of macrolides, azalides, ketolides and clindamycin (Abstract A-1264). Paper presented at 42nd Interscience Conference on Antimicrobial Agents and Chemotherapy. San Diego, California, September 27–30, 2002.

[10] Carbon C. Pharmacodynamics of macrolides, azalides, and streptogramins: effect on extracellular pathogens. Clin Infect Dis 1998;27(1):28–32.

[11] Rodvold KA, Piscitelli SC. New oral macrolide and fluoroquinolone antibiotics: an overview of pharmacokinetics, interactions, and safety. Clin Infect Dis 1993;17(Suppl 1):S192–9.

[12] Bauernfeind A, Jungwirth R, Eberlein E. Comparative pharmacodynamics of clarithromycin and azithromycin against respiratory pathogens. Infection 1995;23(5):316–21.

[13] Stein GE, Schooley S. Comparative serum bactericidal activity of clarithromycin and azithromycin against macrolide-sensitive and resistant strains of Streptococcus pneumoniae. Diagn Microbiol Infect Dis 2001;39(3):181–5.

[14] Craig WA. The hidden impact of antibacterial resistance in respiratory tract infection. Re-evaluating current antibiotic therapy. Respir Med 2001;95(Suppl A):S12–9 [discussion S26].

[15] Dagan R, Johnson CE, McLinn S, et al. Bacteriologic and clinical efficacy of amoxicillin/clavulanate vs. azithromycin in acute otitis media. Pediatr Infect Dis J 2000;19(2):95–104.

[16] Dagan R, Leibovitz E, Fliss DM, et al. Bacteriologic efficacies of oral azithromycin and oral cefaclor in treatment of acute otitis media in infants and young children. Antimicrob Agents Chemother 2000;44(1):43–50.

[17] Kim MK, Zhou W, Tessier PR, et al. Bactericidal effect and pharmacodynamics of cethromycin (ABT-773) in a murine pneumococcal pneumonia model. Antimicrob Agents Chemother 2002;46(10):3185–92.

[18] Wise R, Honeybourne D. Pharmacokinetics and pharmacodynamics of fluoroquinolones in the respiratory tract. Eur Respir J. Jul 1999;14(1):221–9.

[19] Lister PD. Pharmacodynamics of gatifloxacin against Streptococcus pneumoniae in an in vitro pharmacokinetic model: impact of area under the curve/MIC ratios on eradication. Antimicrob Agents Chemother 2002;46(1):69–74.

[20] Woodnutt G. Pharmacodynamics to combat resistance. J Antimicrob Chemother 2000; 46(Suppl T1):25–31.

[21] Wright DH, Brown GH, Peterson ML, Rotschafer JC. Application of fluoroquinolone pharmacodynamics. J Antimicrob Chemother 2000;46(5):669–83.

[22] Preston SL, Drusano GL, Berman AL, et al. Pharmacodynamics of levofloxacin: a new paradigm for early clinical trials. JAMA 1998;279(2):125–9.

[23] Jacobs MR. Optimisation of antimicrobial therapy using pharmacokinetic and pharmacodynamic parameters. Clin Microbiol Infect 2001;7(11):589–96.

[24] Bertino J Jr, Fish D. The safety profile of the fluoroquinolones. Clin Ther 2000;22(7): 798–817 [discussion 797].

[25] Mandell LA, Ball P, Tillotson G. Antimicrobial safety and tolerability: differences and dilemmas. Clin Infect Dis 2001;32(Suppl 1):S72–9.

[26] Zhanel GG, Ennis K, Vercaigne L, et al. A critical review of the fluoroquinolones: focus on respiratory infections. Drugs 2002;62(1):13–59.

[27] Quale J, Landman D, Ravishankar J, Flores C, Bratu S. Streptococcus pneumoniae, Brooklyn, New York: fluoroquinolone resistance at our doorstep. Emerg Infect Dis 2002; 8(6):594–7.

[28] Chen DK, McGeer A, de Azavedo JC, Low DE. Decreased susceptibility of Streptococcus pneumoniae to fluoroquinolones in Canada. Canadian Bacterial Surveillance Network. N Engl J Med 1999;341(4):233–9.

[29] Blum MD, Graham DJ, McCloskey CA. Temafloxacin syndrome: review of 95 cases. Clin Infect Dis 1994;18(6):946–50.

[30] Ball P. Future of the quinolones. Semin Respir Infect 2001;16(3):215–24.

[31] Hooper DC. New uses for new and old quinolones and the challenge of resistance. Clin Infect Dis 2000;30(2):243–54.

[32] Vesga O, Bonnat C, Craig W. In vivo pharmacodynamic activity of HMR3647, a new ketolide. Paper presented at 37th Interscience Conference on Antimicrobial Agents and Chemotherapy. Toronto, Ontario, Canada, September 28-October 1, 1997.

[33] Sindelar G, Zhao X, Liew A, et al. Mutant prevention concentration as a measure of fluoroquinolone potency against mycobacteria. Antimicrob Agents Chemother 2000; 44(12):3337–43.

[34] Zhao X, Drlica K. Restricting the selection of antibiotic-resistant mutants: a general strategy derived from fluoroquinolone studies. Clin Infect Dis 2001;33(Suppl 3):S147–56.

[35] Zhao X, Drlica K. Restricting the selection of antibiotic-resistant mutant bacteria: measurement and potential use of the mutant selection window. J Infect Dis 2002;185(4): 561–5.

[36] Smith HJ, Nichol KA, Hoban DJ, Zhanel GG. Stretching the mutant prevention concentration (MPC) beyond its limits. J Antimicrob Chemother 2003;51(6):1323–5.

[37] Andes D, Craig WA. In vivo activities of amoxicillin and amoxicillin-clavulanate against Streptococcus pneumoniae: application to breakpoint determinations. Antimicrob Agents Chemother 1998;42(9):2375–9.

[38] Magnusdottir AB, Hermansson A, Melhus A. Experimental study of the virulence of Streptococcus pneumoniae with reduced susceptibility to penicillin. Int J Pediatr Otorhinolaryngol 2000;55(1):1–9.

[39] Ba BB, Bernard A, Iliadis A, et al. New approach for accurate simulation of human pharmacokinetics in an in vitro pharmacodynamic model: application to ciprofloxacin. J Antimicrob Chemother 2001;47(2):223–7.

[40] Firsov AA, Zinner SH, Vostrov SN, et al. Comparative pharmacodynamics of azithromycin and roxithromycin with S. pyogenes and S. pneumoniae in a model that simulates in vitro pharmacokinetics in human tonsils. J Antimicrob Chemother 2002;49(1):113–9.

[41] Gustafsson I, Hjelm E, Cars O. In vitro pharmacodynamics of the new ketolides HMR 3004 and HMR 3647 (Telithromycin) against Chlamydia pneumoniae. Antimicrob Agents Chemother 2000;44(7):1846–9.

[42] Lister PD, Pong A, Chartrand SA, Sanders CC. Rationale behind high-dose amoxicillin therapy for acute otitis media due to penicillin-nonsusceptible pneumococci: support from in vitro pharmacodynamic studies. Antimicrob Agents Chemother 1997;41(9):1926–32.

[43] Lister PD, Prevan AM, Sanders CC. Importance of beta-lactamase inhibitor pharmacokinetics in the pharmacodynamics of inhibitor-drug combinations: studies with piperacillin-tazobactam and piperacillin-sulbactam. Antimicrob Agents Chemother 1997;41(4): 721–7.

[44] Odenholt I, Lowdin E, Cars O. Pharmacodynamics of telithromycin In vitro against respiratory tract pathogens. Antimicrob Agents Chemother 2001;45(1):23–9.

[45] Winters M. Basic clinical pharmacokinetics. 3rd edition. Vancouver, WA: Applied Therapeutics, Inc; 1994.

[46] Craig WA. Pharmacokinetics of antibiotics with special emphasis on cephalosporins. Clin Microbiol Infect 2000;6(Suppl 3):46–9.

[47] Turnidge JD. Pharmacodynamic (kinetic) considerations in the treatment of moderately severe infections with cefotaxime. Diagn Microbiol Infect Dis 1995;22(1–2):57–69.

[48] Nightingale CH. Pharmacokinetics and pharmacodynamics of newer macrolides. Pediatr Infect Dis J 1997;16(4):438–43.

[49] Rodvold KA. Clinical pharmacokinetics of clarithromycin. Clin Pharmacokinet 1999; 37(5):385–98.

[50] Canafax DM, Yuan Z, Chonmaitree T, Deka K, Russlie HQ, Giebink GS. Amoxicillin middle ear fluid penetration and pharmacokinetics in children with acute otitis media. Pediatr Infect Dis J 1998;17(2):149–56.

[51] Gee T, Ellis R, Marshall G, Andrews J, Ashby J, Wise R. Pharmacokinetics and tissue penetration of linezolid following multiple oral doses. Antimicrob Agents Chemother 2001; 45(6):1843–6.

[52] Bearden DT, Rodvold KA. Dosage adjustments for antibacterials in obese patients: applying clinical pharmacokinetics. Clin Pharmacokinet 2000;38(5):415–26.

[53] Wurtz R, Itokazu G, Rodvold K. Antimicrobial dosing in obese patients. Clin Infect Dis 1997;25(1):112–8.

[54] Mouton JW, van Ogtrop ML, Andes D, Craig WA. Use of pharmacodynamic indices to predict efficacy of combination therapy in vivo. Antimicrob Agents Chemother 1999; 43(10):2473–8.

[55] Doern GV, Jorgensen JH, Thornsberry C, Preston DA. Prevalence of antimicrobial resistance among clinical isolates of Haemophilus influenzae: a collaborative study. Diagn Microbiol Infect Dis 1986;4(2):95–107.

[56] Jacobs MR, Bajaksouzian S, Zilles A, Lin G, Pankuch GA, Appelbaum PC. Susceptibilities of Streptococcus pneumoniae and Haemophilus influenzae to 10 oral antimicrobial agents based on pharmacodynamic parameters: 1997 US Surveillance study. Antimicrob Agents Chemother 1999;43(8):1901–8.

[57] Thornsberry C, Ogilvie PT, Holley HP Jr, Sahm DF. Survey of susceptibilities of Streptococcus pneumoniae, Haemophilus influenzae, and Moraxella catarrhalis isolates to 26 antimicrobial agents: a prospective US study. Antimicrob Agents Chemother 1999; 43(11):2612–23.

[58] Hoban DJ, Doern GV, Fluit AC, Roussel-Delvallez M, Jones RN. Worldwide prevalence of antimicrobial resistance in Streptococcus pneumoniae, Haemophilus influenzae, and Moraxella catarrhalis in the SENTRY Antimicrobial Surveillance Program, 1997–1999. Clin Infect Dis 2001;32(Suppl 2):S81–93.

[59] Jacobs MR, Felmingham D, Appelbaum PC, Gruneberg RN. The Alexander Project 1998–2000: susceptibility of pathogens isolated from community-acquired respiratory tract infection to commonly used antimicrobial agents. J Antimicrob Chemother 2003;52(2): 229–46.

[60] Garau J. Treatment of drug-resistant pneumococcal pneumonia. Lancet Infect Dis 2002; 2(7):404–15.

[61] Lonks JR, Garau J, Gomez L, et al. Failure of macrolide antibiotic treatment in patients with bacteremia due to erythromycin-resistant Streptococcus pneumoniae. Clin Infect Dis 2002;35(5):556–4.

[62] Jacobs MR. In vivo veritas: in vitro macrolide resistance in systemic Streptococcus pneumoniae infections does result in clinical failure. Clin Infect Dis 2002;35(5):565–9.

[63] Davidson R, Cavalcanti R, Brunton JL, et al. Resistance to levofloxacin and failure of treatment of pneumococcal pneumonia. N Engl J Med 2002;346(10):747–50.

[64] Empey PE, Jennings HR, Thornton AC, Rapp RP, Evans ME. Levofloxacin failure in a patient with pneumococcal pneumonia. Ann Pharmacother 2001;35(6):687–90.

[65] Kelley MA, Weber DJ, Gilligan P, Cohen MS. Breakthrough pneumococcal bacteremia in patients being treated with azithromycin and clarithromycin. Clin Infect Dis 2000;31(4):1008–11.

[66] Musher DM, Dowell ME, Shortridge VD, et al. Emergence of macrolide resistance during treatment of pneumococcal pneumonia. N Engl J Med 2002;346(8):630–1.

[67] Tenover FC, McGowan JE Jr. Reasons for the emergence of antibiotic resistance. Am J Med Sci 1996;311(1):9–16.

[68] Thomas JK, Forrest A, Bhavnani SM, et al. Pharmacodynamic evaluation of factors associated with the development of bacterial resistance in acutely ill patients during therapy. Antimicrob Agents Chemother 1998;42(3):521–7.

[69] Dowell SF, Butler JC, Giebink GS, et al. Acute otitis media: management and surveillance in an era of pneumococcal resistance–a report from the Drug-resistant Streptococcus pneumoniae Therapeutic Working Group. Pediatr Infect Dis J 1999;18(1):1–9.

[70] Anon JB, Jacobs MR, Poole MD, et al. Antimicrobial treatment guidelines for acute bacterial rhinosinusitis. Otolaryngol Head Neck Surg 2004;130(1 Suppl):1–45.

[71] Blondeau JM, Zhao X, Hansen G, Drlica K. Mutant prevention concentrations of fluoroquinolones for clinical isolates of Streptococcus pneumoniae. Antimicrob Agents Chemother 2001;45(2):433–8.

[72] Dong Y, Zhao X, Kreiswirth BN, Drlica K. Mutant prevention concentration as a measure of antibiotic potency: studies with clinical isolates of Mycobacterium tuberculosis. Antimicrob Agents Chemother 2000;44(9):2581–4.

[73] Kaye CM, Allen A, Perry S, et al. The clinical pharmacokinetics of a new pharmacokinetically enhanced formulation of amoxicillin/clavulanate. Clin Ther 2001;23(4):578–84.

[74] Ambrose PG, Grasela DM. The use of Monte Carlo simulation to examine pharmacodynamic variance of drugs: fluoroquinolone pharmacodynamics against Streptococcus pneumoniae. Diagn Microbiol Infect Dis 2000;38(3):151–7.

[75] Ambrose PG, Quintiliani R. Limitations of single point pharmacodynamic analysis. Pediatr Infect Dis J 2000;19(8):769.

[76] Nightingale CH, Grant EM, Quintiliani R. Pharmacodynamics and pharmacokinetics of levofloxacin. Chemotherapy 2000;46(Suppl 1):6–14.

[77] Nicolau DP, Ambrose PG. Pharmacodynamic profiling of levofloxacin and gatifloxacin using Monte Carlo simulation for community-acquired isolates of Streptococcus pneumoniae. Am J Med 2001;111(Suppl 9A):13S–8S [discussion 36S–38S].

[78] Poole MD. A mathematical therapeutic outcomes model for sinusitis. Otolaryngol Head Neck Surg 2004;130(1 Suppl):46–50.

[79] Singer ME, Harding I, Jacobs MR, Jaffe DH. Impact of antimicrobial resistance on health outcomes in the out-patient treatment of adult community-acquired pneumonia: a probability model. J Antimicrob Chemother 2003;51(5):1269–82.

[80] Jacobs MR. Worldwide trends in antimicrobial resistance among common respiratory tract pathogens in children. Pediatr Infect Dis J 2003;22(8 Suppl):S109–19.

[81] Jacobs MR, Koeth LM, Appelbaum PC. Use of appropriate breakpoints in antimicrobial surveillance studies. Clin Infect Dis 2002;35(11):1446–8 [author reply 1448–9].

[82] NCCLS. Performance standards for antimicrobial susceptibility testing; fourteenth informational supplement M100–S14, 2002. Wayne, PA: NCCLS; 2004.

ELSEVIER
SAUNDERS

CLINICS IN
LABORATORY
MEDICINE

Clin Lab Med 24 (2004) 503–530

Susceptibility of *Streptococcus pneumoniae*, *Haemophilus influenzae*, and *Moraxella catarrhalis* to 17 oral antimicrobial agents based on pharmacodynamic parameters: 1998–2001 U.S. Surveillance Study

Michael R. Jacobs, MD, PhD[a,*],
Saralee Bajaksouzian, MS[a], Anne Windau, BS[a],
Caryn E. Good, MA, MPH[a], Gengrong Lin, BS[b],
Glenn A. Pankuch, MS[b], Peter C. Appelbaum, MD, PhD[b]

[a]*Department of Pathology, Case Western Reserve University and University Hospitals of Cleveland, 11100 Euclid Avenue, Cleveland, OH 44106, USA*
[b]*Department of Pathology, Hershey Medical Center, 500 University Drive, Hershey, PA 17033, USA*

The ubiquitous pathogens *Streptococcus pneumoniae* and *Haemophilus influenzae* cause a wide spectrum of community-acquired infections, including sinusitis, acute exacerbations of chronic bronchitis, pneumonia, otitis media, bacteremia, and meningitis. The advent and widespread use of the protein-conjugated type b capsular polysaccharide *H influenzae* vaccine in children has largely eliminated the risk of life-threatening infections due to encapsulated type b strains [1], but localized infections caused by nonencapsulated *H influenzae* strains remain common. The introduction in the United States of a seven-valent protein-conjugated capsular polysaccharide *S pneumoniae* vaccine in children in 2000 has resulted in a 29% decrease in the incidence of invasive pneumococcal disease overall in 2001 compared with 1998 to 1999, and a 35% decrease in penicillin non-susceptible strains [2]. Although the greatest decrease in invasive pneumococcal disease during this period occurred in children under 2 years of age (69%), the incidence of this disease also fell significantly for adults, being

Financial support for this work was provided by Glaxo SmithKline Pharmaceuticals, Philadelphia, PA, USA.
* Corresponding author.
E-mail address: mrj6@cwru.edu (M.R. Jacobs).

32% lower for adults 20 to 39 years of age, 8% lower for those 40 to 64 years of age, and 18% lower for those ≥65 years of age [2].

Antimicrobial resistance to most classes of antimicrobial agents has emerged in both *H influenzae* and *S pneumoniae*, and effective patient management requires physicians to be aware of the patterns and clinical significance of antibiotic resistance in these pathogens. This knowledge is gained, in large measure, from periodic systematic epidemiologic surveillance studies. Emergence of resistance of *H influenzae* to penicillins, mediated by β-lactamase production, first emerged in the United States in 1974 [3,4] and has evolved into an obstacle to effective treatment with older β-lactams. Its prevalence has risen steadily from its appearance in 1974 to 16% in 1986 [5], 33% in 1993 [6], and 36% in 1994 to 1995 [7]. Additionally, investigators have noted higher minimum inhibitory concentrations (MICs) for ampicillin, amoxicillin, cefaclor, and cefprozil with β-lactamase–producing strains [8–10]. Far less common is non-β-lactamase–mediated ampicillin resistance [8]. β-Lactamase–negative, ampicillin-resistant (BLNAR) strains possess altered penicillin-binding proteins (PBPs) that have decreased affinity for many β-lactam agents [11,12]. BLNAR strains are rare in most countries, except for Japan, where they accounted for 2.6% of isolates [13]. Additionally, β-lactamase is produced by most strains of *Moraxella catarrhalis*, and this species is also intrinsically resistant to trimethoprim [13].

Antibiotic-resistant strains of *S pneumoniae* have been reported on all continents in the 2 decades since resistant pneumococcal strains were identified in the United States [14]. In some regions, drug-resistant *S pneumoniae* predominate, with numerous strains resistant to multiple agents [10,14]. Changes in the affinity of PBPs, which are chromosomally mediated, result in β-lactam resistance. Penicillin-resistant strains (penicillin MICs ≥ 2 µg/mL) are now common in many countries, including the United States, France, Spain, Romania, Japan, Korea, and Taiwan [13,14]. Additionally, clinical failure of treatment for patients with meningitis led to the detection of *S pneumoniae* strains highly resistant to third-generation cephalosporins [15,16]. The MICs of these cephalosporins exceeded those of penicillin, in contrast to previous experience, which showed the MICs of these cephalosporins to be lower than those of penicillin.

Current clinical practice generally involves treating community-acquired respiratory tract infections empirically. In 1997, more than 130 million courses of antibiotics were prescribed for outpatient treatment of such infections (including pharyngitis), with almost 90 million courses for adults and almost 42 million for children [17]. Empiric antibiotics should be active against both *S pneumoniae* and *H influenzae* for respiratory tract infections other than pharyngitis, and periodic surveillance of respiratory tract isolates for changes in the susceptibility patterns of these pathogens is therefore essential to manage community-acquired *S pneumoniae* and *H influenzae* infections effectively [1,18]. Accordingly, the present study sought to characterize current levels of resistance in *S pneumoniae* and *H influenzae* to 17 oral antimicrobial agents by evaluating the susceptibility of isolates from adults with community-acquired infections in the United States.

As current susceptibility breakpoints for many oral antimicrobial agents no longer correspond with more recent clinical, microbiologic, pharmaco-kinetic, and investigational experience [19–22], investigators have proposed a new approach based on pharmacokinetic/pharmacodynamic (PK/PD) modeling and on clinical studies that have measured bacteriologic outcome and evaluated this in relation to drug pharmacokinetics and susceptibilities of pathogens [21–25]. The activity of β-lactams and erythromycin has been shown to depend on the time the serum concentration exceeds the MIC of the agent, with clinical success occurring in more than 80% of cases when the unbound blood concentration of the agent exceeds the MIC of an infecting strain for more than 40% to 50% of the dosing interval [19]. Using standard dosing regimens and the serum pharmacokinetics of these agents, the unbound serum drug concentrations that are maintained for at least 40% to 50% of the dosing interval can be determined and used as PK/PD breakpoints. Different PK/PD parameters correlate with clinical outcome for fluoroquinolones and for newer macrolides/azalides, such as azithro-mycin and clarithromycin, and breakpoints can be derived from one of two ratios—the peak unbound serum concentration to the MIC or the 24-hour area under the unbound serum concentration curve (AUC) to the MIC [19,26]. Clinical cure correlates best when the AUC/MIC ratio exceeds 25 to 30 for these agents in immunocompetent animal models [19] and in a human study [27], and MIC breakpoints for susceptibility can therefore be derived from the formula AUC/25.

Materials and methods

Study centers

Between January 1998 and December 2001, isolates of *H influenzae*, *M catarrhalis*, and *S pneumoniae* from patients over 12 years of age with community-acquired respiratory tract infections were collected by selected laboratories representative of six geographic regions in the United States, either from outpatients or from inpatients within 48 hours of admission (Fig. 1). After isolation by the collecting laboratories, strains were frozen at −70°C and transported to reference laboratories at Case Western Reserve University, Cleveland, Ohio (MRJ), or the Hershey Medical Center, Hershey, Pennsylvania (PCA). The demographic information submitted included patient age and sex, specimen collection date, and specimen source. The reference laboratories confirmed the identity and purity of all strains [28].

Susceptibility testing

The 17 oral antimicrobials tested—amoxicillin, amoxicillin/clavulanic acid (2:1 ratio, examined in two formulations: standard formulation

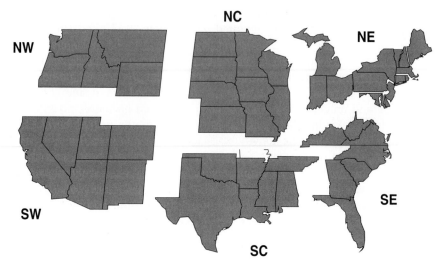

Fig. 1. Isolates were analyzed according to the six regions shown: Northwest (NW), Southwest (SW), North Central (NC), South Central (SC), Northeast (NE), and Southeast (SE).

[500/125 mg threes time a day or 875/125 mg twice a day] and extended-release formulation [2000/125 mg twice a day]), cefaclor, cefuroxime axetil, cefixime, cefprozil, cefdinir, erythromycin, clarithromycin, azithromycin, clindamycin, gemifloxacin, levofloxacin, gatifloxacin, moxifloxacin, doxycy-cline, and trimethoprim/sulfamethoxazole (1:19 ratio)—were selected to reflect agents representative of current oral treatment options. Ampicillin was included to characterize β-lactamase–negative, ampicillin-resistant strains of *H influenzae* and penicillin used to characterize penicillin susceptibility of *S pneumoniae*. Ceftriaxone was also included to reflect its potential for use parenterally in cases failing oral therapy or for patients with severe disease requiring hospitalization. All agents were tested throughout the study period, except for cefdinir (tested 1999 to 2001), and levofloxacin, gatifloxacin, and moxifloxacin (tested 2000 to 2001). Cipro-floxacin was also tested as a marker of fluoroquinolone resistance, and susceptibility of isolates from 1998 to 1999 with ciprofloxacin MICs of >4 μg/mL was determined against levofloxacin, gatifloxacin, and moxifloxacin.

MICs were determined by broth microdilution according to the methods of the National Committee for Clinical Laboratory Standards (NCCLS) [29] in custom dried 96-well microdilution trays (Sensititre Division, TREK Diagnostics, Westlake, Ohio) in two configurations, one for testing *S pneumoniae* and the other for testing *H influenzae* and *M catarrhalis*. Inocula of *Haemophilus* were prepared from chocolate agar plates incubated for a full 24 hours by the direct colony suspension method. *S pneumoniae* inocula were prepared from blood agar plates incubated for 18 to 20 hours, also by direct colony suspension. Growth from these plates was suspended in tubes of Mueller-Hinton broth (Sensititre) to a density equivalent to a 0.5 McFarland standard. Within 30 minutes of preparation, 20 μL of suspension for *H influenzae* and 200 μL for *S pneumoniae* were added to 10-mL tubes of in-house fresh *Haemophilus* test medium or Mueller-Hinton broth (Sensititre) supplemented with 5% lysed horse blood (Cleveland Scientific, Bath, Ohio), respectively. *Haemophilus* test medium was prepared according to the methods of the NCCLS using Mueller-Hinton broth base (Difco), 0.5% yeast extract (Difco), 15 μg NAD per mL and 15 μg hematin per mL (Sigma). *Haemophilus* test medium was prepared in batches, and stored at 4°C for use within 2 weeks of preparation (its performance is known to degrade after this time [28]) or stored at −20°C for up to 6 weeks. Also within 30 minutes of preparation, doseheads were placed on the tubes, and 100-μL volumes dispensed into each well of the Sensititre microdilution trays with an autoinoculator (Sensititre). Trays were then sealed and incubated for 22 to 24 hours at 35°C in ambient air, and the lowest drug concentration showing no growth was read as the MIC. Inoculum checks were performed on all isolates by transferring 10 μL from the inoculating suspensions into tubes containing 6 mL saline; after mixing, 100 μL was transferred to blood or chocolate agar plates and spread over the surface of the plate. Colonies were counted after incubation for 20 to 24 hours at 35°C in a 5% CO_2 atmosphere; 50 to 120 colonies represented the desired range of 3 to 7×10^5 CFU/mL, and strains with inocula beyond this range were retested until the inocula were in the correct range. *M catarrhalis* was tested using the same methods used for *H influenzae*. Quality control of MIC testing is detailed later.

H influenzae and *M catarrhalis* isolates were also tested for β-lactamase production by the nitrocefin disk method (Cefinase, Becton Dickinson Laboratories, Sparks, Maryland), with positive and negative controls used on each day of testing.

Quality control

Initial quality control assessments included evaluation of the performance characteristics of each lot of the Sensititre panels and media used for *S pneumoniae* and *H influenzae*. Quality control strains specified by NCCLS, including *S pneumoniae* ATCC 49619, *H influenzae* ATCC 49247 and 49766, *Enterococcus faecalis* ATCC 29212, and *Escherichia coli* ATCC 25922 and 35218 were used [29]. Inocula of the nonfastidious strains were prepared as for *S pneumoniae*, except that 50 μL of suspension was added to 10-mL tubes of plain Mueller-Hinton broth. MIC values for quality control strains were required to fall within NCCLS-specified ranges [30,31]. In addition, a battery of 50 *S pneumoniae* and 50 *H influenzae* strains with known MIC values were tested on each lot of trays, and each lot accepted for use if results were comparable to results previously obtained using in-house frozen trays.

After the adequacy of the susceptibility testing materials was confirmed, the relevant quality control strains for each organism were tested on each day of testing, and results accepted only if the MICs of the quality control strains were within specified limits. In addition, at the end of the study, all quality control values were analyzed; this analysis confirmed that modal values for all agents were the same as modal NCCLS values and that values from both testing laboratories were comparable.

Susceptibility interpretation criteria

MICs were interpreted as susceptible, intermediate, and resistant according to the most recent NCCLS interpretations [30,31] where available, and according to PK/PD parameters as well [19,23,26]. PK/PD breakpoints were based on standard dosing regimens and criteria appropriate to each agent. For β-lactams and erythromycin, these breakpoints were based on unbound serum concentrations present for 40% to 50% of the dosing interval, whereas for the remaining agents they were based on 24-hour area under unbound serum concentration curve (AUC) to MIC ratios exceeding 25 [19,26]. The agents tested in this study and their interpretative breakpoints are shown in Table 1.

Data collection and analysis

All pertinent data, including demographic and susceptibility data, were entered into a computerized database. The MIC ranges, distributions, and the MIC values that inhibited 50% (MIC_{50}) and 90% (MIC_{90}) of organisms were determined for each agent. Data for *Haemophilus* were analyzed as all strains, β-lactamase–positive strains, and β-lactamase–negative strains. For *S pneumoniae* isolates, analysis included all strains as well as penicillin-susceptible, -intermediate, and -resistant strains. For both these pathogens, data were also analyzed by year, geographic region, isolation site, and patient age. Statistical significance was determined by binomial or chi-squared analysis, and *P* values of ≤ 0.05 were regarded as significant.

Results

This study evaluated 2901 strains of *S pneumoniae*, 2570 untypeable strains of *H influenzae,* and 218 strains of *M catarrhalis* isolated from specimens submitted from patients in 29 states grouped into six geographic regions (Fig. 1). Isolates were cultured predominantly from specimens obtained from the lower respiratory tract, blood, middle ear, nasopharynx, and paranasal sinuses. Among *S pneumoniae* isolates, 1572 were isolated from the lower respiratory tract, 808 from blood, 200 from the nasopharynx, 155 from the paranasal sinus, 98 from the middle ear, and eight from other sources. Sixty *S pneumoniae* isolates did not have a site of origin

Table 1

Breakpoints (µg/mL) used to determine susceptible (S), intermediate (I), and resistant (R), categories, based on pharmacokinetic/pharmacodynamic (PK/PD) and National Committee for Clinical Laboratory Standards (NCCLS) interpretations except as noted

| Antimicrobial Agent | PK/PD breakpoints | | NCCLS breakpoints | | | | | |
| | | | S pneumoniae | | | H influenzae | | |
	S	R	S	I	R	S	I	R
Penicillin	NA[b]	NA	≤0.06	0.12-1	≥2	NA	NA	NA
Ampicillin	NA	NA	NA	NA	NA	≤1	2	≥4
Amoxicillin	≤2	≥4	≤2	4	≥8	NA	NA	NA
Amox/Clav	≤2	≥4	≤2	4	≥8	≤4	NA	≥8
Amox/Clav extended release	≤4	≥8	NA	NA	NA	NA	NA	NA
Cefaclor	≤0.5	≥1	≤1	2	≥4	≤8	16	≥32
Cefuroxime axetil	≤1	≥2	≤1	2	≥4	≤4	8	≥16
Cefixime	≤1	≥2	NA	NA	NA	≤1	NA	NA
Ceftriaxone	≤1	≥2	≤1	2	≥4	≤2	NA	NA
Cefprozil	≤1	≥2	≤2	4	≥8	≤8	16	≥32
Cefdinir[a]	≤0.5	≥1	≤0.5	1	≥2	≤1	NA	NA
Erythromycin	≤0.25	≥0.5	≤0.25	0.5	≥1	NA	NA	NA
Clarithromycin	≤0.25	≥0.5	≤0.25	0.5	≥1	≤8	16	≥32
Azithromycin	≤0.12	≥0.25	≤0.5	1	≥2	≤4	NA	NA
Clindamycin	≤0.25	≥0.5	≤0.25	0.5	≥1	≤1	NA	NA
Gemifloxacin	≤0.25	≥0.5	≤0.12	0.25	≥0.5	≤0.12	NA	NA
Levofloxacin[a]	≤2	≥4	≤2	4	≥8	≤1	NA	NA
Gatifloxacin[c]	≤1	≥2	≤1	2	≥4	≤1	NA	NA
Moxifloxacin[c]	≤1	≥2	≤1	2	≥4	≤2	4	≥8
Doxycycline	≤0.25	≥0.5	NA	NA	NA	NA	NA	NA
Trimethoprim/sulfa	≤0.5	≥1	≤0.5	1 - 2	≥4	≤1	2	≥4

[a] Tested 1999–2001.
[b] NA, not applicable.
[c] Tested 2000–2001.
Data from Refs. [13,28,30,31,44,65].

described. Among the *H influenzae* isolates, 1999 were from the lower respiratory tract, 281 from the nasopharynx, 107 from the paranasal sinus, 74 from the middle ear, 51 from blood, and four from other sources. Fifty-four *H influenzae* isolates did not have a site of origin described. Virtually all isolates of *M catarrhalis* were isolated from the lower respiratory tract. Susceptibility of *S pneumoniae* (overall and by penicillin and macrolide susceptibilities) and *H influenzae* (overall and by β-lactamase production and trimethoprim/sulfamethoxazole susceptibility) by year, region, specimen type, and patient age are shown in Tables 2–11.

Streptococcus pneumoniae susceptibility

The MIC and susceptibility data for the 2901 strains of *S pneumoniae* tested are summarized in Tables 2–7. Penicillin-susceptible strains accounted for 63.6% of isolates, whereas 13.2% were penicillin intermediate, and

Table 2
Penicillin and erythromycin susceptibility of S pneumoniae, and β-lactamase production and trimethoprim/sulfamethoxazole susceptibility of H influenzae isolates by years

Year	S pneumoniae					H influenzae		
	No. of strains tested	% Penicillin susceptible	% Penicillin intermediate	% Penicillin resistant	% Macrolide (ERY) resistant	No. of strains tested	% β-Lactamase positive[a]	% Trimethoprim/ sulfamethoxazole resistant
1998	567	65.1	13.6	21.3	24.5	707	31.8	23.6
1999	741	59.1	12.7	28.2	32.8	783	30.3	22.0
2000	1037	67.1	10.7	22.1	26.1	583	25.9	19.0
2001	556	61.5	17.8	20.7	28.8	497	24.7	22.5
All strains	2901	63.6	13.2	23.2	28.0	2570	28.6	21.9

[a] β-Lactamase production fell significantly between 1998–1999 and 2000–2001 (P = 0.002).

Table 3
Regional variation in *H influenzae* β-lactam production and *S pneumoniae* penicillin and macrolide susceptibility (statistically significant differences in prevalence of resistance between regions and overall resistance are indicated, with *P* values shown in footnotes)

Region	*S pneumoniae*[a]			*H influenzae*[b]
	% Penicillin intermediate	% Penicillin resistant	% Macrolide (ERY) resistant	% β-Lactamase positive
Northeast	13.4	26.2	29.8	31.8
North Central	11.6	24.1	27.0	31.8
Northwest	12.9	17.4[d]	23.0[c]	29.5
Southeast	16.4	23.7	27.1	29.4
South Central	12.3	25.9	26.6	27.7
Southwest	12.2	22.4	29.5	23.5[c]
Overall	13.2	23.2	28.0	28.6

[a] 14.6%–17.6% of strains from each region.
[b] 12.1%–20.4% of strains from each region.
[c] $P < 0.05$.
[d] $P < 0.005$.

23.2% were penicillin resistant (see Table 2). The MIC_{50} and MIC_{90} values and susceptibilities, by PK/PD and NCCLS parameters, for all strains and by penicillin susceptibility are shown in Tables 6 and 7. Penicillin and macrolide resistance rose by 7% to 8% from 1998 to 1999, but then fell by about 6% in 2000, with little change in 2001 (see Table 2).

The most highly active agents overall, based on PK/PD breakpoints, were amoxicillin (91.6%), amoxicillin/clavulanic acid (92.1% to 95.2%), ceftriaxone (96.3%), clindamycin (90.6%), and the respiratory fluoroquinolones (99.1% to 99.7%) (Table 7). Twenty-six strains (0.9%) were resistant to levofloxacin and gatifloxacin, 24 (0.8%) to moxifloxacin, and eight (0.3%) to gemifloxacin. Doxycycline was active against 80.4% of isolates. The macrolides/azalides and oral cephalosporins, except for cefaclor (19.7%), were active against 66.3% to 72.6% of isolates.

Activity based on penicillin susceptibility showed that most agents were active against 91.8% to 100% of penicillin-susceptible isolates, except for cefaclor (30.3% at PK/PD breakpoint; 69.9% at NCCLS breakpoint) (see Table 7). Whereas amoxicillin, amoxicillin/clavulanic acid, and ceftriaxone were active against 99.5% to 100% of penicillin-intermediate strains of *S pneumoniae* at PK/PD breakpoints, cefdinir and cefprozil were only active against 63.1% to 64.6% of strains, cefixime against 35.3% and cefaclor against 2.9%. Against penicillin-resistant strains of *S pneumoniae*, several of the β-lactam agents were largely inactive. Cefaclor, cefuroxime axetil, cefixime, cefprozil, and cefdinir all had high $MIC_{90}s$ (>64, 8, 32, 32, and 8 μg/mL, respectively), and the susceptibilities of penicillin-resistant strains to these agents were less than 1% by both PK/PD and NCCLS interpretations. Ceftriaxone (84.6% susceptible) was the most active, followed by the extended release amoxicillin/clavulanic acid (79.4%), amoxicillin/clavulanic

Table 4

Distribution of *S pneumoniae* and *H influenzae* isolates by specimen source (statistically significant differences in prevalence of resistance between specimen sources and overall resistance are indicated, with *P* values shown in footnotes)

Source	S pneumoniae						H influenzae	
	No. (%) of strains tested	% Penicillin susceptible	% Penicillin intermediate	% Penicillin resistant	% Macrolide (ERY) resistant		No. (%) of strains tested	% β-Lactamase positive
Blood	808 (27.9)	72.0[d]	11.5	16.5[d]	20.3[d]		51 (2.0)	19.6
Lower respiratory tract	1572 (54.2)	61.2	14.3	24.5	30.9[a]		1999 (77.8)	27.4
Nasopharynx	200 (6.9)	59.5	12.0	28.5	29.5		281 (10.9)	32.7
Paranasal sinus	155 (5.3)	50.3[d]	12.3	37.4[d]	38.7[c]		107 (4.2)	32.7
Middle ear	98 (3.4)	65.3	7.1	27.6	39.5[a]		74 (2.9)	43.2[b]
All strains	2901[e] (100)	63.6	13.2	23.2	28.0		2570[e] (100)	28.6

[a] *P* < 0.05.
[b] *P* < 0.01.
[c] *P* < 0.005.
[d] *P* < 0.001.
[e] 68 (2.3%) of *S pneumoniae* and 58 (2.3%) of *H influenzae* were excluded from this analysis if from sources with low numbers or if source was not provided.

Table 5
Distribution and susceptibility of S pneumoniae and H influenzae isolates by patient age

Age group (years)	Number	No. (%) Penicillin intermediate	No. (%) Penicillin resistant	No. (%) Macrolide[a] resistant	Number	No. (%) β-lactamase positive
13–20	116	13 (11.2)	25 (21.6)	35 (30.2)	136	30 (22.1)
21–30	200	28 (14.0)	49 (24.5)	54 (27.0)	231	67 (29.0)
31–40	460	67 (14.6)	106 (23.0)	131 (28.5)	361	96 (26.6)
41–50	524	63 (12.0)	112 (21.4)	119 (22.7)	390	106 (27.2)
51–60	480	70 (14.6)	107 (22.3)	135 (28.1)	365	111 (30.4)
61–70	391	50 (12.8)	96 (24.6)	120 (30.7)	372	103 (27.7)
> 70	593	75 (12.6)	140 (23.6)	180 (30.4)	542	161 (29.7)
Unknown	137	16 (11.7)	39 (28.5)	39 (28.5)	173	62 (35.8)
Total	2901	382 (13.2)	674 (23.2)	813 (28.0)	2570	736 (28.6)

In the header, "S pneumoniae" spans the No. Penicillin intermediate, No. Penicillin resistant, No. Macrolide resistant columns, and "H influenzae" spans the last two columns.

[a] Macrolide resistance represented by erythromycin.

acid standard formulation (66.3%), and amoxicillin (63.6%). Only three penicillin-resistant strains (0.4%) had ceftriaxone MICs higher than penicillin MICs. However, 219 penicillin-resistant strains (7.5% of all isolates) had amoxicillin MICs higher than penicillin MICs.

Table 6
MIC_{50} and MIC_{90} values (μg/mL) of S pneumoniae isolates for all isolates and by penicillin susceptibility

Antimicrobial agent	All isolates (n = 2901)		Penicillin susceptible (n = 1845)		Penicillin intermediate (n = 382)		Penicillin resistant (n = 674)	
	MIC_{50}	MIC_{90}	MIC_{50}	MIC_{90}	MIC_{50}	MIC_{90}	MIC_{50}	MIC_{90}
Penicillin	0.03	2	0.015	0.03	0.25	1	4	4
Amoxicillin	0.03	2	0.03	0.03	0.25	1	2	8
Amox/Clav	0.03	2	0.03	0.03	0.25	1	2	8
Cefaclor	2	> 64	1	2	4	32	> 64	> 64
Cefuroxime axetil	0.06	8	0.03	0.12	0.5	4	8	8
Cefixime	0.25	32	0.25	0.5	2	16	32	32
Ceftriaxone	0.03	1	0.03	0.03	0.25	0.5	1	2
Cefprozil	0.25	16	0.25	0.5	1	4	16	32
Cefdinir	0.06	8	0.06	0.12	0.5	4	8	8
Erythromycin	0.06	8	0.06	0.06	0.25	64	4	64
Clarithromycin	0.03	8	0.03	0.06	0.25	64	4	64
Azithromycin	0.12	16	0.06	0.12	0.5	64	8	64
Clindamycin	0.06	0.12	0.06	0.12	0.06	4	0.06	4
Gemifloxacin	0.015	0.03	0.015	0.03	0.015	0.03	0.015	0.03
Levofloxacin	1	1	1	1	1	1	1	1
Gatifloxacin	0.25	0.5	0.25	0.5	0.25	0.5	0.25	0.25
Moxifloxacin	0.12	0.25	0.12	0.25	0.12	0.25	0.12	0.12
Doxycycline	0.12	8	0.12	0.25	0.25	16	0.5	8
Trimethoprim/ sulfamethoxazole	0.25	8	0.25	1	1	8	4	16

Table 7
Susceptibilities by Pharmacokinetic/Pharmacodynamic (PK/PD) and National Committee for Clinical Laboratory Standards (NCCLS) breakpoints of S pneumoniae for all isolates and by penicillin susceptibility

Antimicrobial agent	All isolates (n = 2901)			Penicillin susceptible (n = 1845)			Penicillin intermediate (n = 382)			Penicillin resistant (n = 674)		
	PK/PD	NCCLS		PK/PD	NCCLS		PK/PD	NCCLS		PK/PD	NCCLS	
	%S	%S	%R	%S	%S	%R	%S	%S	%R	%S	%S	%R
Penicillin	NA	63.6	23.2	NA	100	0.0	NA	0.0	0.0	NA	0.0	100
Amoxicillin	91.6	91.6	4.8	100	100	0.0	100	100	0.0	63.6	63.6	20.6
Amox/Clav	92.1	92.1	4.8	100	100	0.0	99.7	99.7	0.0	66.3	66.3	20.6
Amox/Clav extended release	95.2	NA	NA	100	NA	NA	100	NA	NA	79.4	NA	NA
Cefaclor	19.7	46.1	34.1	30.3	69.9	3.4	2.9	12.0	67.0	0.1	0.3	99.4
Cefuroxime axetil	72.6	72.6	25.2	99.9	99.9	0.1	68.8	68.8	16.5	0.0	0.0	99.0
Cefixime	66.3	NA	NA	96.7	NA	NA	35.3	NA	NA	0.4	NA	NA
Ceftriaxone	96.3	96.3	1.0	100	100	0.0	99.5	99.5	0.3	84.6	84.6	4.3
Cefprozil	71.8	74.4	23.6	99.7	99.9	0.1	63.1	81.2	9.2	0.4	0.9	96.1
Cefdinir	71.8	71.8	26.0	99.9	99.9	0.0	64.6	64.6	19.3	0.5	0.5	98.9
Erythromycin	72.0	72.0	27.9	92.6	92.6	7.3	49.7	49.7	49.5	28.0	28.0	72.0
Clarithromycin	72.3	72.3	26.9	92.8	92.8	6.9	51.0	51.0	46.3	28.2	28.2	70.8
Azithromycin	71.0	72.1	27.4	91.8	92.7	6.9	48.4	50.3	47.6	27.2	28.0	71.8
Clindamycin	90.6	90.6	9.1	97.9	97.9	1.8	81.4	81.4	18.1	75.8	75.8	23.9
Gemifloxacin	99.7	99.4	0.3	99.7	99.2	0.3	100	100	0.0	99.7	99.4	0.3
Levofloxacin	99.1	99.1	0.9	99.0	99.0	1.0	99.7	99.7	0.3	99.1	99.1	0.9
Gatifloxacin[a]	99.1	99.1	0.8	99.0	99.0	1.0	99.7	99.7	0.0	99.1	99.1	0.4
Moxifloxacin[a]	99.2	99.2	0.5	99.0	99.0	0.7	100	100	0.0	99.3	99.3	0.3
Doxycycline	80.4	NA	NA	95.2	NA	NA	65.2	NA	NA	48.7	NA	NA
Trimethoprim/sulfamethoxazole	63.7	63.7	29.5	86.4	86.4	8.0	46.1	46.1	39.8	11.3	11.3	82.6

Abbreviation: NA, not applicable.

[a] Isolates from 1998–1999 with ciprofloxacin MIC >4 μg/mL were tested against these agents (see methods) to allow comparisons for the entire study period.

Table 8
Resistance of 1424 isolates of *S pneumoniae* resistant to one or more drug classes (1477 isolates were susceptible to all agents tested)

Resistance to:	Number of isolates resistant to any drug class	Number of isolates resistant to drug class shown						
		Penicillin (≥0.12 µg/mL)[a]	Erythromycin (≥1 µg/mL)	Clindamycin (≥1 µg/mL)	Doxycycline (≥0.5 µg/mL)	Trimethoprim/ sulfamethoxazole (≥1 µg/mL)	Levofloxacin (≥8 µg/mL)
1 drug class	421	165	38	0	36	169	13
2 drug classes	269	193	80	4	38	218	5
3 drug classes	308	280	265	22	82	274	1
4 drug classes	242	234	241	51	228	211	5
5 drug classes	182	182	182	182	182	182	–
6 drug classes	2	2	2	2	2	2	2
Totals	1424	1056	808	261	568	1056	26

[a] Includes penicillin-intermediate and -resistant isolates.

Table 9
Cross-resistance between isolates of *S pneumoniae* resistant to two or more drug classes
(N = 1003)

No. of drug classes resistant	Drug classes resistant	No. (%) of isolates resistant to drug classes indicated
3	Pen, Ery, SXT	214 (21.3%)
4	Pen, Ery, Doxy, SXT	187 (18.6%)
5	Pen, Ery, Cli, Doxy, SXT	182 (18.1%)
2	Pen, SXT	163 (16.3%)
3	Pen, Doxy, SXT	43 (4.3%)
2	Ery, SXT	40 (4.0%)
4	Pen, Ery, Cli, Doxy	33 (3.3%)
3	Pen, Ery, Doxy	21 (2.1%)
2	Pen, Ery	20 (2.0%)
2	Doxy, SXT	14 (1.4%)

The 10 most common patterns are shown, accounting for 917 isolates (91.4%).

Abbreviations for drug classes with minimum inhibitory concentration breakpoints used for this analysis in parentheses: Cli, clindamycin ($\geq$1 mg/mL); Doxy, doxycycline ($\geq$0.5 mg/mL); Ery, erythromycin ($\geq$1 µg/mL); Pen, penicillin ($\geq$0.12 mg/mL); SXT, trimethoprim/sulfamethoxazole ($\geq$1 µg/mL).

Analysis of macrolide/azalide and penicillin cross-resistance in *S pneumoniae* strains showed approximately 7% of penicillin-susceptible strains were resistant to macrolides/azalides, whereas 46.3% to 49.5% of penicillin-intermediate strains and 70.8% to 72.0% of penicillin-resistant strains were macrolide/azalide resistant (see Table 7). Clindamycin resistance also increased with increasing penicillin resistance but to a lesser degree, with 1.8%, 18.1%, and 23.9% clindamycin cross-resistance with penicillin-susceptible, -intermediate, and -resistant strains, respectively.

Among the other agents tested, doxycycline was highly active against penicillin-susceptible strains of *S pneumoniae* (95.2% susceptible). Doxycycline activity decreased against penicillin-nonsusceptible isolates, with 65.2% and 48.7% of penicillin-intermediate and -resistant strains, respectively, susceptible to this agent. Finally, trimethoprim/sulfamethoxazole susceptibility was 63.7% overall and was 86.4%, 46.1%, and 11.3% among penicillin-susceptible, -intermediate, and -resistant strains, respectively.

Overall, slightly more than half (1477) of the 2901 isolates of *S pneumoniae* were susceptible to all six classes of agent tested: penicillins, macrolides, clindamycin, tetracyclines, trimethoprim/sulfamethoxazole, and quinolones. Of the 1424 isolates resistant to one or more of these drug classes, 421 were resistant to a single drug class, whereas 1003 were resistant to two or more classes (see Table 8). Two isolates were resistant to all six drug classes. The 10 most common patterns of resistance in isolates resistant to two or more drug classes are shown in Table 9. Four patterns accounted for 74.3% of these isolates, with all of these isolates being resistant to penicillin and trimethoprim/sulfamethoxazole alone (16.3%), or in addition

Table 10
MIC$_{50}$ and MIC$_{90}$ values (µg/mL) of *H. influenzae* for all isolates and by β-lactamase production

Antimicrobial agent	All isolates (N = 2570)		β-Lactamase negative (n = 1834)		β-Lactamase positive (n = 736)	
	MIC$_{50}$	MIC$_{90}$	MIC$_{50}$	MIC$_{90}$	MIC$_{50}$	MIC$_{90}$
Ampicillin	0.25	> 16	0.25	0.5	> 16	> 16
Amoxicillin	0.5	> 16	0.5	1	> 16	> 16
Amox/Clav	0.5	1	0.5	1	1	2
Amox/Clav extended release	0.5	1	0.5	1	1	2
Cefaclor	4	16	4	8	8	32
Cefuroxime axetil	1	2	1	2	1	2
Cefixime	0.03	0.06	0.003	0.06	0.03	0.06
Ceftriaxone	≤0.004	0.008	0.004	0.008	0.004	0.008
Cefprozil	2	8	2	8	4	32
Cefdinir	0.25	0.5	0.25	0.5	0.25	0.5
Erythromycin	4	8	4	8	4	8
Clarithromycin	8	16	8	16	8	16
Azithromycin	1	2	1	2	1	2
Gemifloxacin	0.004	0.008	0.004	0.008	0.004	0.008
Levofloxacin	0.015	0.015	0.015	0.015	0.015	0.015
Gatifloxacin	0.008	0.015	0.008	0.015	0.008	0.015
Moxifloxacin	0.015	0.03	0.015	0.03	0.015	0.03
Doxycycline	0.5	1	0.5	1	0.5	1
Trimethoprim/ sulfamethoxazole	0.12	> 4	0.12	4	0.12	> 4

Abbreviation: MIC, minimum inhibitory concentration.

to erythromycin (21.3%), erythromycin and doxycycline (18.6%), or erythromycin, doxycycline and clindamycin (18.1%). Other patterns were less common, with none accounting for >5% of these isolates.

Haemophilus influenzae susceptibility

Of the 2570 *H influenzae* strains tested, 28.6% (736 strains) were β-lactamase positive by the nitrocefin disk method (see Table 2). The MIC$_{50}$ and MIC$_{90}$ values and susceptibilities, by PK/PD and NCCLS parameters, for all strains and for β-lactamase–positive and –negative strains are shown in Tables 10 and 11. Five strains (0.2%) demonstrated the features of β-lactamase–negative ampicillin-resistant (BLNAR) strains, with ampicillin MIC values of 4 µg/mL or greater. Four of these five strains were similarly resistant to amoxicillin and amoxicillin/clavulanic acid. Amoxicillin/clavulanic acid MICs of all β-lactamase–positive strains were ≤4 µg/mL, with 98.5% being ≤2 µg/mL.

Some changes in susceptibility were noted over the study period. β-Lactamase production fell significantly, from 30.3% to 31.8% in 1998 to 1999 to 24.7% to 25.9% in 2000 to 2001 (*P* = 0.002) (see Table 2). However,

Table 11
Susceptibilities by Pharmacokinetic/Pharmacodymaic (PK/PD) and National Committee for Clinical Laboratory Standards (NCCLS) breakpoints, of H influenzae for all isolates and by β-lactamase production

Antimicrobial agent	All isolates (N = 2570)			β-Lactamase negative (n = 1834)			β-Lactamase positive (n = 736)		
	PK/PD	NCCLS		PK/PD	NCCLS		PK/PD	NCCLS	
	%S	%S	%R	%S	%S	%R	%S	%S	%R
Ampicillin	NA	70.5	28.4	NA	98.7	0.3	NA	0.1	98.6
Amoxicillin	70.2	71.6	28.4	98.1	99.7	0.3	0.4	1.8	98.2
Amox/Clav	98.3	99.8	0.2	98.2	99.7	0.3	98.5	100	0.0
Amox/Clav extended release	99.8	99.8	0.2	99.7	NA	NA	100	NA	NA
Cefaclor	3.7	86.0	4.7	4.7	93.0	1.0	1.0	68.5	14.1
Cefuroxime axetil	82.8	98.8	0.2	81.8	99.0	0.2	85.3	98.5	0.1
Cefixime	>99.9	>99.9	<0.1	99.9	99.9	0.1	100	100	0.0
Ceftriaxone	>99.9	>99.9	<0.1	99.9	99.9	0.1	100	100	0.0
Cefprozil	23.2	90.5	3.5	30.8	95.6	0.6	4.3	78.0	10.9
Cefdinir	93.5	98.9	1.1	92.9	98.8	1.2	94.9	99.0	1.0
Erythromycin	0.0	NA	NA	0.0	NA	NA	0.0	NA	NA
Clarithromycin	0.0	80.7	2.3	0.0	83.5	1.9	0.0	73.6	3.4
Azithromycin	2.3	98.8	1.2	2.5	98.7	1.3	1.8	99.0	1.0
Gemifloxacin	99.8	99.8	0.2	99.7	99.7	0.3	100	100	0.0
Levofloxacin	100	100	0.0	100	100	0.0	100	100	0.0
Gatifloxacin	100	100	0.0	100	100	0.0	100	100	0.0
Moxifloxacin	100	100	0.0	100	100	0.0	100	100	0.0
Doxycycline	25.1	NA		27.3	NA		19.6	NA	
Trimethoprim/sulfamethoxazole	78.1	78.1	16.3	80.4	80.4	13.7	72.4	72.4	22.8

trimethoprim/sulfamethoxazole resistance remained fairly constant during the study, varying from a low of 19.0% in 2000 to a high of 23.6% in 1998. β-Lactamase–positive (BLP) strains of *H influenzae* demonstrated high MIC_{90} values to many of the β-lactam agents, with MIC_{90} values of ≥16 μg/mL noted for ampicillin, amoxicillin, cefaclor, and cefprozil (see Table 10). Less than 5% of BLP isolates were susceptible to these agents by PK/PD parameters (see Table 11). However, whereas almost all β-lactamase–negative isolates were susceptible to amoxicillin, only 30.8% of these were susceptible to cefprozil and <5% to cefaclor at PK/PD breakpoints. Among the other β-lactam agents, >98% of strains were susceptible to amoxicillin/clavulanic acid, cefixime, and ceftriaxone by both PK/PD and NCCLS breakpoints, and 94.9% were susceptible to cefdinir by PK/PD parameters (99.0% by NCCLS). Finally, 85.3% were susceptible to cefuroxime axetil by PK/PD parameters (98.5% by NCCLS).

Macrolides had low activity against *H influenzae* strains according to PK/PD parameters, regardless of β-lactamase production. Fluoroquinolones were consistently highly active, with only five strains (0.3%) resistant to gemifloxacin. Doxycycline was active against 25.1% of strains, by PK/PD-established breakpoints, and trimethoprim/sulfamethoxazole active against 78.1% according to either PK/PD or NCCLS parameters.

M catarrhalis susceptibility

Of the 218 strains tested, 92.7% (202 strains) were β-lactamase positive by the nitrocefin disk method. The MIC_{50} and MIC_{90} values and susceptibilities by PK/PD parameters are shown in Table 12. Most isolates of *M catarrhalis* were resistant to amoxicillin, cefaclor, cefprozil, and trimethoprim/sulfamethoxazole. Most isolates were susceptible to the other agents tested, except for cefuroxime axetil, where only 50.5% were susceptible.

Susceptibility variations by region, specimen source, and age

Susceptibility patterns were determined for each of the six regions in the United States (see Table 3). The highest prevalences of penicillin-intermediate and -resistant strains of *S pneumoniae* were from the Southeast (16.4% and 23.7%, respectively) and Northeast (13.4% and 26.2%, respectively) regions, whereas the Northwest (12.9% and 17.4%, respectively) ($P < 0.01$) region had the lowest in comparison to the overall prevalence. In all regions more strains of *S pneumoniae* were resistant than intermediate. Overall, the proportion of penicillin-intermediate and -resistant strains from the east (39.9%, $P = 0.05$) was higher than the west regions (32.4%, $P < 0.05$), with the central regions (37.0%, not statistically significant) falling between the two and similar to the overall prevalence. The proportion of macrolide-resistant strains from the northwest region (23.0%) was significantly lower than the other regions and overall (28.0%, $P < 0.05$). Macrolide

Table 12
MIC$_{50}$ and MIC$_{90}$ values (µg/mL) and susceptibilities by Pharmacokinetic/Pharmacodymaic breakpoints of *M catarrhalis* (N = 218)

Antimicrobial agent	MIC$_{50}$	MIC$_{90}$	%S
Ampicillin	8	> 16	7.3[a]
Amoxicillin	8	> 16	7.3[a]
Amox/Clav	≤0.12	0.25	100
Amox/Clav extended release	≤0.12	0.25	100
Cefaclor	2	8	8.7
Cefuroxime axetil	1	4	50.5
Cefixime	0.12	0.5	100
Ceftriaxone	0.12	1	93.6
Cefprozil	4	16	9.2
Cefdinir[b]	0.25	0.25	100
Erythromycin[c]	≤0.5	≤0.5	100
Clarithromycin[c]	≤0.5	≤0.5	100
Azithromycin	0.06	0.12	100
Gemifloxacin	0.015	0.015	100
Levofloxacin[b]	0.03	0.06	100
Gatifloxacin[b]	0.03	0.03	100
Moxifloxacin[b]	0.06	0.06	100
Doxycycline	0.25	0.25	96.3
Trimethoprim/sulfamethoxazole	1	2	19.3

Abbreviation: MIC, minimum inhibitory concentration.
[a] Based on β-lactamase production.
[b] N = 85.
[c] Lowest concentration tested (0.5 µg/mL) used as breakpoint.

resistance was highest in the Northeast (29.8%) and Southwest (29.5%), but neither difference was statistically different from the overall value.

The highest prevalences of β-lactamase–positive strains of *H influenzae* were found in the Northeast (31.8%) and North Central (31.8%) regions compared to the overall prevalence of 28.6%, whereas the lowest was from the Southwest (23.5%, $P < 0.05$). No significant differences were found comparing east, west, and central, or north and south regions.

The prevalence of penicillin resistance in *S pneumoniae* was highest in isolates from the paranasal sinus (37.4%, $P < 0.001$ versus overall 23.2%) specimens (see Table 4) and lowest in isolates from blood (16.5%, $P < 0.001$ versus overall). Macrolide resistance was 28.0% overall in *S pneumoniae* isolates with a significantly lower prevalence in isolates from blood (20.3%, $P < 0.001$) and higher prevalence in isolates from the paranasal sinus (38.7%, $P < 0.005$) and middle ear (39.5%, $P < 0.05$). *H influenzae* isolates from middle ear specimens had a significantly higher prevalence of β-lactamase–positive strains (43.2%, $P < 0.01$) than the overall prevalence of 28.6%; this difference was not found to be age associated. The lowest prevalence of β-lactamase–positive strains was in specimens isolated from blood (19.6%); this was not a statistically significant difference, though the sample size of 51 blood isolates was small.

Within the age groups included in this study, age was not found to be a significant predictor of penicillin resistance in *S pneumoniae* or β-lactamase production in *H influenzae* (see Table 5).

Discussion

The continuing high prevalence of resistance to oral antimicrobial agents in the major respiratory pathogens, *H influenzae* and *S pneumoniae*, has produced a need to re-evaluate treatment options for respiratory tract infections [18,32]. This is particularly important for the established oral agents, many of which have decreased activity against contemporary isolates, and also for newer agents like the fluoroquinolones, which currently have broader spectra of activity against these and other respiratory tract pathogens. Recent studies have shown that up to 33% of strains of *S pneumoniae* are now penicillin intermediate or resistant in many parts of the country [10,33]. Furthermore, more than 30% of strains of *H influenzae* and 90% of strains of *M catarrhalis* now produce β-lactamases [9,10]. This severely limits the activity of many oral antimicrobial agents [14,18,34–38].

We used interpretative MIC breakpoints based primarily on PK/PD-derived values as these are applicable to all three species studied. Although many NCCLS and FDA-approved breakpoints differ considerably between *S pneumoniae* and *H influenzae*, neither has breakpoints for *M catarrhalis*. As the dosing regimen and site of infection determine the limit of activity of an antimicrobial agent, the breakpoint that defines this limit applies to all pathogens with similar disease pathogenesis, such as *S pneumoniae*, *H influenzae*, and *M catarrhalis*, which are all extracellular pathogens. PK/PD parameters can also be used to determine breakpoints applicable to intracellular pathogens, although this is more complex due to variations in intracellular location of different pathogens and differences in pH of these locations [39]. The origins of different NCCLS and FDA breakpoints can be traced to inadequate clinical studies of diseases with high rates of spontaneous resolution, such as acute sinusitis, acute exacerbation of chronic bronchitis (AECB), and acute otitis media, or failure to stratify patients by disease severity in community acquired pneumonia (CAP) and AECB [19,40–46].

Applying PK/PD breakpoints to the results of this study has identified the respiratory fluoroquinolones as active against more than 99.1% of strains of both *S pneumoniae* and *H influenzae*. These fluoroquinolones, levofloxacin, gemifloxacin, gatifloxacin, and moxifloxacin, are regarded as being very active against pneumococci as their breakpoints are higher than baseline MIC distributions of strains, and few resistant strains have been detected [14]. Gemifloxacin was active against 99.7% of isolates, with 18 of 26 isolates resistant to levofloxacin and gatifloxacin being susceptible to this agent. Amoxicillin/clavulanic acid and ceftriaxone are also highly active against both species, with 99.8% of *H influenzae* and 92.1% to 95.2% of

S pneumoniae strains being susceptible to amoxicillin/clavulanic acid and >99.9% and 96.3%, respectively, susceptible to ceftriaxone at PK/PD breakpoints. Although >99.9% of *H influenzae* strains are susceptible to cefixime, only 66.3% of *S pneumoniae* strains are susceptible. However, 82.8% of *H influenzae* and 72.6% of *S pneumoniae* are susceptible to cefuroxime axetil. In contrast, although 91.6% of *S pneumoniae* strains are susceptible to amoxicillin, only 70.2% of *H influenzae* are susceptible. Cefprozil and cefdinir have similar activity against *S pneumoniae* (71.8% and 71.8%, respectively, susceptible), but cefprozil has poor activity against *H influenzae* (23.2% susceptible at PK/PD breakpoint). Cefdinir is a recently approved agent with a NCCLS susceptible breakpoint of 0.5 μg/mL, which we also have used as the PK/PD breakpoint as its pharmacokinetic properties have not been adequately established. Additionally, its pharmacokinetic profile varies with its dosing regimen, which can be once or twice daily, so that the PK/PD breakpoint may be found to be lower when more experience has been obtained with this agent. Whereas lowering the cefdinir breakpoint to 0.12 or 0.25 μg/mL would have some effect on *S pneumoniae* (reducing overall susceptibility from 71.8% at 0.5 μg/mL to 68.8% at 0.25 μg/mL and 61.2% at 0.12 μg/mL), this would reduce its activity against *H influenzae* from 93.5% at 0.5 μg/mL to 78.2% at 0.25 μg/mL and to 15.9% at 0.12 μg/mL. An in vitro pharmacokinetic model has shown that cefdinir concentrations simulating human serum values based on a once daily dosing regimen failed to inhibit the growth of four strains of *H influenzae* over the 24-hour dosing interval; three strains had cefdinir MICs of 0.25 μg/mL and 1 of 0.5 μg/mL [47]. However, growth of three of the four strains was reduced to below detectable levels at concentrations simulating twice daily dosing. Cefaclor has poor activity against both species, with only 19.7% of *S pneumoniae* and 3.7% of *H influenzae* isolates, respectively, being susceptible at the PK/PD breakpoint. Although 72.0%, 72.3%, and 71.0% of *S pneumoniae* strains were susceptible to erythromycin, clarithromycin, and azithromycin, respectively, no *H influenzae* strains were susceptible to erythromycin and clarithromycin and only 2.3% were susceptible to azithromycin based on PK/PD parameters. A human volunteer study on the intrapulmonary distribution of clarithromycin and azithromycin demonstrated much higher concentrations of these agents in epithelial lining fluid (ELF) than in serum [48]. ELF concentrations present for ≥50% the dosing interval were 15 to 30 μg/mL (mean of five values, 26.1 μg/mL) for clarithromycin and <0.1 to 1 μg/mL (mean of five values excluding one value of <0.1 μg/mL, 0.95 μg/mL) for azithromycin. These concentrations exceed the MICs for clarithromycin observed with most strains of *H influenzae* and some strains of macrolide-resistant *S pneumoniae*, and the MICs for azithromycin for some strains of *H influenzae*. However, serum rather than ELF concentrations appear to correlate with clinical outcome of pulmonary infections [49,50], and recent PK/PD studies in animals or in vitro have shown that both azithromycin and clarithromycin are concentration-dependent agents, with serum AUC:MIC and peak:MIC ratios being predictive of activity [51–54].

Development of tetracycline resistance in *S pneumoniae* has limited the use of this class of agents. However, 80.4% of isolates were susceptible to doxycycline in this study, and the only oral agents with better activities were fluoroquinolones (>99% susceptible), amoxicillin (91.6%), amoxicillin/ clavulanic acid (92.1% to 95.2%) and clindamycin (90.6%). Doxycyline is more active than the oral cephalosporins (66.3% to 72.6% susceptible), macrolides/azalides (71% to 72.3% susceptible), or trimethoprim/sulfame-thoxazole (63.7% susceptible), and offers an alternative for penicillin-allergic patients. However, doxycycline has limited activity against *H influenzae*, with its breakpoint (0.25 μg/mL) falling within the baseline MIC distribution for this species (0.12 to 1 μg/mL).

Analysis of the pathogen distribution obtained in this study by patient age, specimen source, and geographic area shows some interesting patterns. As seen in other studies, blood isolates of *S pneumoniae* had a significantly lower prevalence of penicillin and macrolide resistance than mean values, whereas lower respiratory, sinus, and middle ear isolates had significantly higher values. Additionally, middle ear isolates of *H influenzae* had a significantly higher prevalence of β-lactamase production. The differences may reflect the fact that blood isolates represent primary disease more often than isolates from specimens that are frequently only obtained when patients fail to respond to therapy or undergo surgical procedures.

This study documents stabilization of the previously rising prevalence of β-lactam and macrolide/azalide resistance in *S pneumoniae* noted in the past decade [28]. Case reports have documented the clinical failure of macrolides/ azalides [49,55,56], and the clinical value of these agents for empiric use in respiratory tract infections remains controversial [37,57]. Amoxicillin and amoxicillin/clavulanic acid still retain their activity, however, with >90% of *S pneumoniae* strains being susceptible in our study. We did, however, note that the proportion of penicillin-resistant isolates of *S pneumoniae* suscep-tible to amoxicillin decreased from 80.2% in our 1997 study [28] to 63.6% in this study, and that 32.5% of penicillin-resistant isolates had amoxicillin MICs that were higher than penicillin MICs, whereas only 4.8% of isolates had this feature in our earlier study [28]. Nevertheless, amoxicillin and amoxicillin/clavulanate remained the most active oral β-lactam agents tested overall and for all subsets of isolates based on penicillin susceptibility (see Table 7). The only oral agents with better activity were the respiratory quinolones. In contrast, ceftriaxone-resistant strains with lower penicillin MICs remained rare (only three strains were found in this study), and most patients infected with strains causing nonmeningeal infections should respond to this agent administered intravenously or intramuscularly. An appropriate PK/PD breakpoint for this agent in nonmeningeal infections is 1 μg/mL [19], with 96.3% of strains being susceptible at this concentration in our study. Treating meningitis with ceftriaxone may be a problem, however, because only 79.7% of strains were susceptible at the meningitis breakpoint of 0.5 µg/mL, and a further 16.7% of strains had MICs of 1 µg/ mL, the current intermediate value in meningitis.

Although few fluoroquinolone-resistant strains were found in this study, the indiscriminate use of these agents to treat respiratory tract infections could lead to the development and spread of resistance as has occurred in other countries [10,13,24]. However, 34.6% of isolates were resistant to two or more of the six drug classes tested in this study, with most of these being resistant to penicillin and trimethoprim/sulfamethoxazole.

In contrast to *S pneumoniae,* our results showed no major changes in susceptibility in *H influenzae* isolates, although the prevalence of β-lactamase positivity has decreased to 28.6% of the 2570 strains tested in this study. The MIC_{50} and MIC_{90} values were generally unchanged from previous studies, however, despite the fact that the proportions of strains susceptible to many agents differ markedly from those in other studies due to our use of PK/PD breakpoints [7,9,10,34,58,59]. As with *S pneumoniae,* significant fluoroquinolone resistance has not yet emerged in *H influenzae,* although a few resistant strains were detected. Additionally, no major shift in non-β-lactamase–mediated β-lactam resistance was found, with only five β-lactamase–negative ampicillin-resistant strains found. Few amoxicillin/ clavulanic acid resistant strains were found, accounting for only 1.7% of strains for the current formulation and 0.2% of strains for the extended-release formulation.

Penicillin susceptibility of *S pneumoniae* in this study (63.6% susceptible, 13.2% intermediate, 23.2% resistant) was similar to that found in adults in our previous study (45.3% to 78.1% susceptible; 10.6% to 24.2% intermediate; 21.3% to 30.5% resistant), whereas β-lactamase production in *H influenzae* fell considerably (from 30.9%–46.3% to 28.6%) [28]. Additionally, the proportion of penicillin-nonsusceptible blood isolates in this study (28%) was similar to that found over the same time period from invasive pneumococcal disease (24% to 26%) in the Active Bacterial Core Surveillance of the Centers for Disease Control and Prevention, with similar differentiation into penicillin-intermediate and -resistant groups [2]. Introduction of a seven-valent protein-conjugated capsular polysaccharide *S pneumoniae* vaccine in children in 2000 resulted in a greater decrease in penicillin nonsusceptible strains (35%) than in the overall decrease in the incidence of invasive pneumococcal disease (29%) in 2001 compared to 1998 to 1999 [2], which may be explained by the fact that most resistant isolates belong to serotypes included in or related to vaccine serotypes [60]. Another *S pneumoniae* surveillance study over 1998 to 1999 and 2001 to 2002 found an increase in penicillin resistance (from 14.7% to 18.4%) and in azithromycin resistance (from 22.7% to 27.5%) [59,61]. Although azithromycin resistance in that study (28%) was similar to our findings (27.4%), penicillin resistance in our study (23.2%) was higher, and the reasons for these findings are unclear. Additional differences in geographic distribution of resistance were found between these studies. Whereas we found that penicillin and macrolide resistance was lowest in the Northwest, Karlowsky et al [61] found the lowest prevalence in the New England region and highest in the West South Central region. Jones et al [62] also reported resistance to be highest in the South Central and South East regions of the United States. Additionally, whereas trimethoprim/sulfamethoxazole resistance in *H influenzae* in our study (21.9%) was similar to that found by Karlowsky [59] in comparable age groups (17.9% to 22.2%), β-lactamase production was somewhat higher in our study (28.6% versus 17.9 to 25.6%).

This study shows that significant β-lactam and macrolide/azalide resistance in *S pneumoniae* and β-lactamase production and trimethoprim/ sulfamethoxazole resistance in untypeable *H influenzae* are still present. In addition, pharmacodynamic parameters have been used to interpret susceptibility data in a more clinically meaningful way. The results of this study should be applied to clinical practice based on the clinical presentation of the patient, the probability of the patient's having a bacterial rather than a viral infection, the natural history of the disease, the potential of pathogens to be susceptible to various oral antimicrobial agents, the potential for cross-resistance between agents with *S pneumoniae*, and the potential for pathogens to develop further resistance [63]. Antibiotics should be used judiciously to maintain remaining activity [32,64] and chosen carefully based on activity determined by PK/PD based breakpoints [19] to avoid these bacteria developing further resistance, particularly to fluoroquinolones.

Summary

The susceptibility of *Streptococcus pneumoniae* (2901 strains), untypeable *Haemophilus influenzae* (2570 strains), and *Moraxella catarrhalis* (218 strains) from adults with community-acquired respiratory tract infections was determined in six regions of the United States. MIC data were interpreted according to pharmacodynamically derived breakpoints applicable to the oral agents tested. Among *S pneumoniae* isolates, 63.6% were penicillin susceptible, 13.2% were intermediate, and 23.2% were resistant. Overall, 91.6% of *S pneumoniae* were susceptible to amoxicillin, 92.1% to amoxicillin/ clavulanic acid (95.2% at the extended-release formulation breakpoint), 90.6% to clindamycin, 80.4% to doxycycline, 71.0% to azithromycin, 72.3% to clarithromycin, 71.8% to cefprozil and cefdinir, 72.6% to cefuroxime axetil, 66.3% to cefixime, 63.7% to trimethoprim/sulfamethoxazole, and 19.7% to cefaclor. Only 26 isolates (0.9%) were resistant to levofloxacin and gatifloxacin, 24 to moxifloxacin (0.8%), and eight (0.3%) to gemifloxacin. Among *H influenzae* strains, 28.6% were β-lactamase positive, but virtually all were susceptible to amoxicillin/clavulanic acid (98.3%, with 99.8% at the extended-release formulation breakpoint), cefixime (100%), and fluoroquinolones (≥99.8%), whereas 93.5% were susceptible to cefdinir, 82.8% to cefuroxime axetil, 78.1% to trimethoprim/sulfamethoxazole, 70.2% to amoxicillin, 25.1% to doxycycline, 23.2% to cefprozil, and <5% to cefaclor, azithromycin and clarithromycin. Significant resistance was found in both pathogens in all six geographic regions. Most isolates of *M catarrhalis* were resistant to amoxicillin, cefaclor, cefprozil, and trimethoprim/sulfamethoxazole. Judicious use of oral antimicrobial agents is necessary to prevent further increases in antimicrobial resistance.

Acknowledgments

The authors thank Laura Koeth for coordinating collection of strain. We also thank the following for collecting and submitting isolates for testing in this study: B. Grover, S. Gamble, M. Bay, D. Lamb, S. Munroe, G. Teskie, P. Wong, S. Cyprian, T. Cleary, M. Rivera, C. Watkins, H. Phillips, D. Prince, S. Walker, M. Beard, R. Carey, B. Droege, J. Tjhio, G. Denys, R. Cheek, G. Munier, B. Cato, W. Eppling, D. Cosmidis, D. DeMarco, L. McDermott, D. Schwartz, M. Welty, R. Van Enk, J. Loomis, L. McClure, L. Temme, S. Matthey, M. Hostetter, L. Buck, G. Overturf, R. Cammarata, S. Jenkins, L. Rosenstein, J.R. DiPersio, C. Hogan, B. Rourke, L. Kaufmann, J. Griffin, B. Smith, L. Brown, B. Cavagnolo, N. Lee, L. Mann, K. Korgenski, K. Hazen, W. Winn, J. Claridge, M. Coyle, M. Patera, J. Quick, and M. Schmitz.

References

[1] Black SB, Shinefield HR. Immunization with oligosaccharide conjugate *Haemophilus influenzae* type b (HbOC) vaccine on a large health maintenance organization population: extended follow-up and impact on *Haemophilus influenzae* disease epidemiology. The Kaiser Permanente Pediatric Vaccine Study Group. Pediatr Infect Dis J 1992;11(8):610–3.

[2] Whitney CG, Farley MM, Hadler J, et al. Decline in invasive pneumococcal disease after the introduction of protein-polysaccharide conjugate vaccine. N Engl J Med 2003;348(18): 1737–46.

[3] Khan W, Ross S, Rodriguez W, Controni G, Saz AK. *Haemophilus influenzae* type B resistant to ampicillin. A report of two cases. JAMA 1974;229(3):298–301.

[4] Tomeh MO, Starr SE, McGowan JE Jr, Terry PM, Nahmias AJ. Ampicillin-resistant *Haemophilus influenzae* type B infection. JAMA 1974;229(3):295–7.

[5] Doern GV, Jorgensen JH, Thornsberry C, et al. National collaborative study of the prevalence of antimicrobial resistance among clinical isolates of *Haemophilus influenzae*. Antimicrob Agents Chemother 1988;32(2):180–5.

[6] Rittenhouse SF, Miller LA, Kaplan RL, Mosely GH, Poupard JA. A survey of beta-lactamase-producing *Haemophilus influenzae*. An evaluation of 5750 isolates. Diagn Microbiol Infect Dis 1995;21(4):223–5.

[7] Jones RN, Jacobs MR, Washington JA, Pfaller MA. A 1994–95 survey of *Haemophilus influenzae* susceptibility to ten orally administered agents. A 187 clinical laboratory center sample in the United States. Diagn Microbiol Infect Dis 1997;27(3):75–83.

[8] Jacobs MR, Bajaksouzian S. Microbiologic evaluation of contemporary *Haemophilus influenzae* isolates having elevated MICs to amoxicillin-clavulanic acid. Diagn Microbiol Infect Dis 1997;28:105–12.

[9] Doern GV, Brueggemann AB, Pierce G, Holley HP Jr, Rauch A. Antibiotic resistance among clinical isolates of *Haemophilus influenzae* in the United States in 1994 and 1995 and detection of beta-lactamase- positive strains resistant to amoxicillin-clavulanate: results of a national multicenter surveillance study. Antimicrob Agents Chemother 1997;41(2):292–7.

[10] Thornsberry C, Ogilvie P, Kahn J, Mauriz Y. Surveillance of antimicrobial resistance in *Streptococcus pneumoniae*, *Haemophilus influenzae*, and *Moraxella catarrhalis* in the United States in 1996–1997 respiratory season. The Laboratory Investigator Group. Diagn Microbiol Infect Dis 1997;29(4):249–57.

[11] Ubukata K, Shibasaki Y, Yamamoto K, et al. Association of amino acid substitutions in penicillin-binding protein 3 with beta-lactam resistance in beta-lactamase-negative ampicillin-resistant *Haemophilus influenzae*. Antimicrob Agents Chemother 2001;45(6): 1693–9.

[12] Hasegawa K, Yamamoto K, Chiba N, et al. Diversity of ampicillin-resistance genes in *Haemophilus influenzae* in Japan and the United States. Microb Drug Resist 2003;9(1): 39–46.

[13] Jacobs MR, Felmingham D, Appelbaum PC, Gruneberg RN, Alexander Project G. The Alexander Project 1998–2000: susceptibility of pathogens isolated from community-acquired respiratory tract infection to commonly used antimicrobial agents. J Antimicrob Chemother 2003;52(2):229–46.

[14] Jacobs MR, Appelbaum PC. Antibiotic-resistant pneumococci. Rev Med. Microbiol 1995; 6:77–93.

[15] Bradley JS, Connor JD. Ceftriaxone failure in meningitis caused by *Streptococcus pneumoniae* with reduced susceptibility to beta-lactam antibiotics. Pediatr Infect Dis J 1991;10(11):871–3.

[16] Sloas MM, Barrett FF, Chesney PJ, et al. Cephalosporin treatment failure in penicillin- and cephalosporin- resistant *Streptococcus pneumoniae* meningitis. Pediatr Infect Dis J 1992;11(8):662–6.

[17] Scott-Levin I. Physician drug and diagnosis audit (PDDA). Newton, PA: PMSI Scott-Levin, Inc.; 1997.

[18] Green M, Wald ER. Emerging resistance to antibiotics: impact on respiratory infections in the outpatient setting. Ann Allergy Asthma Immunol 1996;77(3):167–73; quiz 173–5.

[19] Craig WA. Pharmacokinetic/pharmacodynamic parameters: rationale for antibacterial dosing of mice and men. Clin Infect Dis 1998;26(1):1–10; quiz 11–2.

[20] Dagan R, Abramson O, Leibovitz E, et al. Impaired bacteriologic response to oral cephalosporins in acute otitis media caused by pneumococci with intermediate resistance to penicillin. Pediatr Infect Dis J 1996;15(11):980–5.

[21] Dagan R, Abramson O, Leibovitz E, et al. Bacteriologic response to oral cephalosporins: are established susceptibility breakpoints appropriate in the case of acute otitis media? J Infect Dis 1997;176(5):1253–9.

[22] Dagan R, Piglansky L, Yagupsky P, Fliss DM, Lieberman A, Leibovitz E. Bacteriologic response in acute otitis media (AOM): comparison between azithromycin (AZ), cefaclor (CEC) and amoxicillin (AMOX). Abstracts of the 37th Interscience Conference on Antimicrobial Agents and Chemotherapy. Abstr. No. K-103:345. Washington, DC: American Society for Microbiology; 1997.

[23] Craig WA, Andes D. Pharmacokinetics and pharmacodynamics of antibiotics in otitis media. Pediatr Infect Dis J 1996;15(3):255–9.

[24] Drusano GL, Goldstein FW. Relevance of the Alexander Project: pharmacodynamic considerations. J Antimicrob Chemother 1996;(38 Suppl A):141–54.

[25] Drusano GL, Craig WA. Relevance of pharmacokinetics and pharmacodynamics in the selection of antibiotics for respiratory tract infections. J Chemother 1997;9(Suppl 3):38–44.

[26] Nightingale CH. Pharmacokinetics and pharmacodynamics of newer macrolides. Pediatr Infect Dis J 1997;16(4):438–43.

[27] Preston SL, Drusano GL, Berman AL, et al. Pharmacodynamics of levofloxacin: a new paradigm for early clinical trials. JAMA 1998;279(2):125–9.

[28] Jacobs MR, Bajaksouzian S, Zilles A, Lin G, Pankuch GA, Appelbaum PC. Susceptibilities of Streptococcus pneumoniae and Haemophilus influenzae to 10 oral antimicrobial agents based on pharmacodynamic parameters: 1997 U.S. Surveillance study. Antimicrob Agents Chemother 1999;43(8):1901–8.

[29] National Committee for Clinical Laboratory Standards. Methods for dilution antimicrobial susceptibility tests for bacteria that grow aerobically. Approved Standard M7–A4. Villanova (PA): National Committee for Clinical Laboratory Standards; 1997.

[30] National Committee for Clinical Laboratory Standards. Performance standards for antimicrobial susceptibility testing; thirteenth informational supplement: M100–S13. Wayne (PA): National Committee for Clinical Laboratory Standards; 2003.

[31] National Committee for Clinical Laboratory Standards. Performance standards for antimicrobial susceptibility testing; fourteenth informational supplement: M100–S14. Wayne (PA): National Committee for Clinical Laboratory Standards; 2004.

[32] Dowell SF, Butler JC, Marcy SM, Phillips WR, Gerber MA, Schwartz B. Principles of judicious use of antimicrobial agents for pediatric upper respiratory tract infections. Pediatrics 1998;101:163–5.

[33] Doern GV, Brueggemann A, Holley HP Jr, Rauch AM. Antimicrobial resistance of Streptococcus pneumoniae recovered from outpatients in the United States during the winter months of 1994 to 1995: results of a 30-center national surveillance study. Antimicrob Agents Chemother 1996;40(5):1208–13.

[34] Barry AL, Pfaller MA, Fuchs PC, Packer RR. In vitro activities of 12 orally administered antimicrobial agents against four species of bacterial respiratory pathogens from U.S. Medical Centers in 1992 and 1993. Antimicrob Agents Chemother 1994;38(10):2419–25.

[35] Barry AL, Fuchs PC. In vitro activities of a streptogramin (RP59500), three macrolides, and an azalide against four respiratory tract pathogens. Antimicrob Agents Chemother 1995;39(1):238–40.

[36] Barry AL. Antimicrobial agents for community-acquired respiratory tract infections. Infection 1995;23(Suppl 2):S59–63; discussion S64.

[37] Bartlett JG. Empirical therapy of community-acquired pneumonia: macrolides are not ideal choices. Semin Respir Infect 1997;12(4):329–33.

[38] Pelton SI. Defining resistance: breakpoints and beyond implications for pediatric respiratory infection. Diagn Microbiol Infect Dis 1996;25(4):195–9.

[39] Seral C, Van Bambeke F, Tulkens PM. Quantitative analysis of gentamicin, azithromycin, telithromycin, ciprofloxacin, moxifloxacin, and oritavancin (LY333328) activities against intracellular Staphylococcus aureus in mouse J774 macrophages. Antimicrob Agents Chemother. Jul 2003;47(7):2283–92.

[40] Fine MJ, Auble TE, Yealy DM, et al. A prediction rule to identify low-risk patients with community-acquired pneumonia. N Engl J Med 1997;336(4):243–50.

[41] Fine MJ. Risk stratification for patients with community-acquired pneumonia. Int J Clin Pract Suppl 2000;(115):14–7.

[42] Ball P, Baquero F, Cars O, et al. Antibiotic therapy of community respiratory tract infections: strategies for optimal outcomes and minimized resistance emergence. J Antimicrob Chemother 2002;49(1):31–40.

[43] Dagan R, Klugman KP, Craig WA, Baquero F. Evidence to support the rationale that bacterial eradication in respiratory tract infection is an important aim of antimicrobial therapy. J Antimicrob Chemother 2001;47(2):129–40.

[44] Jacobs MR. Optimisation of antimicrobial therapy using pharmacokinetic and pharmacodynamic parameters. Clin Microbiol Infect 2001;7(11):589–96.

[45] Fendrick AM, Saint S, Brook I, Jacobs MR, Pelton S, Sethi S. Diagnosis and treatment of upper respiratory tract infections in the primary care setting. Clin Ther 2001;23(10):1683–706.

[46] Sethi S. Infectious exacerbations of chronic bronchitis: diagnosis and management. J Antimicrob Chemother 1999;43(Suppl A):97–105.

[47] Ross GH, Hovde LB, Ibrahim KH, Ibrahim YH, Rotschafer JC. Comparison of once-daily versus twice-daily administration of cefdinir against typical bacterial respiratory tract pathogens. Antimicrob Agents Chemother 2001;45(10):2936–8.

[48] Rodvold KA, Gotfried MH, Danziger LH, Servi RJ. Intrapulmonary steady-state concentrations of clarithromycin and azithromycin in healthy adult volunteers. Antimicrob Agents Chemother 1997;41(6):1399–402.

[49] Lonks JR, Garau J, Medeiros AA. Implications of antimicrobial resistance in the empirical treatment of community-acquired respiratory tract infections: the case of macrolides. J Antimicrob Chemother 2002;50(Suppl S2):87–92.

[50] Jacobs MR. In vivo veritas: in vitro macrolide resistance in systemic *Streptococcus pneumoniae* infections does result in clinical failure. Clin Infect Dis 2002;35(5):565–9.

[51] Zhanel GG, DeCorby M, Noreddin A, et al. Pharmacodynamic activity of azithromycin against macrolide-susceptible and -resistant *Streptococcus pneumoniae* simulating clinically achievable free serum, epithelial lining fluid and middle ear fluid concentrations. J Antimicrob Chemother 2003;52(1):83–8.

[52] Noreddin AM, Roberts D, Nichol K, Wierzbowski A, Hoban DJ, Zhanel GG. Pharmacodynamic modeling of clarithromycin against macrolide-resistant [PCR-positive mef(A) or erm(B)] *Streptococcus pneumoniae* simulating clinically achievable serum and epithelial lining fluid free-drug concentrations. Antimicrob Agents Chemother 2002;46(12): 4029–34.

[53] Novelli A, Fallani S, Cassetta MI, Arrigucci S, Mazzei T. In vivo pharmacodynamic evaluation of clarithromycin in comparison to erythromycin. J Chemother 2002;14(6): 584–90.

[54] den Hollander JG, Knudsen JD, Mouton JW, et al. Comparison of pharmacodynamics of azithromycin and erythromycin in vitro and in vivo. Antimicrob Agents Chemother 1998; 42(2):377–82.

[55] Jackson MA, Burry VF, Olson LC, Duthie SE, Kearns GL. Breakthrough sepsis in macrolide-resistant pneumococcal infection. Pediatr Infect Dis J 1996;15(11): 1049–51.

[56] Reid R Jr, Bradley JS, Hindler J. Pneumococcal meningitis during therapy of otitis media with clarithromycin. Pediatr Infect Dis J 1995;14(12):1104–5.

[57] Vergis EN, Yu VL. Macrolides are ideal for empiric therapy of community-acquired pneumonia in the immunocompetent host. Semin Respir Infect 1997;12(4):322–8.

[58] Doern GV. Antimicrobial resistance among lower respiratory tract isolates of *Haemophilus influenzae*: results of a 1992-93 western Europe and USA collaborative surveillance study. The Alexander Project Collaborative Group. J Antimicrob Chemother 1996;38(Suppl A): 59–69.

[59] Karlowsky JA, Thornsberry C, Critchley IA, et al. Susceptibilities to levofloxacin in *Streptococcus pneumoniae*, *Haemophilus influenzae*, and *Moraxella catarrhalis* clinical isolates from children: results from 2000–2001 and 2001–2002 TRUST studies in the United States. Antimicrob Agents Chemother 2003;47(6):1790–7.

[60] Joloba ML, Windau A, Bajaksouzian S, Appelbaum PC, Hausdorff WP, Jacobs MR. Pneumococcal conjugate vaccine serotypes of *Streptococcus pneumoniae* isolates and the antimicrobial susceptibility of such isolates in children with otitis media. Clin Infect Dis 2001;33(9):1489–94.

[61] Karlowsky JA, Thornsberry C, Jones ME, Evangelista AT, Critchley IA, Sahm DF. Factors associated with relative rates of antimicrobial resistance among *Streptococcus pneumoniae* in the United States: results from the TRUST Surveillance Program (1998–2002). Clin Infect Dis 2003;36(8):963–70.

[62] Jones RN, Jenkins SG, Hoban DJ, Pfaller MA, Ramphal R. In vitro activity of selected cephalosporins and erythromycin against staphylococci and pneumococci isolated at

38 North American medical centers participating in the SENTRY Antimicrobial Surveillance Program, 1997–1998. Diagn Microbiol Infect Dis 2000;37(2):93–8.

[63] Rosenfeld RM. An evidence-based approach to treating otitis media. Pediatr Clin North Am 1996;43(6):1165–81.

[64] Dowell SF, Butler JC, Giebink GS, et al. Acute otitis media: management and surveillance in an era of pneumococcal resistance—a report from the Drug-resistant Streptococcus pneumoniae Therapeutic Working Group. Pediatr Infect Dis J 1999;18(1):1–9.

[65] Sinus and Allergy Health Partnership. Antimicrobial treatment guidelines for acute bacterial rhinosinusitis. Sinus and Allergy Health Partnership. Otolaryngol Head Neck Surg 2000;123(Suppl.):S1–32.

CLINICS IN
LABORATORY
MEDICINE

ELSEVIER
SAUNDERS

Clin Lab Med 24 (2004) 531–551

Evolution of amoxicillin/clavulanate in the treatment of adults with acute bacterial rhinosinusitis and community-acquired pneumonia in response to antimicrobial-resistance patterns

Thomas M. File Jr, MD, MS[a,b,*],
Michael S. Benninger, MD[c],
Michael R. Jacobs, MD, PhD[d,e]

[a]Department of Internal Medicine, Northeastern Ohio Universities College of Medicine,
Rootstown, OH, USA
[b]Infectious Disease Service, Summa Health System, 75 Arch Street,
Suite 105, Akron, OH 44304, USA
[c]Department of Otolaryngology–Head and Neck Surgery, Henry Ford Hospital,
2799 West Grand Boulevard, Detroit, MI 48202, USA
[d]Department of Pathology and Medicine, Case Western Reserve University,
Cleveland, OH, USA
[e]Clinical Microbiology, University Hospitals of Cleveland, 11100 Euclid Avenue,
Pathology 529, Cleveland, OH 44106, USA

Acute bacterial rhinosinusitis (ABRS) and community-acquired pneumonia (CAP) are common community-acquired respiratory tract infections and represent a significant burden to the health care system. *Streptococcus pneumoniae* and *Haemophilus influenzae* are two of the most common bacterial causes of ABRS and CAP [1,2]. Pneumococcal resistance to commonly used antimicrobials among *S pneumoniae* has increased at an alarming rate, and current antimicrobial therapies need to be tailored to combat this surge in resistance.

According to 1996 figures, there are approximately 20 million cases of ABRS in the United States each year [3]. Between 1985 and 1992, ABRS

This work was supported by GlaxoSmithKline.
* Corresponding author. Infectious Disease Service, Akron Infectious Disease, Inc., 75 Arch Street, Suite 105, Akron, OH 44304.
E-mail address: Filet@summa-health.org (T.M. File, Jr).

accounted for 7% to 12% of all antimicrobial prescriptions [4], and a recent audit of prescriptions from the National Ambulatory Medical Care Survey indicates that ABRS is responsible for 21% of antimicrobial prescriptions for adults [5]. In adults, *S pneumoniae* is responsible for 20% to 43% of ABRS cases, and *H influenzae* and *Moraxella catarrhalis* are identified in 22% to 35% and 2% to 10% of cases, respectively [6].

Pneumonia is the sixth leading cause of death in the United States and the number one cause of death from infectious diseases [7,8]. *S pneumoniae* is responsible for two thirds of cases of CAP [9]. *H influenzae* is involved in 2% to 12% of CAP cases, and *M catarrhalis* is responsible for less than 1% of CAP cases [10,11].

Since discovery of the bacteriocidal effects of penicillin in 1929, many β-lactam antimicrobials, as well as other classes of antimicrobials, have been developed to counteract increasing antimicrobial resistance among respiratory tract pathogens (Table 1) [12–14]. The purpose of this article is to review the timeline of β-lactam discovery, the development of antimicrobial resistance, and the rationale for a new pharmacokinetically enhanced formulation of amoxicillin/clavulanate (Augmentin XR GlaxoSmithKline, Collegeville, Pennsylvania).

Prevalence and mechanisms of β-lactam resistance among common respiratory pathogens

The first penicillin-nonsusceptible *S pneumoniae* isolate (minimum inhibitory concentration [MIC] = 0.25 µg/mL) in the United States was reported in 1974 [15]. National surveillance studies have indicated a constant increase in the rate of resistance among *S pneumoniae* in the 1990s (Fig. 1) [16–19]. Between the years 1998 and 1999 and 1999 to 2000, clinical *S pneumoniae* isolates demonstrated a statistically significant increase in resistance to amoxicillin/clavulanate (3.7%, $P < 0.001$), cefuroxime (2.2%, $P < 0.05$), clarithromycin (3.1%, $P < 0.001$), and trimethoprim/sulfamethoxazole (TMP/SMX) (2.0%, $P < 0.05$) [20]. In a recent U.S. study, 37% of *S pneumoniae* isolates were penicillin nonsusceptible (MIC $\geq$ 0.12 µg/mL), with 12% being penicillin intermediate (MICs 0.12–1 µg/mL) and 25% resistant (MIC $\geq$ 2 µg/mL) to penicillin [21]. Increasing resistance to commonly used antimicrobials among *S pneumoniae* isolates is extremely concerning, and many isolates are resistant to multiple drug classes.

β-Lactam resistance is mediated by two primary mechanisms: production of β-lactamase enzymes and alteration of penicillin-binding proteins (PBPs) [22]. β-Lactam resistance among *H influenzae* and *M catarrhalis* is most commonly mediated by production of β-lactamase enzymes, which hydrolyze bonds within the β-lactam ring of penicillins and some cephalosporins, resulting in inactivation of the antimicrobial [23]. The production of β-lactamase destroys β-lactam antimicrobials before they reach the cell and exert their bacteriocidal effects. This mechanism of resistance can be over-

Table 1
Timeline of β-lactam discovery, bacterial resistance, and approval for use in the United States

Year	Landmarks in β-lactam discovery and bacterial resistance
1929	Antimicrobial effects of penicillin first reported by Alexander Fleming
1940	Penicillin isolated by Howard Florey
1944	*Staphylococcus aureus* reported as first penicillin (β-lactam)-resistant bacteria
1946	Penicillin G approved
1960	Methicillin approved
1961	Ampicillin released as the first penicillin with activity against Gram-negative bacteria, including *Haemophilus influenzae*
	Oxacillin approved
1962	Tetracycline-resistant *Streptococcus pneumoniae* reported
1963	Ampicillin approved
1964	Nafcillin and cephalothin approved
1965	Penicillin-intermediate *Streptococcus pneumoniae* first reported
1970	Carbenicillin approved
1973	Amoxicillin widely adopted as broad-spectrum oral penicillin, potent against *Streptococcus pneumoniae*
	Cefazolin approved
1974	Ampicillin-resistant *Haemophilus influenzae* reported
1976	Clavulanate, a β-lactamase inhibitor, discovered
	Ticarcillin approved
1977	Penicillin-, chloramphenicol-, and multidrug-resistant *Streptococcus pneumoniae* first reported in South Africa
	Ampicillin-resistant *Moraxella catarrhalis* reported
1978	Cefamandole and cefoxitin approved
1981	Cefotaxime and piperacillin approved
1982	Cefoperazone approved
1983	Ceftizoxime and cefuroxime axetil approved
1984	Amoxicillin/clavulanate and ceftriaxone approved
1985	Ticarcillin/clavulanate, ceftazidime, and cefotetan approved
1986	Ampicillin/sulbactam approved
1993	Piperacillin/tazobactam approved
2001	Amoxicillin/clavulanate 600 mg/5 mL oral suspension approved (90/6.4 mg/kg/day twice a day)
2002	Extended-release amoxicillin/clavulanate (2000/125 mg twice a day) approved

Adapted from Medeiros AA. Evolution and dissemination of beta-lactamases accelerated by generations of beta-lactam antibiotics. Clin Infect Dis 1997;(24 Suppl 1):S19–45.

come by using a combination of a β-lactam plus a β-lactamase inhibitor, which renders the β-lactamase enzyme inactive and allows more of the β-lactam drug to reach the cell and exert its bacteriocidal effect. In 1984, the first β-lactamase inhibitor, clavulanic acid, was introduced in combination with amoxicillin for clinical use in the United States [24]. A bi-cyclic β-lactam derived from *Streptomyces clavuligerus,* clavulanate acts as a specific inhibitor of many β-lactamase enzymes [23], broadening the antimicrobial spectrum of amoxicillin to include many β-lactamase–producing pathogens. Of the currently available oral β-lactam antimicrobials and macrolides, amoxicillin/clavulanate is the only oral agent that inhibits more than 90% of strains of the three most common respiratory tract pathogens [25]. β-

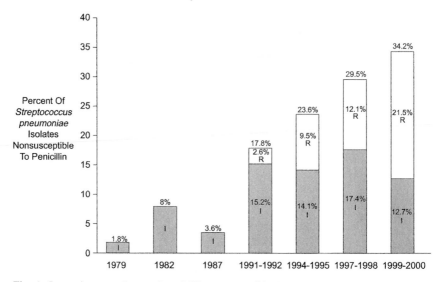

Fig. 1. Increasing prevalence of penicillin-nonsuceptible *Streptococcus pneumoniae* isolates based on national surveillance studies [16–19]. I = intermediate (penicillin minimum inhibitory concentration [MIC] = 0.12–1 µg/mL); R = resistant (MIC ≥ 2 µg/mL).

Lactamase inhibitors, therefore, only work effectively in organisms that are inherently susceptible to β-lactam antimicrobials. β-Lactamase production, the primary mechanism of resistance to penicillins among *H influenzae*, was first reported in 1974 [26]. In 1990, 16.5% of *H influenzae* were reported to produce β-lactamase [27]. By 1994 to 1995, the rate of β-lactamase production among *H influenzae* isolates peaked at 36.4% [28]. The percentage of *H influenzae* isolates that produce β-lactamase seems to have leveled off in recent years at approximately 30% [17,21,29,30] but needs to be considered when selecting an antimicrobial. Inactivation of β-lactamase in β-lactamase–producing isolates by the inhibitor, clavulanate, results in more than 98% of *H influenzae* isolates worldwide being susceptible (based on pharmacokinetic/pharmacodynamic [PK/PD] breakpoints) to the pharmacokinetically enhanced formulation of amoxicillin/clavulanate (4 g amoxicillin component/day), cefixime, ceftriaxone, and the fluoroquinolones (ciprofloxacin, ofloxacin, gemifloxacin, levofloxacin, gatifloxacin, and moxifloxacin), whereas less than 1.5% of isolates were susceptible to erythromycin, azithromycin, and clarithromycin [21].

National surveillance studies also have demonstrated that more than 90% of *M catarrhalis* isolates produce β-lactamase [21,30,31] and are resistant to penicillin, ampicillin, and amoxicillin. However, using PK/PD breakpoints, virtually all *M catarrhalis* isolates were susceptible to the pharmacokinetically enhanced formulation of amoxicillin/clavulanate, regular amoxicillin/clavulanate, azithromycin, clarithromycin, cefixime, cefdinir, erythromycin, and the respiratory fluoroquinolones [21].

In contrast to the resistance mechanism of β-lactamase production by *H influenzae* and *M catarrhalis*, β-lactam resistance among *S pneumoniae* is dependent on alterations in PBPs [32], which are membrane-bound proteins that catalyze the transfer of peptide chains involved in peptidoglycan cross-linking within the bacterial cell wall. β-Lactams, through their interaction with PBPs, block the cross-linking of peptide chains that support the peptidoglycan structure. As a result of this interaction, the cell wall becomes weak and unable to provide osmotic support, and eventually the cell is lysed. When the active transpeptidation site of the PBP is altered, the affinity for the antimicrobial is reduced and higher drug concentrations are required for enzyme inhibition. Furthermore, because there are several PBPs and three regions of each PBP that make up the active transpeptidation site, *S pneumoniae* isolates demonstrate varying degrees of resistance to different β-lactams based on the number of PBP alterations that have occurred. This mechanism of resistance can often be overcome if clinically achievable concentrations exceed the concentration required to inhibit the infecting strain for a sufficient length of time, which can usually be achieved with appropriate parenteral dosing regimens or, in some cases, by increasing the oral dose of the antimicrobial [33]. For example, higher daily doses of amoxicillin (4 g/day) may successfully eradicate *S pneumoniae* isolates that are resistant to conventional therapy (eg, daily amoxicillin doses of 1.5 to1.75 g) [2].

Cross-resistance

Multiple drug resistance (ie, resistance to $\geq$ 3 classes of antimicrobials) has been reported worldwide in pneumococci and can be attributed to genes carried on DNA segments and transferred among different strains of bacteria [7]. Pneumococcal resistance to non-β-lactam antimicrobials has increased along with use of such agents [34–37]. *S pneumoniae* strains that are penicillin resistant often are resistant to macrolides, cephalosporins, sulfonamides, and tetracyclines [30]. Penicillin-resistant pneumococci more commonly exhibit multidrug resistance than pneumococci that are penicillin susceptible [16,38]. For example, of *S pneumoniae* isolates that were resistant to penicillin (MIC $\geq$ 2 µg/mL), 75% also were resistant to TMP/SMX, 41% to erythromycin, 24% to tetracycline, and 79% demonstrated resistance to multiple drug classes [39]. In addition, significant cross-resistance was noted for the penicillins and macrolides. In a surveillance study by Jacobs and colleagues [21], less than 10% of penicillin-susceptible *S pneumoniae* were cross-resistant to azithromycin and clarithromycin, whereas approximately 72% of isolates resistant to penicillin also were cross-resistant to azithromycin and clarithromycin (Table 2). Furthermore, there have been reports of clinical treatment failures with macrolide therapy in patients with macrolide-resistant *S pneumoniae* infections [40–45].

It is important to consider the incidence of multidrug resistance among *S pneumoniae* isolates because resistance to antimicrobials limits the available

Table 2
Susceptibility of respiratory tract isolates to oral antimicrobial agents at pharmacokinetic/pharmacodynamic (PK/PD) breakpoints (1998–2000)

| Agent | Susceptibility breakpoint (µg/mL) | Percentage of isolates susceptible at PK/PD breakpoints | | | | | |
		Streptococcus pneumoniae (all) (N = 2901)	Penicillin-susceptible Streptococcus pneumoniae[a] (N = 1845)	Penicillin-intermediate Streptococcus pneumoniae[b] (N = 382)	Penicillin-resistant Streptococcus pneumoniae[c] (N = 674)	Haemophilus influenzae (N = 1919)	Moraxella catarrhalis (N = 204)
High-dose amoxicillin[d]	≤4	95.2	100	100	79.4	70.2	7.3
Amoxicillin/clavulanate[e]	≤2[e]	92.1	100	99.7	66.3	98.3	100
High-dose amoxicillin/clavulanate[e]	≤4[e,f]	95.2	100	100	79.4	99.8	100
Cefaclor	≤0.5	19.7	30.3	2.9	0.1	3.7	8.7
Cefdinir	≤0.25	68.8	98.4	49.2	0.5	78.2	77.6
Cefixime	≤1	66.3	96.7	35.3	0.4	>99.9	100
Cefpodoxime	≤0.5	75.4	99.7	67.4	0.7	100	85
Cefprozil	≤1	71.8	99.7	63.1	0.4	23.2	9.2
Cefuroxime axetil	≤1	72.6	99.9	68.8	0	82.8	50.5
Loracarbef	≤0.5	7.6	10.3	6.5	0	9.6	
Azithromycin	≤0.12	71.0	91.8	48.4	27.2	2.3	100
Clarithromycin	≤0.25	72.3	92.8	51.0	28.2	0	100
Erythromycin	≤0.25	72.0	92.6	49.7	28.0	0	100
Clindamycin[g]	≤0.25	90.6	97.9	81.4	75.8	0	0
Doxycycline	≤0.25	80.4	95.2	65.2	48.7	25.1	96.3

	MIC	[h]	[h]	[h]	[h]	
Ciprofloxacin	≤1	99.1	99.9	99.7		100
Gatifloxacin	≤1	99.1	99.0	99.7	99.1	100
Levofloxacin	≤2	99.1	99.0	99.7	99.1	100
Moxifloxacin	≤1	99.2	99.0	100	99.3	100
Trimethoprim/sulfamethoxazole[g,i]	≤0.5	63.7	86.4	46.1	11.3	19.3

[a] MIC_{90} ≤0.06 µg/mL.
[b] MICs 0.12–1 µg/mL.
[c] MIC ≥2 µg/mL.
[d] High-dose amoxicillin = 4 g/day.
[e] Amoxicillin component of amoxicillin/clavulanate.
[f] This breakpoint is not approved by the US Food and Drug Administration.
[g] NCCLS breakpoints are used for clindamycin and trimethoprim/sulfamethoxazole.
[h] Ciprofloxacin MICs are higher than the PK/PD breakpoints for some isolates of S pneumoniae; therefore, ciprofloxacin does have reliable coverage against S pneumoniae.
[i] Shown as trimethoprim component.
Adapted from Anon JB, Jacobs MR, Poole MD, et al. Antimicrobial treatment guidelines for acute bacterial rhinosinusitis. Otolaryngol Head Neck Surg 2004;130(1 Suppl):1–45.

treatment options [20]. This can be especially concerning in patients who have failed previous therapies or are limited by allergies to certain antimicrobial agents.

There are many antimicrobial agents available for the treatment of ABRS and CAP, including β-lactams, macrolides, tetracyclines, TMP/SMX, and fluoroquinolones, but increased use of some of these agents has led to increased resistance among common pathogens [32,35,37]. Increasing antimicrobial resistance and factors that may place a patient at higher risk for infection with resistant pathogens have a significant impact on antimicrobial selection. Several treatment guidelines have been developed to assist physicians in the selection of an appropriate antimicrobial for use in the treatment of patients with ABRS or CAP [1,2,46,47].

Treatment guidelines

Acute bacterial rhinosinusitis

Because it is impractical to routinely obtain cultures for isolation of pathogens from the sinuses, patients with ABRS are usually treated empirically. Recently updated guidelines from the Sinus and Allergy Health Partnership [2] stratify patients according to their severity of disease, disease progression rate, and previous antimicrobial exposure. Recent antimicrobial therapy (within the previous 4 to 6 weeks) is a risk factor for infection with resistant strains. In areas with a high incidence of penicillin-resistant or drug-resistant S pneumoniae, guidelines suggest that amoxicillin/clavulanate therapy should be prescribed at a total dose of 4 g/day (amoxicillin component) [2]. In addition, susceptibility data based on PK/PD breakpoints can aid the clinician when selecting an antimicrobial agent (see Table 2). PK/PD breakpoints are based on PK/PD parameters of antimicrobials that correlate with successful clinical outcomes, and selection of an antimicrobial based on high rates of susceptibility at the determined antimicrobial breakpoints may be associated with better clinical outcomes with that particular agent [2].

Adult patients can be stratified into two categories. The first includes patients with mild disease who have not received recent antimicrobial treatment; the second includes patients with mild disease who have taken antimicrobials in the previous 4 to 6 weeks or those with moderate disease regardless of recent antimicrobial exposure. The degree of disease severity (mild or moderate) is left to the judgment of the physician treating the patient. Agents recommended for adults with mild disease who have not received antimicrobial treatment in the previous 4 to 6 weeks include amoxicillin (1.5 to 4 g/day), amoxicillin/clavulanate (1.75 to 4 g/250 mg/day), cefpodoxime proxetil, cefuroxime axetil, or cefdinir [2]. Antimicrobial choices for initial therapy in adults in the other category include high-dose amoxicillin/clavulanate (4 g of amoxicillin component/day) or a respiratory fluoroquinolone (gatifloxacin, levofloxacin, or moxifloxacin). However, prudent use of the fluoroquinolones is recommended because widespread use of these agents in patients with milder disease may promote resistance [46].

Based on a therapeutic outcome model, predicted clinical efficacy of first-line oral treatment is higher than 90% with high-dose amoxicillin/clavulanate (4 g/250 mg), amoxicillin/clavulanate (1.75 g/250 mg), and the respiratory fluoroquinolones (gatifloxacin, levofloxacin, and moxifloxacin), and 83% to 88% with high-dose amoxicillin (4 g/day) and amoxicillin (1.5 g/day) [2]. Although estimated clinical efficacy with cefuroxime axetil, cefpodoxime proxetil, cefixime, cefdinir, and TMP/SMX is generally between 83% and 88%, these agents have low rates of activity against penicillin-resistant S pneumoniae isolates [21] and therefore may not be appropriate for use in patients at risk for infection with this pathogen.

Broader-spectrum antimicrobials should be considered in adult patients with mild disease who have taken antimicrobials in the previous 4 to 6 weeks or in those with moderate disease regardless of recent antimicrobial exposure because such patients are at risk for therapeutic failure or infection with resistant pathogens [2]. Additional considerations for antimicrobial therapies in these patients include parenteral ceftriaxone or combination Gram-positive and Gram-negative coverage with high-dose amoxicillin or clinda-mycin plus cefixime, or high-dose amoxicillin or clindamycin plus rifampin.

Community-acquired pneumonia

Treatment guidelines for outpatient management of CAP have been established by the American Thoracic Society (ATS) [1], the Infectious Diseases Society of America (IDSA) [47], and the Centers for Disease Control and Prevention (CDC) [46]. Treatment guidelines for CAP published by the ATS stratify patients according to risk for infection with specific pathogens and recommend a newer macrolide (clarithromycin or azithromycin) or doxycycline for outpatients who are not at risk for infection with penicillin-resistant or drug-resistant S pneumoniae [1]. Therapy with an oral β-lactam (ie, amoxicillin/clavulanate, high-dose amoxicillin [1 g every 8 hours], cefpodox-ime proxetil, or cefuroxime axetil) plus a newer macrolide or doxycycline, or monotherapy with a respiratory fluoroquinolone (ie, levofloxacin, gatiflox-acin, or moxifloxacin) is recommended for the treatment of outpatients with cardiopulmonary disease (ie, congestive heart failure or chronic obstructive pulmonary disease) and other disease-modifying factors, such as age older than 65 years. These recommendations provide for coverage of the "typical" as well as the atypical pathogens (Mycoplasma pneumoniae, Chlamydia pneumoniae, and Legionella pneumophila). M pneumoniae can be found in up to 37% of CAP episodes [1], whereas C pneumoniae is responsible for approximately 5% to 15% of CAP cases each year and L pneumophila is identified in 2% to 6% of cases [7].

The Pneumonia Patient Outcome Research Team (PORT) study demonstrated that the mortality rate from CAP is more closely associated with age and disease severity than with the causative pathogen [48]. Therefore, outpatient treatment can be considered for patients in PORT risk classes I or II (those aged 50 years or younger with up to one comorbid illness or laboratory abnormality). In a study of patients with CAP, atypical pathogens were identified in 14% of outpatients [49]. It is not clear if any patient benefit is achieved in treating outpatients with CAP caused by *M pneumoniae* or *C pneumoniae* with an agent active against these pathogens, because no differences in clinical outcomes were found when agents with no activity against atypicals were used [50–52]. However, the ability to differentiate a clinical effect in these studies may be limited by the study designs and the tendency for many of these infections to be self-limited. However, several older studies have shown that specific treatment for mild *M pneumoniae* CAP reduces morbidity of pneumonia and shortens the duration of symptoms [53]. Although macrolides and doxycycline provide coverage of atypical pathogens such as *M pneumoniae, C pneumoniae,* and *L pneumophila*, they have limited activity against drug-resistant *S pneumoniae* (DRSP) [46].

The most recent IDSA guidelines recommend a macrolide or doxycycline for patients who were previously healthy and had not received recent antimicrobial therapy. An antipneumococcal fluoroquinolone (ie, levofloxacin, gatifloxacin, moxifloxacin, or gemifloxacin [not currently marketed]), an advanced macrolide (ie, azithromycin or clarithromycin) plus high-dose amoxicillin (1 g 3 times daily), an advanced macrolide plus high-dose amoxicillin/clavulanate (2 g twice daily) is preferred for the outpatient empiric treatment of CAP in patients who are at greater risk for DRSP [47]. These treatment guidelines emphasize that the cause of CAP should be determined whenever possible and that pathogen-directed therapy should be used once the etiologic agent has been identified. The oral β-lactam drug of choice for treating penicillin-susceptible pneumococcal pneumonia (MIC ≤ 1.0 μg/mL) is amoxicillin. Although penicillin and amoxicillin MICs against pneumococci are similar, oral amoxicillin therapy is preferred because of its reliable absorption, excellent bioavailability, and longer half-life than penicillin [7]. Higher doses (ie, 3 to 4 g/day) of amoxicillin are required for activity against more than 90% of *S pneumoniae* isolates [47]. When *H influenzae* or *M catarrhalis* are likely pathogens, amoxicillin/clavulanate is among the preferred antimicrobials for CAP.

The recommendations of the Drug-Resistant *Streptococcus pneumoniae* Therapeutic Working Group of the CDC for empirical therapy of CAP are similar to those of the IDSA and the ATS, but they emphasize that fluoroquinolones should not be used as first-line treatment because of their broad spectrum of activity and concerns that pneumococcal resistance will develop with widespread fluoroquinolone use [46]. Furthermore, the CDC recommends that treatment with these agents should be reserved for use in patients who have failed first-line therapy or those with highly penicillin-resistant pneumococcal pneumonia (penicillin MICs $\geq$ 4 µg/mL), for which there are few alternative oral therapies available. The CDC statement recommends a macrolide (erythromycin, clarithromycin, or azithromycin) or doxycycline as empiric therapy for outpatients with CAP; however, the CDC also recommends antipneumococcal β-lactams (ie, amoxicillin/clavulanate, amoxicillin, or cefuroxime axetil) as empiric first-line therapy choices (with the acknowledgment that these do not cover the "atypical" pathogens).

Role of amoxicillin/clavulanate in acute bacterial rhinosinusitis and community-acquired pneumonia

Based on the previous discussion, amoxicillin/clavulanate is clearly an appropriate option for antimicrobial therapy for use in the empiric outpatient treatment of ABRS or CAP disease, in which *S pneumoniae, H influenzae,* or *M catarrhalis* are the predominant bacterial pathogens. Specifically, amoxicillin/clavulanate is a preferred choice in patients with ABRS who have failed other antimicrobial therapies, have recently received antimicrobial therapy, or have substantive symptoms. Introduced in 1984, the combination of amoxicillin/clavulanate is now available in several oral formulations (tablets, chewable tablets, suspensions, and extended-release tablets) to accommodate both adult and pediatric patients in ambulatory practice. This review focuses on adult patients; therefore, the pediatric formulations will not be discussed. The newest formulation of amoxicillin/clavulanate is an extended-release tablet that contains 1000 mg of amoxicillin and 62.5 mg of clavulanate. This formulation should be administered as 2 tablets twice daily for a total daily dose of 4 g amoxicillin. The total daily dose of clavulanate is 250 mg, which is the same as immediate-release amoxicillin/clavulanate 875/125-mg tablet taken twice daily. Extended-release amoxicillin/clavulanate was recently introduced as a much-needed therapy to treat ABRS and CAP caused by respiratory pathogens, given the current environment of antimicrobial resistance. This new formulation of amoxicillin/clavulanate, with activity against isolates of *S pneumoniae* with reduced susceptibility to penicillin, is an important development in light of antimicrobial resistance patterns and decreased susceptibility to penicillin among *S pneumoniae* that has developed during the past decade.

Extended-release amoxicillin/clavulanate

The new, high-dose, extended-release formulation of amoxicillin/clavulanate (16:1 ratio), which became available in 2002, was developed in response to treatment guidelines for ABRS [6] and CAP [1,7,46], which recommend higher doses of amoxicillin to combat reduced penicillin susceptibility among *S pneumoniae*, while retaining activity against β-lactamase-producing strains of *H influenzae* and *M catarrhalis*. This new tablet formulation consists of an immediate-release layer of amoxicillin trihydrate and clavulanate potassium, and an extended-release layer of amoxicillin sodium. The extended-release amoxicillin layer maintains higher plasma amoxicillin concentrations for a longer duration than other oral formulations, a phenomenon associated with maximum bacteriocidal activity [54]. The clavulanate component provides coverage of β-lactamase–producing pathogens.

Improved pharmacokinetic profile

The efficacy of β-lactam antimicrobials is dependent on nonprotein-bound serum concentrations, which must be greater than the MIC for at least 40% to 50% of the dosing interval [33]. Amoxicillin is the only oral β-lactam that can be dosed to achieve serum concentrations above the MIC at which 90% of isolates of pneumococci are inhibited (MIC_{90}) for at least 40% of the dosing interval. The sustained-release layer of the new extended-release amoxicillin/clavulanate formulation results in plasma amoxicillin concentrations remaining elevated longer than with immediate-release amoxicillin/clavulanate (Fig. 2) [54], and the higher amoxicillin concentrations achieved with this new formulation allow coverage of most *S pneumoniae* with reduced susceptibility to penicillin, specifically *S pneumoniae* with a penicillin MIC of 2 μg/mL, which are considered resistant.

Efficacy of extended-release amoxicillin/clavulanate in adults with acute bacterial rhinosinusitis

Extended-release amoxicillin/clavulanate was evaluated in three clinical studies of adults with ABRS (one comparative and two noncomparative

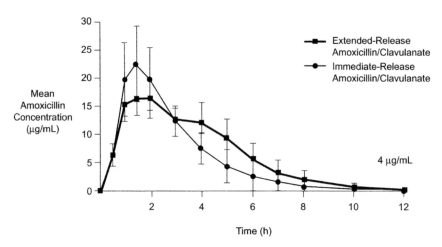

Fig. 2. Mean plasma concentration-time profile for amoxicillin after oral administration of extended-release amoxicillin/clavulanate (2000/125 mg) compared with that of immediate-release amoxicillin/clavulanate (2000/125 mg). From Kaye CM, Allen A, Perry S, et al. The clinical pharmacokinetics of a new pharmacokinetically enhanced formulation of amoxicillin/clavulanate. Clin Ther 2001;23(4)578–84; with permission.

trials). In the comparative trial, 363 patients were randomized to either extended-release amoxicillin/clavulanate (2000/125 mg twice daily) or levofloxacin (500 mg daily) for 10 days [55,56]. Combined clinical and radiologic success at test of cure (days 17 to 28) in the per-protocol population, the primary endpoint, was 83.7% in patients receiving extended-release amoxicillin/clavulanate and 84.3% in patients receiving levofloxacin. Although the ability to differentiate between agents is very limited by the trial design for noninferiority, these results show comparable efficacy in the two treatment groups.

Two noncomparative, multicenter trials evaluated the bacteriologic and clinical efficacies of extended-release amoxicillin/clavulanate for the treatment of ABRS in 1554 patients [55]. In the combined studies, extended-release amoxicillin/clavulanate "eradicated" 97.7% of *S pneumoniae* isolates and 100% of highly penicillin-resistant (MIC $\geq$ 4 µg/mL) *S pneumoniae* isolates in the per-protocol population (Table 3) [55]. "Eradication" is presumed in this study design and is defined as clinical success in the absence of bacteriologically documented failure. In addition, combined bacteriologic eradication and presumed bacteriologic eradication rates were 94.1% for *H influenzae* and 98.4% for *M catarrhalis*. Clinical success rates at test of cure (days 17 to 28) were 92.5% and 94.0% in the two studies. Results from the three trials of extended-release amoxicillin/clavulanate in patients with ABRS demonstrate that extended-release amoxicillin/clavulanate has comparable clinical efficacy to levofloxacin and higher than 90% presumed bacteriologic efficacy against *S pneumoniae*, including isolates with reduced susceptibility to penicillin, and β-lactamase–producing *H influenzae* and *M catarrhalis*.

Table 3
Combined bacteriologic eradication at test of cure (days 17–28) in the per-protocol population for two noncomparative clinical trials of extended-release amoxicillin/clavulanate (2000/125 mg twice daily) in 442 patients with acute bacterial rhinosinusitis [55].

Pathogen	Bacteriologic eradication n/N(%)	95% confidence interval[a]
Streptococcus pneumoniae, all	210/215 (97.7)	NA
Streptococcus pneumoniae, penicillin MIC $\geq$2 µg/mL	22/23 (95.7)	78.1, 99.9
Streptococcus pneumoniae, penicillin MIC = 2 µg/mL	13/14 (92.9)	66.1, 99.8
Streptococcus pneumoniae, penicillin MIC $\geq$4 µg/mL	9/9 (100)	66.4, 100
Haemophilus influenzae	160/170 (94.1)	NA
Moraxella catarrhalis	61/62 (98.4)	NA

Diagnosis was determined by culture of sinus aspirates obtained by sinus puncture; 1554 patients were studied in these two studies.

Abbreviations: MIC, minimum inhibitory concentration; NA, not available.

[a] Calculated using exact probabilities.

Efficacy of extended-release amoxicillin/clavulanate in adults with community-acquired pneumonia

Five clinical trials evaluated the efficacy of extended-release amoxicillin/clavulanate in the treatment of CAP (one noncomparative study and four randomized, double-blind, multicenter studies) [55,57]. These studies included a total of 2337 patients. In one comparative trial, 347 patients with CAP were randomized to either extended-release amoxicillin/clavulanate (2000/125 mg twice daily) or immediate-release amoxicillin/clavulanate (1000/125 mg three times daily) for 10 days [58]. In this comparative trial, clinical success in the per-protocol population at test of cure (days 18 to 39), the primary endpoint, occurred in 91.5% of patients receiving extended-release amoxicillin/clavulanate and 93% of those receiving 1000/125 mg amoxicillin/clavulanate (Table 4). Radiologic success rates were 92.4% and 93.9%, and presumed bacteriologic success rates were 90.6% and 84.4%, respectively. More than 85% of patients in the per-protocol population experienced clinical, bacteriologic, and radiologic success at end of therapy (days 11 to17) in both groups. The results of this study demonstrate that, within the limitations of this type of study design developed to demonstrate noninferiority, the efficacy of extended-release amoxicillin/clavulanate is similar to that of amoxicillin/clavulanate 1000/125 mg three times daily.

In a similar trial, 319 patients received either extended-release amoxicillin/clavulanate or amoxicillin/clavulanate 875/125 mg three times daily for 7 or 10 days [59]. Clinical success at test of cure in the per-protocol population, the primary endpoint, occurred in 94.7% of patients receiving extended-release amoxicillin/clavulanate and 88.8% of patients receiving amoxicillin/clavulanate 875/125 mg 3 times daily (Table 4). Presumed bacteriologic success in the bacteriology per-protocol population was 85% with extended-release amoxicillin/clavulanate and 77.3% in the comparator group.

Results from a comparative trial of amoxicillin/clavulanate 2000/125 mg versus amoxicillin/clavulanate 875/125 mg twice daily demonstrate that more than 85% of the per-protocol population at test of cure (TOC) experienced clinical, radiologic, and presumed bacteriologic success with amoxicillin/clavulanate 2000/125 mg twice daily for 7 days (see Table 4) [57].

Similar results were observed in another comparative trial of extended-release amoxicillin/clavulanate and amoxicillin/clavulanate 875/125 mg twice daily and a noncomparative trial (N = 1122) of extended-release amoxicillin/clavulanate for 7 days [55]. The latter study had a clinical success rate of 85.6%. Results from the five clinical trials in patients with CAP demonstrate that extended-release amoxicillin/clavulanate has comparable efficacy to several immediate-release amoxicillin/clavulanate formulations and dosing regimens.

Tolerability

A total of 4144 patients received extended-release amoxicillin/clavulanate in phase III clinical trials. Extended-release amoxicillin/clavulanate was

Table 4
Treatment outcomes at test of cure (days 18–39) in the per-protocol population for three comparative clinical trials of extended-release amoxicillin/clavulanate in patients with community-acquired pneumonia[55,57–59]

Treatment outcome	Amoxicillin/ clavulanate 2000/125 mg BID n/N(%)	Amoxicillin/ clavulanate 1000/125 mg TID n/N(%)	Amoxicillin/ clavulanate 2000/125 mg BID n/N(%)	Amoxicillin/ clavulanate 875/125 mg TID n/N(%)	Amoxicillin/ clavulanate 2000/125 mg BID n/N(%)	Amoxicillin/ clavulanate 875/125 mg BID n/N(%)
Clinical success	108/118 (91.5)	106/114 (93)	108/114 (94.7)	103/116 (88)	223/247 (90.3)	198/226 (87.6)
Radiologic success	109/118 (92.4)	107/114 (93.9)	NR	NR	230/247 (93.1)	204/226 (90.3)
Bacteriologic success (presumed)	29/32 (90.6)	27/32 (84.4)	17/20 (85)	17/22 (77.3)	58/67 (86.6)	40/51 (78.4)

Abbreviations: BID, twice daily; NR, not reported; TID, three times daily.

generally safe and well tolerated. Most of the reported side effects were mild and transient, and the most frequently reported adverse events were diarrhea (15.6%), nausea (2.2%), genital moniliasis (2.1%), and abdominal pain (1.6%) [55]. The adverse-effect profile of extended-release amoxicillin/clavulanate is similar to that of the immediate-release 875/125-mg twice-daily regimen [57].

Role in therapy

Extended-release amoxicillin/clavulanate (2000/125 mg) was developed in accordance with treatment guidelines for the management of ABRS [6] and CAP [1,7,46], which recommend higher doses of amoxicillin in patients at risk for infection with S pneumoniae with reduced susceptibility to penicillin and adequate coverage of β-lactamase–producing pathogens.

Available data show that extended-release amoxicillin/clavulanate is a suitable choice for the treatment of patients with ABRS or CAP caused by confirmed or suspected β-lactamase–producing pathogens (ie, H influenzae, M catarrhalis, Haemophilus parainfluenzae, Klebsiella pneumoniae, or methicillin-susceptible Staphylococcus aureus) and S pneumoniae with reduced susceptibility to penicillin (penicillin MICs ≤ 2 μg/mL; amoxicillin MICs ≤ 4 μg/mL). The recommended dosage for extended-release amoxicillin/clavulanate in the treatment of patients with ABRS is two tablets (2000/125 mg) twice a day for 10 days. The dosing regimen for patients with CAP is two tablets (2000/125 mg) twice a day for 7 to 10 days.

Summary

ABRS and CAP are two of the most common community-acquired respiratory tract infections in the United States and are a significant burden to the health care system. The pathogens most frequently isolated from patients with ABRS or CAP include S pneumoniae, H influenzae, and M catarrhalis. Increasing resistance among these pathogens to commonly used antimicrobials complicates the selection of an effective treatment regimen that is also well tolerated.

A new extended-released formulation of amoxicillin/clavulanate was developed to achieve higher amoxicillin concentrations that can eradicate S pneumoniae with reduced susceptibility to penicillin, as recommended in current ABRS and CAP treatment guidelines. Several features of this new formulation make it a highly appropriate antimicrobial to be considered for empiric outpatient treatment of ABRS and CAP with suspected or confirmed β-lactamase–producing pathogens (ie, H influenzae, M catarrhalis, H parainfluenzae, K pneumoniae, or methicillin-susceptible S aureus) or S pneumoniae with reduced susceptibility to penicillin (penicillin MICs ≤ 2 μg/mL; amoxicillin MICs ≤ 4 μg/mL). The improved pharmacokinetic profile of the extended-release formulation achieves higher amoxicillin concentrations that remain elevated longer than immediate-release formulations. In addition, extended-release amoxicillin/clavulanate demonstrated comparable clinical efficacy to levofloxacin 500 mg once daily for 10 days for the treatment of ABRS and to immediate-release amoxicillin/clavulanate (875/125 mg twice daily, 875/125 mg three times daily, and 1000/125 mg three times daily) for the treatment of CAP, while providing improved coverage of penicillin-nonsusceptible *S pneumoniae*.

Extended-release amoxicillin/clavulanate is generally well tolerated and has a similar safety profile to older formulations of amoxicillin/clavulanate. The combination β-lactam/β-lactamase inhibitor was launched in 1984 and has a 20-year history of use worldwide. Extended-release amoxicillin/ clavulanate is a much-needed and important antimicrobial agent in the armamentarium against *S pneumoniae* with reduced susceptibility to penicillin and β-lactamase–producing pathogens.

Development of antimicrobials throughout the past 50 years has changed to fulfill the needs of combating infection and overcoming increasing antimicrobial resistance. Current treatment guidelines for community-acquired respiratory tract infections no longer depend solely on the characteristics of the patient and the clinical syndrome, but on those of the offending pathogen, including presence and level of antimicrobial resistance. The most common respiratory tract pathogens known to cause ABRS and CAP include *Streptococcus pneumoniae* and *Haemophilus influenzae*. In addition, *Moraxella catarrhalis* is commonly found in patients with ABRS, and the atypical pathogens (*Mycoplasma pneumoniae* and *Chlamydia pneumoniae*) are frequently found in patients with CAP. The prevalence of antimicrobial resistance, especially β-lactam and macrolide resistance, among *S pneumoniae* and *H influenzae* has increased dramatically during the past 2 decades, diminishing the activity of many older antimicrobials against resistant organisms. For this reason, pharmacokinetic considerations, such as the achievable serum drug concentration and the amount of time this concentration exceeds the minimum inhibitory concentration (T > MIC) of antimicrobials against pathogens, are increasingly important in the formulation of new antimicrobials. A pharmacokinetically enhanced formulation of amoxicillin/clavulanate has been developed to fulfill the need for an oral β-lactam antimicrobial that achieves greater T > MIC than conventional formulations to improve activity against *S pneumoniae* with reduced susceptibility to penicillin. The β-lactamase inhibitor clavulanate allows for coverage of β-lactamase–producing pathogens, such as *H influenzae* and *M catarrhalis*. This article reviews the rationale for, and evolution of, oral amoxicillin/clavulanate formulations for ABRS and CAP.

References

[1] Niederman MS, Mandell LA, Anzueto A, et al. Guidelines for the management of adults with community-acquired pneumonia. Diagnosis, assessment of severity, antimicrobial therapy, and prevention. Am J Respir Crit Care Med 2001;163(7):1730–54.

[2] Anon JB, Jacobs MR, Poole MD, et al. Antimicrobial treatment guidelines for acute bacterial rhinosinusitis. Otolaryngol Head Neck Surg 2004;130(1 Suppl):1–45.

[3] Ray NF, Baraniuk JN, Thamer M, et al. Healthcare expenditures for sinusitis in 1996: contributions of asthma, rhinitis, and other airway disorders. J Allergy Clin Immunol 1999;103(3 Pt 1):408–14.

[4] McCaig LF, Hughes JM. Trends in antimicrobial drug prescribing among office-based physicians in the United States. JAMA 1995;273(3):214–9.

[5] Scott Levin Prescription Audit from Verispan. LLC. January–December 2002.

[6] Antimicrobial treatment guidelines for acute bacterial rhinosinusitis. Sinus and Allergy Health Partnership. Otolaryngol Head Neck Surg 2000;123(1 Pt 2):5–31.

[7] Bartlett JG, Dowell SF, Mandell LA, File TM Jr, Musher DM, Fine MJ. Practice guidelines for the management of community-acquired pneumonia in adults. Infectious Diseases Society of America. Clin Infect Dis 2000;31(2):347–82.

[8] Prevention of pneumococcal disease: recommendations of the Advisory Committee on Immunization Practices (ACIP). MMWR Recomm Rep 1997;46(RR-8):1–24.

[9] Fine MJ, Smith MA, Carson CA, et al. Prognosis and outcomes of patients with community-acquired pneumonia. A meta-analysis. JAMA 1996;275(2):134–41.

[10] Gotfried MH. Epidemiology of clinically diagnosed community-acquired pneumonia in the primary care setting: results from the 1999–2000 respiratory surveillance program. Am J Med 2001;111(Suppl 9A):25S–9S [discussion 36S–8S].

[11] Jacobs MR. Emergence of antibiotic resistance in upper and lower respiratory tract infections. Am J Manag Care 1999;5(11 Suppl):S651–61.

[12] Appelbaum PC, Bhamjee A, Scragg JN, Hallett AF, Bowen AJ, Cooper RC. Streptococcus pneumoniae resistant to penicillin and chloramphenicol. Lancet 1977;2(8046):995–7.

[13] GlaxoSmithKline. Antibiotic treatment and resistance timeline. Available at: http://www.augmentin.com. Accessed August 2, 2002.

[14] Jacobs MR, Koornhof HJ, Robins-Browne RM, et al. Emergence of multiply resistant pneumococci. N Engl J Med 1978;299(14):735–40.

[15] Naraqi S, Kirkpatrick GP, Kabins S. Relapsing pneumococcal meningitis: isolation of an organism with decreased susceptibility to penicillin. G. J Pediatr 1974;85(5):671–3.

[16] Doern GV, Heilmann KP, Huynh HK, Rhomberg PR, Coffman SL, Brueggemann AB. Antimicrobial resistance among clinical isolates of *Streptococcus pneumoniae* in the United States during 1999–2000, including a comparison of resistance rates since 1994–1995. Antimicrob Agents Chemother 2001;45(6):1721–9.

[17] Doern GV, Brueggemann AB, Huynh H, Wingert E. Antimicrobial resistance with Streptococcus pneumoniae in the United States, 1997–98. Emerg Infect Dis 1999;5(6):757–65.

[18] Doern GV, Brueggemann A, Holley HP Jr, Rauch AM. Antimicrobial resistance of Streptococcus pneumoniae recovered from outpatients in the United States during the winter months of 1994 to 1995: results of a 30-center national surveillance study. Antimicrob Agents Chemother 1996;40(5):1208–13.

[19] Spika JS, Facklam RR, Plikaytis BD, Oxtoby MJ. Antimicrobial resistance of Streptococcus pneumoniae in the United States, 1979–1987. The Pneumococcal Surveillance Working Group. J Infect Dis 1991;163(6):1273–8.

[20] Thornsberry C, Sahm DF, Kelly LJ, et al. Regional trends in antimicrobial resistance among clinical isolates of Streptococcus pneumoniae, Haemophilus influenzae, and Moraxella catarrhalis in the United States: results from the TRUST Surveillance Program, 1999–2000. Clin Infect Dis 2002;34(Suppl 1):S4–S16.

[21] Jacobs MR, Felmingham D, Appelbaum PC, Gruneberg RN. The Alexander Project 1998–2000: susceptibility of pathogens isolated from community-acquired respiratory tract infection to commonly used antimicrobial agents. J Antimicrob Chemother 2003;52(2):229–46.

[22] Chambers HF. Penicillin-binding protein-mediated resistance in pneumococci and staphylococci. J Infect Dis 1999;179(Suppl 2):S353–9.

[23] Bush K. Beta-lactamase inhibitors from laboratory to clinic. Clin Microbiol Rev 1988;1(1): 109–23.

[24] Medeiros AA. Evolution and dissemination of beta-lactamases accelerated by generations of beta-lactam antibiotics. Clin Infect Dis 1997;24(Suppl 1):S19–45.

[25] Jacobs MR. Drug-resistant Streptococcus pneumoniae: rational antibiotic choices. Am J Med 1999;106(5A):19S–25S [discussion 48S–52S].

[26] Khan W, Ross S, Rodriguez W, Controni G, Saz AK. Haemophilus influenzae type B resistant to ampicillin. A report of two cases. JAMA 1974;229(3):298–301.

[27] Jorgensen JH, Doern GV, Maher LA, Howell AW, Redding JS. Antimicrobial resistance among respiratory isolates of Haemophilus influenzae, Moraxella catarrhalis, and Streptococcus pneumoniae in the United States. Antimicrob Agents Chemother 1990; 34(11):2075–80.

[28] Doern GV, Brueggemann AB, Pierce G, Holley HP Jr, Rauch A. Antibiotic resistance among clinical isolates of Haemophilus influenzae in the United States in 1994 and 1995 and detection of beta-lactamase-positive strains resistant to amoxicillin-clavulanate: results of a national multicenter surveillance study. Antimicrob Agents Chemother 1997;41(2):292–7.

[29] Jones ME, Karlowsky JA, Blosser-Middleton R, Critchley IA, Thornsberry C, Sahm DF. Apparent plateau in beta-lactamase production among clinical isolates of Haemophilus influenzae and Moraxella catarrhalis in the United States: results from the LIBRA Surveillance initiative. Int J Antimicrob Agents 2002;19(2):119–23.

[30] Thornsberry C, Ogilvie PT, Holley HP Jr, Sahm DF. Survey of susceptibilities of Streptococcus pneumoniae, Haemophilus influenzae, and Moraxella catarrhalis isolates to 26 antimicrobial agents: a prospective US study. Antimicrob Agents Chemother 1999; 43(11):2612–23.

[31] Doern GV, Jones RN, Pfaller MA, Kugler K. Haemophilus influenzae and Moraxellacatarrhalis from patients with community-acquired respiratory tract infections: antimicrobial susceptibility patterns from the SENTRY antimicrobial Surveillance Program (United States and Canada, 1997). Antimicrob Agents Chemother 1999;43(2): 385–9.

[32] Hakenbeck R, Kaminski K, Konig A, et al. Penicillin-binding proteins in beta-lactam-resistant streptococcus pneumoniae. Microb Drug Resist 1999;5(2):91–9.

[33] Craig WA. Pharmacokinetic/pharmacodynamic parameters: rationale for antibacterial dosing of mice and men. Clin Infect Dis 1998;26(1):1–10 [quiz 11–2].

[34] Chen DK, McGeer A, de Azavedo JC, Low DE. Decreased susceptibility of Streptococcus pneumoniae to fluoroquinolones in Canada. Canadian Bacterial Surveillance Network. N Engl J Med 1999;341(4):233–9.

[35] Ho PL, Yung RW, Tsang DN, et al. Increasing resistance of Streptococcus pneumoniae to fluoroquinolones: results of a Hong Kong multicentre study in 2000. J Antimicrob Chemother 2001;48(5):659–65.

[36] Hyde TB, Gay K, Stephens DS, et al. Macrolide resistance among invasive Streptococcus pneumoniae isolates. JAMA 2001;286(15):1857–62.

[37] Pihlajamaki M, Kotilainen P, Kaurila T, Klaukka T, Palva E, Huovinen P. Macrolide-resistant Streptococcus pneumoniae and use of antimicrobial agents. Clin Infect Dis 2001; 33(4):483–8.

[38] Appelbaum PC. Resistance among Streptococcus pneumoniae: implications for drug selection. Clin Infect Dis 2002;34(12):1613–20.

[39] Hofmann J, Cetron MS, Farley MM, et al. The prevalence of drug-resistant Streptococcus pneumoniae in Atlanta. N Engl J Med 1995;333(8):481–6.

[40] Fogarty C, Goldschmidt R, Bush K. Bacteremic pneumonia due to multidrug-resistant pneumococci in 3 patients treated unsuccessfully with azithromycin and successfully with levofloxacin. Clin Infect Dis 2000;31(2):613–5.

[41] Kelley MA, Weber DJ, Gilligan P, Cohen MS. Breakthrough pneumococcal bacteremia in patients being treated with azithromycin and clarithromycin. Clin Infect Dis 2000;31(4): 1008–11.

[42] Lonks JR, Garau J, Gomez L, et al. Failure of macrolide antibiotic treatment in patients with bacteremia due to erythromycin-resistant Streptococcus pneumoniae. Clin Infect Dis 2002;35(5):556–64.

[43] Musher DM, Dowell ME, Shortridge VD, et al. Emergence of macrolide resistance during treatment of pneumococcal pneumonia. N Engl J Med 2002;346(8):630–1.

[44] Reid R Jr, Bradley JS, Hindler J. Pneumococcal meningitis during therapy of otitis media with clarithromycin. Pediatr Infect Dis J 1995;14(12):1104–5.

[45] Waterer GW, Wunderink RG, Jones CB. Fatal pneumococcal pneumonia attributed to macrolide resistance and azithromycin monotherapy. Chest 2000;118(6):1839–40.

[46] Heffelfinger JD, Dowell SF, Jorgensen JH, et al. Management of community-acquired pneumonia in the era of pneumococcal resistance: a report from the Drug-Resistant Streptococcus pneumoniae Therapeutic Working Group. Arch Intern Med 2000;160(10): 1399–408.

[47] Mandell LA, Bartlett JG, Dowell SF, File TM Jr, Musher DM, Whitney C. Update of practice guidelines for the management of community-acquired pneumonia in immuno-competent adults. Clin Infect Dis 2003;37(11):1405–33.

[48] Fine MJ, Auble TE, Yealy DM, et al. A prediction rule to identify low-risk patients with community-acquired pneumonia. N Engl J Med 1997;336(4):243–50.

[49] Nicholson SC, Conetta BJ, Mayer HB. Difference in pathogens isolated from outpatients and inpatients with community-acquired pneumonia. Presented at the 40th Interscience Conference on Antimicrobial Agents and Chemotherapy. Toronto, Ontario, Canada, September 17–20, 2000.

[50] Donowitz GR, Brandon ML, Salisbury JP, et al. Sparfloxacin versus cefaclor in the treatment of patients with community-acquired pneumonia: a randomized, double-masked, comparative, multicenter study. Clin Ther 1997;19(5):936–53.

[51] Lode H, Garau J, Grassi C, et al. Treatment of community-acquired pneumonia: a randomized comparison of sparfloxacin, amoxycillin-clavulanic acid and erythromycin. Eur Respir J 1995;8(12):1999–2007.

[52] Mundy LM, Oldach D, Auwaerter PG, et al. Implications for macrolide treatment in community-acquired pneumonia. Hopkins CAP Team. Chest 1998;113(5):1201–6.

[53] File TM Jr, Tan JS, Plouffe JF. The role of atypical pathogens: Mycoplasma pneumoniae, Chlamydia pneumoniae, and Legionella pneumophila in respiratory infection. Infect Dis Clin North Am Sep 1998;12(3):569–92 [vii.].

[54] Kaye CM, Allen A, Perry S, et al. The clinical pharmacokinetics of a new pharmacokineti-cally enhanced formulation of amoxicillin/clavulanate. Clin Ther 2001;23(4):578–84.

[55] Augmentin XR prescribing information. Research Triangle Park. NC: GlaxoSmithKline; 2002.

[56] File TM Jr, Jacobs MR, Poole MD, Wynne B. Outcome of treatment of respiratory tract infections due to Streptococcus pneumoniae, including drug-resistant strains, with pharmacokinetically enhanced amoxycillin/clavulanate. Int J Antimicrob Agents 2002; 20(4):235–47.

[57] File T, Lode H, Kurz H, Crann R and the 600 Study Group. Comparative efficacy/safety of pharmacokinetically enhanced amoxicillin/clavulanate 200/125 mg vs amoxicillin/ clavulanate 875/125 mg in community-acquired pneumonia (CAP). Presented at the 99th International Conference of the American Thoracic Society. Seattle, Washington, May 16–21, 2003.

[58] Petitpretz P, Chidiac C, Soriano F, Garau J, Stevenson K, Rouffiac E. The efficacy and safety of oral pharmacokinetically enhanced amoxycillin-clavulanate 2000/125 mg, twice daily, versus oral amoxycillin-clavulanate 1000/125 mg, three times daily, for the treatment

of bacterial community-acquired pneumonia in adults. Int J Antimicrob Agents Aug Aug 2002;20(2):119–29.

[59] Garau J, Twynholm M, Garcia-Mendez E. and the 557 study group. Comparative efficacy and safety of pharmacokinetically enhanced amoxicillin/clavulanate 2000/125 mg b.d. versus amoxicillin/clavulanate 875/125 mg t.d.s. in community-acquired pneumonia (CAP) [poster]. Presented at the 12th European Congress of Clinical Microbiology and Infectious Diseases. Milan, Italy, April 24–27, 2002.

ELSEVIER
SAUNDERS

Clin Lab Med 24 (2004) 553–558

CLINICS IN
LABORATORY
MEDICINE

Index

Note: Page numbers of article titles are in **boldface** type.

A

Acinetobacter, antibiotic-resistant, in pediatric patients, 361

Agar screen test, for methicillin susceptibility, 410

Ambler classification, of beta-lactamases, 345–346

Amoxicillin
  for respiratory tract infections
    distribution of, 486
    dosing of, 485, 490, 492, 494
    resistance to, 495
    susceptibility testing of, 501–528

Amoxicillin/clavulanate, **529–549**
  development of, beta-lactam resistance and, 530–536
  extended-release, 539–544
  for pneumonia, 537–539, 541–544
  for respiratory tract infections, 490–491
  for rhinosinusitis, 536–537, 539–544
  pharmacokinetics of, 540
  resistance to, 495
  susceptibility testing of, 501–528

Amp C beta-lactamases (cephalosporinases), 346, 348–353

Ampicillin, susceptibility testing of, 501–528

Analytical isoelectric focusing, for beta-lactamase identification, 353

Antibiograms, for antibiotic therapy optimization, in critical illness, 331

Antimicrobial resistance. *See also specific antibiotics.*
  in critical illness, **329–341**
  in Gram-negative bacteria, in hospitalized children, **361–378**
  in *Haemophilus influenzae,* **453–473, 501–528**
  in institutionalized elderly persons, **343–360**

  in *Moraxella catarrhalis.* See *Moraxella catarrhalis.*
  in respiratory pathogens
    amoxicillin/clavulanate evolution for, **529–549**
    mechanisms of, **417–451**
    pharmacodynamics and pharmacokinetics of, **475–500**
  in *Staphylococcus aureus,* 442
    methicillin, **401–416**
    vancomycin, **379–400**
  in *Streptococcus pneumoniae.* See *Streptococcus pneumoniae.*
  selection of, 423–426

Athletes, methicillin-resistant *Staphylococcus aureus* transmission among, 406–407

Azithromycin
  for respiratory tract infections
    distribution of, 486
    dosing of, 479–480
    resistance to, 488
  resistance to, 457, 461, 488, 495
  susceptibility testing of, 501–528

B

BBL Crystal MRSA ID System, for methicillin resistance, 412

Beta-lactamases
  Amp C type (cephalosporinases), 347–348
  classification of, 345–346
  description of, 344
  extended spectrum, 346–351
  Gram-negative bacteria, 361–362
  Haemophilus influenzae, 421–422, 434
  inhibitors of, 435–436
  molecular epidemiology of, 353–355
  Moraxella catarrhalis, 422, 434–435
  nomenclature of, 344–345
  non-SHV, 348
  non-TEM, 348

Your *Clinics* subscription just got better!

You can now access the FULL TEXT of this publication online at no additional cost! Activate your online subscription today and receive...

- Full text of all issues from 2002 to the present
- Photographs, tables, illustrations, and references
- Comprehensive search capabilities
- Links to MEDLINE and Elsevier journals

Activate Your Online Access Today!

Plus, you can also sign up for E-alerts of upcoming issues or articles that interest you, and take advantage of exclusive access to bonus features!

To activate your individual online subscription:

1. Visit our website at **www.TheClinics.com**.

2. Click on "Register" at the top of the page, and follow the instructions.

3. To activate your account, you will need your subscriber account number, which you can find on your mailing label (note: the number of digits in your subscriber account number varies from six to ten digits). See the sample below where the subscriber account number has been circled.

This is your subscriber account number

```
*******************************************3-DIGIT 001
FEB00   J0167   C7   123456-89   10/00   Q: 1

J.H. DOE, MD
531 MAIN ST
CENTER CITY, NY  10001-001
```

4. That's it! Your online access to the most trusted source for clinical reviews is now available.

theclinics.com

ELSEVIER

Changing Your Address?

Make sure your subscription changes too! When you notify us of your new address, you can help make our job easier by including an exact copy of your Clinics label number with your old address (see illustration below.) This number identifies you to our computer system and will speed the processing of your address change. Please be sure this label number accompanies your old address and your corrected address—you can send an old Clinics label with your number on it or just copy it exactly and send it to the address listed below.

We appreciate your help in our attempt to give you continuous coverage. Thank you.

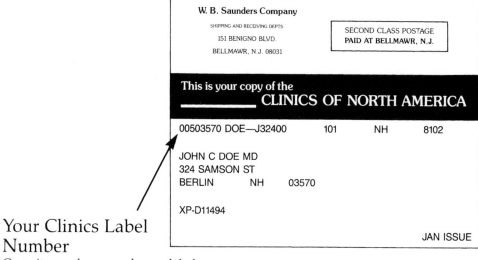

W. B. Saunders Company

SHIPPING AND RECEIVING DEPTS.
151 BENIGNO BLVD.
BELLMAWR, N.J. 08031

SECOND CLASS POSTAGE
PAID AT BELLMAWR, N.J.

This is your copy of the
_____ **CLINICS OF NORTH AMERICA**

00503570 DOE—J32400   101   NH   8102

JOHN C DOE MD
324 SAMSON ST
BERLIN   NH   03570

XP-D11494

JAN ISSUE

Your Clinics Label Number
Copy it exactly or send your label
along with your address to:
W.B. Saunders Company, Customer Service
Orlando, FL 32887-4800
Call Toll Free 1-800-654-2452

Please allow four to six weeks for delivery of new subscriptions and for processing address changes.

YES! Please start my subscription to the **CLINICS** checked below with the ❑ first issue of the calendar year or ❑ current issues. If not completely satisfied with my first issue, I may write "cancel" on the invoice and return it within 30 days at no further obligation.

Please Print:

Name _____

Address _____

City_____ State _____ ZIP _____

Method of Payment

❑ Check (payable to **Elsevier**; add the applicable sales tax for your area)

❑ VISA ❑ MasterCard ❑ AmEx ❑ Bill me

Card number _____ Exp. date _____

Signature _____

Staple this to your purchase order to expedite delivery

❑ **Adolescent Medicine Clinics**
  ❑ Quarterly $92
  ❑ Institutions $121

❑ **Anesthesiology**
  ❑ Quarterly $167
  ❑ Institutions $230
  ❑ *Residents $84

❑ **Cardiology**
  ❑ Quarterly $161
  ❑ Institutions $246
  ❑ *Residents $81

❑ **Chest Medicine**
  ❑ Quarterly $179
  ❑ Institutions $260

❑ **Child and Adolescent Psychiatry**
  ❑ Quarterly $167
  ❑ Institutions $243
  ❑ *Residents $81

❑ **Critical Care**
  ❑ Quarterly $161
  ❑ Institutions $243
  ❑ *Residents $81

❑ **Dental**
  ❑ Quarterly $145
  ❑ Institutions $221

❑ **Emergency Medicine**
  ❑ Quarterly $162
  ❑ Institutions $243
    ❑ Send CME info

❑ **Facial Plastic Surgery**
  ❑ Quarterly $191
  ❑ Institutions $280

❑ **Foot and Ankle**
  Quarterly $153
  Institutions $212

❑ **Gastroenterology**
  ❑ Quarterly $183
  ❑ Institutions $256

❑ **Gastrointestinal Endoscopy**
  ❑ Quarterly $183
  ❑ Institutions $256

❑ **Hand**
  ❑ Quarterly $196
  ❑ Institutions $291

❑ **Hematology/ Oncology**
  ❑ Bimonthly $199
  ❑ Institutions $286

❑ **Immunology & Allergy**
  ❑ Quarterly $162
  ❑ Institutions $243

❑ **Infectious Disease**
  ❑ Quarterly $159
  ❑ Institutions $248

❑ **Clinics in Liver Disease**
  ❑ Quarterly $161
  ❑ Institutions $214

❑ **Medical**
  ❑ Bimonthly $130
  ❑ Institutions $209
  ❑ *Residents $65
    ❑ Send CME info

❑ **MRI**
  ❑ Quarterly $184
  ❑ Institutions $265
    ❑ Send CME info .

❑ **Neuroimaging**
  ❑ Quarterly $184
  ❑ Institutions $265
    ❑ Send CME inf0

❑ **Neurologic**
  ❑ Quarterly $169
  ❑ Institutions $267

❑ **Obstetrics & Gynecology**
  ❑ Quarterly $168
  ❑ Institutions $263

❑ **Occupational and Environmental Medicine**
  ❑ Quarterly $114
  ❑ Institutions $152
  ❑ *Residents $57

❑ **Ophthalmology**
  ❑ Quarterly $184
  ❑ Institutions $297

❑ **Oral & Maxillofacial Surgery**
  ❑ Quarterly $172
  ❑ Institutions $255
  ❑ *Residents $81

❑ **Orthopedic**
  ❑ Quarterly $175
  ❑ Institutions $269
  ❑ *Residents $88

❑ **Otolaryngologic**
  ❑ Bimonthly $195
  ❑ Institutions $321

❑ **Pediatric**
  ❑ Bimonthly $129
  ❑ Institutions $226
  ❑ *Residents $65
    ❑ Send CME info

❑ **Perinatology**
  ❑ Quarterly $148
  ❑ Institutions $217
    ❑ Send CME inf0

❑ **Plastic Surgery**
  ❑ Quarterly $233
  ❑ Institutions $346

❑ **Podiatric Medicine & Surgery**
  ❑ Quarterly $160
  ❑ Institutions $243

❑ **Primary Care**
  ❑ Quarterly $131
  ❑ Institutions $203

❑ **Psychiatric**
  ❑ Quarterly $165
  ❑ Institutions $263

❑ **Radiologic**
  ❑ Bimonthly $213
  ❑ Institutions $302
  ❑ *Residents $107
    ❑ Send CME info

❑ **Sports Medicine**
  ❑ Quarterly $174
  ❑ Institutions $253

❑ **Surgical**
  ❑ Bimonthly $183
  ❑ Institutions $273
  ❑ *Residents $92

❑ **Urologic**
  ❑ Quarterly $186
  ❑ Institutions $280
    ❑ Send CME info

BUSINESS REPLY MAIL

FIRST-CLASS MAIL   PERMIT NO 7135   ORLANDO FL

POSTAGE WILL BE PAID BY ADDRESSEE

PERIODICALS ORDER FULFILLMENT DEPT
ELSEVIER
6277 SEA HARBOR DR
ORLANDO FL 32821-9816